vestment casting, plastics, ultrasonic machining, dielectric heating, electronic printed circuits, and automation. The chapter on assembly processes emphasizes the tremendous savings that can be made in this, often neglected, phase of manufacturing.

"It summarizes in one volume the answers to questions on the newest developments in manufacturing methods, the products to which they are adapted and the economics of their use. The many illustrations are more effective than thousands of words in giving a clear idea of the type of equipment used in various industries and the types of products made by various methods. . . . Summarized in easily assimilated form."—Grace G. Burns, President, Grayborn Steel Company; Director, Vertol Air-Craft Corporation.

ABOUT THE AUTHOR

Arthur C. Ansley has had over 30 years' experience as an executive at the head of his own manufacturing company and his broad interest in mechanical and scientific developments has given him the perspective necessary to present this very technical material in simple, readable style. Mr. Ansley does not pretend to give experts instruction in their own fields, but to present the latest processes that are being used in a comprehensive view.

Manufacturing Methods and Processes

Manufacturing

A CHILTON BOOK

Methods and Processes

ARTHUR C. ANSLEY

President, Arthur Ansley Mfg. Co. and Technical Sales
Company; Member, American Society of Tool Engineers, Acoustical Society of America, and the Institute
of Radio Engineers

Publishers · CHILTON COMPANY · Philadelphia

Foreword

New engineering designs are the basis for the rapid development of the aviation industry. This is as it should be; however, the engineer must keep in sight the fact that he has at his disposal those production methods and processes also constantly changing for manufacturing a product more economically.

In the aircraft industry it is often said that "Our problems are different—manufacturing methods used in the mass-production industries are not adaptable to the manufacture of aircraft." Though there may be some truth in this statement, the aircraft industry should continue its attempt to utilize the applicable mass-production techniques to their advantage.

On the other hand, small-run methods have been developed that show great promise and effect economies for the size of production runs found in the aircraft industry. The use of plastic tooling for sheet-metal forming and the adaptation of electronic controls to complex machine tools are only two of these new developments emphasized in Mr. Ansley's book. Therefore, a continuous careful study of new assembly methods is of increasing importance in aircraft manufacturing efforts toward reduced costs.

Anyone associated with design or production in manufacturing industries will find MANUFACTURING METHODS AND PROCESSES stimulating, for not only does it illustrate the latest manufacturing methods but also it should help to bridge the gap between the drawing board and the final product.

FRANK N. PIASECKI

President, Piasecki Aircraft Corporation

v

Introduction

The increasing complexity of modern industry makes it more and more difficult for the executive to keep up with developments outside his own immediate sphere. Up to a certain point, this specialization is necessary and desirable. The sales executive becomes thoroughly familiar with his own products and their market. The purchasing executive knows his sources of supply and his company's policies on inventories and market fluctuations. The design engineer becomes highly proficient in his specialized field, and the production man a real expert in the processes involved in his day-to-day work. However, too much specialization leads to a narrow viewpoint and a lack of perspective.

Very few of us find the time or have the inclination to follow all of the excellent magazines and technical books featuring one or several of the processes, methods, or materials involved in today's manufacturing. However, a broad view of the latest developments in production methods is most helpful to any executive in an industry related, directly or indirectly, to the manufacture or the distribution of mechanical or technical products. It is also a necessary background for those in production, inspection, purchasing, sales, and engineering work who wish to improve their understanding of their own field and that of related industries.

This book seems to me to fill the need for just such information as these people require. It summarizes in one volume the answers to questions on the newest developments in manufacturing methods, the products to which they are adapted, and the economics of their use. The many illustrations are more effective than thousands of words in giving a clear idea of the type of equipment used in various industries and the types of products made by various methods.

Considerable research has gone into the preparation of this book which is summarized in easily assimilated form. Mr. Ansley's long experience as head of his own manufacturing company and his broad interest in mechanical and scientific developments give him just the viewpoint needed to present this technical material in simple terms and readable style.

GRACE G. BURNS

President, Grayborn Steel Company
Director, Vertol Aircraft Corporation
Member, National Association of Manufacturers

Preface

Modern manufacturing is based on the production of parts or assemblies by means of various processes and methods. New processes, and new developments in old ones, are continually improving manufactured products and reducing costs. There are many excellent books available to engineers and production men covering, very completely, one or more of these old and new processes and giving details of the methods of application and requirements of design.

In this book the author does not pretend to give these experts instruction in their own fields. He does try to present in a nontechnical manner for the executive, the purchasing agent, the engineer, and the production man, a comprehensive view of the latest processes that are being used, with a general picture of their application and, most important of all, their cost. Even technical men may find it helpful in giving them a broad picture of modern production methods and possibly in suggesting applications of some of the newer processes to their own problems. Some of these newer developments have been given more space than their present application may justify because it is felt that they will have particular interest to the reader.

The many illustrations have been selected to give an idea of the processes described, and especially to suggest the type of products made by each method. Thanks are due to the following companies who have furnished illustrations, and, in some cases, have reviewed portions of the text:

ACF Electronics, Div. of ACF Industries, Inc., Alexandria, Virginia
Acme Broach Corporation, Milan, Michigan
Admiral Corporation, Chicago 54, Illinois
The Aetna-Standard Enginering Company, Pittsburgh 30, Pennsylvania
Air Reduction Sales Company, New York 17, New York
The Ajax Manufacturing Co., Cleveland 17, Ohio
Alcaloy, Inc., Trenton, New Jersey
The Allen Mfg. Co., Hartford 2, Connecticut
Aluminum Company of America, Pittsburgh 19, Pennsylvania
American Airlines, Inc., New York 17, New York
American Cyanamid Company, New York 20, New York
American Die Casting Institute, Inc., New York 17, New York

American Hot Dip Galvanizers Association, Inc., Pittsburgh 22, Pennsylvania

American Luggage Works, Inc., West Warwick, Rhode Island

American Sinterings, Div. of Engineered Plastics, Inc., Watertown, Connecticut

American Smelting & Refining Co., Barber, New Jersey

Amplex Division, Chrysler Corporation, Detroit 31, Michigan

Arthur Ansley Mfg. Co., New Hope, Pennsylvania

Austenal Laboratories, Inc., New York 16, New York

The Auto-Nailer Company, Atlanta 3, Georgia

Bakelite Company, New York 17, New York

Baldwin-Lima-Hamilton Corp., Eddystone, Pennsylvania

Barber-Colman Company, Rockford, Illinois

Wallace Barnes Company, Bristol, Connecticut

The Bead Chain Manufacturing Co., Bridgeport 5, Connecticut

Morris Bean & Company, Yellow Springs, Ohio

Bethlehem Steel Company, Inc., Bethlehem, Pennsylvania

The Black Brothers Company, Inc., Mendota, Illinois

The Blanchard Machine Company, Cambridge 39, Massachusetts

E. W. Bliss Co., Canton, Ohio

Bone Engineering Corporation, Glendale 4, California

Borkland Laboratories, Marion, Indiana

Borkland Manufacturing Co., Marion, Indiana

Bronze Bearings, Inc., Cranford, New Jersey

Brown & Sharpe Mfg. Co., Providence 1, Rhode Island

Bruno-New York Industries Corporation, New York 1, New York

The Bullard Company, Bridgeport 2, Connecticut

Burndy Engineering Company, Inc., Norwalk, Connecticut

Burroughs Corporation, Paoli, Pennsylvania

Campbell Machine Div., American Chain & Cable Company, Inc., Bridgeport 2, Connecticut

The Carlton Machine Tool Co., Cincinnati, Ohio

Cast-Master, Inc., Bedford, Ohio

Catalin Corporation of America, New York 16, New York

Celanese Corporation of America, New York 16, New York

Centralab, Div. of Globe Union, Inc., Milwaukee 1, Wisconsin

Cerro de Pasco Corporation, New York 22, New York

Chambersburg Engineering Company, Chambersburg, Pennsylvania

Chem Products, Inc., Rocky Hill, Connecticut

The Cincinnati Milling Machine Co., Cincinnati 9, Ohio

The Cincinnati Shaper Co., Cincinnati 25, Ohio

C. K. L. Machinery Company, Oshkosh, Wisconsin

Frank A. Clarici & Sons, Trenton 10, New Jersey

Clearing Machine Corporation, Chicago, Illinois

The Clearview Co., New York 2, New York

The Cleveland Twist Drill Co., Cleveland 14, Ohio

The Colorado Fuel and Iron Corporation, Wickwire Spencer Steel Division, New York 22, New York

Conforming Matrix Corp., Toledo 2, Ohio
The Dawson Corporation, North Pelham, New York
The Dean Company, Chicago 11, Illinois
The DeVilbiss Company, Toledo 1, Ohio
DeWalt, Inc., Lancaster, Pennsylvania
Henry Disston Division, H. K. Porter Company, Inc., Philadelphia 35, Pennsylvania
The DoAll Company, Des Plaines, Illinois
Hunter Douglas Corporation, Riverside, California
The Dow Chemical Company, Midland, Michigan
Dow Corning Corporation, Midland, Michigan
Drop Forging Association, Cleveland 15, Ohio
Allen B. DuMont Laboratories, Inc., Clifton, New Jersey
The Dumore Company, Racine, Wisconsin
E. I. du Pont de Nemours & Company, Wilmington 98, Delaware
Eastman Chemical Products, Inc., subsidiary of Eastman Kodak Company, New York 16, New York
Eastman Kodak Company, Rochester 4, New York
Ekstrom, Carlson & Co., Rockford, Illinois
Elastic Stop Nut Corporation of America, Union, New Jersey
The Electric Furnace Company, Salem, Ohio
Electromold Corp., Trenton 9, New Jersey
Electronics, a McGraw-Hill publication, New York 36, New York
Elox Corporation of Michigan, Royal Oak 3, Michigan
Emmaus Foundry & Machine Company, Inc., Emmaus, Pennsylvania
The Engelberg Huller Co., Inc., Syracuse 4, New York
Erie Resistor Corporation, Erie 6, Pennsylvania
Ettco Tool Co., Inc., Brooklyn 37, New York
Fairbanks, Morse & Co., Chicago 5, Illinois
Fastener Corporation, Chicago 14, Illinois
Federal Products Corporation, Providence 1, Rhode Island
The Fellows Gear Shaper Co., Springfield, Vermont
Ferro Corporation, Cleveland 5, Ohio
Fine Hardwoods Association, Chicago 11, Illinois
Frenchtown Porcelain Company, Trenton 9, New Jersey
Furane Plastics, Inc., Los Angeles 39, California
General American Transportation Corporation, Chicago 90, Illinois
General Electric Company, Schenectady 5, New York
B. F. Goodrich Chemical Company, Cleveland 15, Ohio
The B. F. Goodrich Company, Akron, Ohio
The Goodyear Tire & Rubber Company, Inc., Chemical Division, Akron 16, Ohio
George Gorton Machine Co., Racine, Wisconsin
The G. A. Gray Company, Cincinnati 7, Ohio
Gray Iron Founders' Society, Inc., Cleveland 14, Ohio
Gries Reproducer Corp., New Rochelle, New York
Handy & Harman, New York 38, New York
Harrington and King Perforating Co., Chicago 44, Illinois

The Heald Machine Company, Worcester 6, Massachusetts
Heintz Manufacturing Company, Philadelphia 20, Pennsylvania
Heli-Coil Corporation, Danbury, Connecticut
Hercules Fastener Company, Chicago 14, Illinois
The A. F. Holden Company, Detroit 27, Michigan
R. M. Hollingshead Corporation, Camden 2, New Jersey
Hunter Spring Company, Lansdale, Pennsylvania
Induction Heating Corporation, Brooklyn 11, New York
Industrial Fasteners Institute, Cleveland 13, Ohio
International Harvester Company, Chicago 1, Illinois
Investment Casting Company, Springfield, New Jersey
C. E. Johansson Gage Co., Dearborn, Michigan
Jones & Lamson Machine Company, Springfield, Vermont
Jones & Laughlin Steel Corporation, Pittsburgh 30, Pennsylvania
Kearney & Trecker Corporation, Milwaukee 14, Wisconsin
Keller Tool Division, Gardner-Denver Company, Grand Haven, Michigan
Kolcast Industries, Inc., Willoughby, Ohio
Koppers Company, Inc., Pittsburgh 19, Pennsylvania
Lebanon Steel Foundry, Lebanon, Pennsylvania
Lester-Phoenix, Incorporated, Cleveland 13, Ohio
The Lincoln Electric Company, Cleveland 17, Ohio
Linde Air Products Company, New York 17, New York
Link-Belt Company, Chicago 1, Illinois
Locke Department, General Electric Company, Baltimore 3, Maryland
The Lodge & Shipley Company, Cincinnati 25, Ohio
The Lufkin Rule Co., Saginaw, Michigan
Malleable Founders' Society, Cleveland 14, Ohio
The Marblette Corporation, Long Island City 1, New York
McInnes Steel Company, Corry, Pennsylvania
Meehanite Metal Corporation, New Rochelle, New York
Metallizing Engineering Company, Inc., Westbury, L. I., New York
The Method X Company, Pittsburgh 30, Pennsylvania
Michigan Spline Gage Co., Hazel Park, Michigan
Michigan Tool Company, Detroit 12, Michigan
Micromatic Hone Corporation, Detroit 38, Michigan
Micrometrical Manufacturing Co., Ann Arbor, Michigan
Minnesota Mining & Mfg. Co., Detroit 2, Michigan
Modern Pattern & Plastics Co., Toledo, Ohio
Moraine Products Div., General Motors Corporation, Dayton 1, Ohio
Morse Twist Drill & Machine Co., New Bedford, Massachusetts
Mueller Brass Company, Port Huron, Michigan
Mueller Laboratory, Pasadena, California
Mycalex Corporation of America, Clifton, New Jersey
The National Acme Company, Cleveland 8, Ohio
National Lead Company, Doehler-Jarvis Division, Toledo 1, Ohio
Nelson Stud Welding, Div. of Gregory Industries, Inc., Lorain, Ohio
New Hermes Engraving Machine Corp., New York 3, New York
Niagara Machine & Tool Works, Buffalo 11, New York

Nopco Chemical Company, Inc., Harrison, New Jersey
North American Aviation, Inc., Los Angeles 45, California
Norton Company, Worcester 6, Massachusetts
Oakite Products, Inc., New York 6, New York
The Ohio Crankshaft Co., Cleveland 5, Ohio
Ohio Precision Castings, Inc., Dayton 3, Ohio
Oliver Machinery Co., Grand Rapids 2, Michigan
The Osborn Manufacturing Company, Cleveland 14, Ohio
O'Sullivan Rubber Corporation, Winchester, Virginia
The Palnut Company, Mountainside, New Jersey
Pangborn Corporation, Hagerstown, Maryland
Parker-Kalon Division, General American Transportation Corporation, Clifton, New Jersey
Parker Rust Proof Company, Detroit 11, Michigan
Paul & Beekman, Inc., Philadelphia 40, Pennsylvania
Pemco Corporation, Baltimore 24, Maryland
Penn Engineering & Manufacturing Corp., Doylestown, Pennsylvania
The Phelps Manufacturing Co., Westport, Connecticut
Photocircuits Corporation, Glen Cove, New York
Pioneer-Central, Div. of Bendix Aviation Corp., Davenport, Iowa
Polymer Processes, Inc., Reading, Pennsylvania
Pontiac Motor Division, General Motors Corporation, Pontiac 11, Michigan
Pratt & Whitney Company, West Hartford 1, Connecticut
Quality Control Company, Los Angeles 27, California
Radio Corporation of America, RCA Victor Division, Camden 2, New Jersey
Radio Receptor Company, Inc., New York 11, New York
Ransburg Electro-Coating Corp., Indianapolis, Indiana
Raytheon Manufacturing Company, Waltham 54, Massachusetts
Reading Gray Iron Castings, Inc., Reading, Pennsylvania
Reed Rolled Thread Die Co., Worcester 1, Massachusetts
Reynolds Metals Co., Louisville 1, Kentucky
Rezolin, Inc., Los Angeles 45, California
Rigidized Metals Corporation, Buffalo 3, New York
Rockford Machine Tool Co., Rockford, Illinois
Rockwell Manufacturing Company, Delta Power Tool Division, Pittsburgh 8, Pennsylvania
Roll Formed Products Company, Youngstown, Ohio
B. M. Root Company, York, Pennsylvania
L. G. Rose Associates, New York 7, New York
Roto-Finish Company, Kalamazoo, Michigan
Rubber and Asbestos Corp., Bloomfield, New Jersey
George Scherr Co., Inc., New York 12, New York
Sciaky Bros., Inc., Chicago 38, Illinois
Shakeproof Division of Illinois Tool Works, Elgin, Illinois
Sheffield Plastics Inc., Sheffield, Massachusetts
Sheldon Machine Co., Inc., Chicago 41, Illinois

Simmons Fastener Corp., Albany, New York
Sintox, Inc., Allentown, Pennsylvania
Spincraft, Inc., Milwaukee 8, Wisconsin
The L. S. Starrett Company, Athol, Massachusetts
Steel Founders' Society of America, Cleveland 13, Ohio
F. J. Stokes Machine Company, Philadelphia 20, Pennsylvania
Sun Oil Company, Philadelphia 3, Pennsylvania
The Taft-Peirce Manufacturing Company, Woonsocket, Rhode Island
The Tannewitz Works, Grand Rapids 2, Michigan
The Tappan Stove Company, Mansfield, Ohio
The Taylor-Winfield Corporation, Warren, Ohio
Thomson Electric Welder Company, Lynn, Massachusetts
Thriftmaster Products Corporation, Lancaster, Pennsylvania
The Timken Roller Bearing Company, Canton 6, Ohio
Tinnerman Products, Inc., Cleveland 1, Ohio
The Torrington Company, Torrington, Connecticut
United Shoe Machinery Corp., Boston 7, Massachusetts
United States Pipe and Foundry Company, Birmingham 2, Alabama
United States Plywood Corporation, New York 36, New York
U.S. Tool Company, Inc., East Orange, New Jersey
Urbauer Engineering Co., Freeport, Illinois
Utica Drop Forge & Tool Corp., Utica 4, New York
The Van Keuren Co., Boston, Massachusetts
Vapor Blast Manufacturing Company, Milwaukee 16, Wisconsin
Verson Allsteel Press Company, Chicago 19, Illinois
Waldes Kohinoor, Inc., Long Island City 1, New York
Wales-Strippit Corporation, North Tonawanda, New York
Westinghouse Electric Corporation, X-Ray Division, Baltimore 3, Maryland
Wheelabrator Corporation, Mishawaka, Indiana
S. B. Whistler & Sons, Inc., Buffalo 23, New York
The S. S. White Dental Mfg. Co., Industrial Division, New York 16, New York
Whitney Metal Tool Company, Rockford, Illinois
Wiedemann Machine Company, Philadelphia 32, Pennsylvania
Wilson Mechanical Instrument Division, American Chain & Cable Company, Inc., Bridgeport 2, Connecticut
Winner Manufacturing Co., Inc., Trenton 3, New Jersey
Winzeler Mfg. & Tool Co., Chicago 12, Illinois
R. D. Wood Company, Philadelphia 5, Pennsylvania
Wyman-Gordon Company, Worcester 1, Massachusetts
The Yoder Company, Cleveland 2, Ohio

Thanks are due also to my wife, Anne Klein Ansley, who, patiently or otherwise, transcribed my sometimes illegible scrawls, and to my sister, Delight Ansley, who compiled the index.

THE AUTHOR

Contents

Casting Processes

All of the various casting processes are methods of injecting molten metal into molds, where it hardens into the desired form. The various processes differ principally in the material of the molds and the method of injecting the metal, such as pouring or forcing under pressure. Some processes can be used with any castable metal, while others are adapted to only a few of the lower melting point alloys. The resulting pieces differ greatly in accuracy, finish, complexity, and cost. No one process is best for every part, but each is best and most economical for certain types of cast pieces. The principal casting processes are sand casting, shell mold casting, plaster mold casting, permanent mold casting, investment casting, and die or pressure casting.

SAND CASTING

This is the earliest, and still the most commonly used, of all casting processes. It can be used with all castable metals: iron, steel, brass, aluminum, bronze, copper, and magnesium. The pattern cost is low, wood patterns often being used, although metal patterns are preferred for long runs. Intricate pieces can be cast by the use of sand cores which can be broken out after the metal has hardened. The piece cost is fairly low, and pieces of almost any size can be cast. Large machine frames weighing many tons are made regularly, as well as small parts weighing only a few ounces. Although it is adapted primarily to small- or medium-quantity production, many large production parts, like automobile cylinder blocks and heating radiators for the home, are regularly sand-cast.

The principal advantages of sand casting are low cost of pattern and low piece cost; also, intricate pieces with elaborate interior cavities can be made by the use of sand cores.

The chief disadvantages are the rough surface and the low accuracy of the castings. This often means that expensive finishing and machining operations are required that might be eliminated by some of the other casting processes.

The process is basically simple, although great skill and long experience are required to apply it successfully to difficult jobs and materials. The pattern is made of wood or metal in the form of the piece desired. Allowance must be made in the dimensions for the shrinkage of the metal, but this usually is done by the patternmaker, the drawings showing the dimensions of the desired casting.

Usually the pattern and the mold are made in two parts to allow for removal of the pattern from the mold, which is made of a special mixture of moist sand and clay packed firmly around the pattern in a wood or metal box called a flask. The upper mold is called the cope; the lower, the drag. For more accurate work, the two halves of the pattern may be mounted on match plates which provide for exact alignment of the two halves. In this case, the pattern and the plates usually are made of metal.

The mold material may be moist "green" sand, or may be held together by a binder and dried or baked (dry sand). Dry-sand molds cost more, but they give a better finish, sharper detail, and greater accuracy. Holes or cavities are formed by cores which are molded separately of special sand mixed with a binder and baked for added strength, and are located in recesses in the mold before the metal is poured. One or more openings, called gates, are provided into which the metal is poured. Sometimes additional passages, called risers, are required to let the metal flow properly to all parts of the mold. The excess metals that harden in these gates and risers are called sprues. The location of the gates and the risers is usually determined by the foundry. Proper design at this stage contributes materially to the soundness of the final casting.

After the metal has hardened, the sand mold is broken away and the cores are broken out; then, after the piece is cool, the gate and the riser sprues are cut off roughly and the casting is cleaned, by sand blasting or tumbling, of any adhering sand. The rough casting is then ready for delivery.

Since tolerances in sand castings have to be very large, any surfaces requiring a smooth finish or a close fit require machining. Usually ⅛ in. to ¼ in. excess material is allowed, to be removed by the machine operations. If too little is allowed, the cutting tools wear very fast, because of abrasive particles in the surface layer of the casting.

Gray iron is the most commonly used material for sand castings. It is hard and brittle but machines well, is low in cost, and is an excellent material for general use. Some 80 percent of all metal castings, on a tonnage basis, are made of gray iron. Gray iron is basically steel with graphite distributed microscopically throughout it. Recent metallurgical studies have made it possible to control the distribution of the graphite and greatly improve the strength of gray iron castings. Various specifications are used to cover the different classes of gray iron, the most commonly used being ASTM #A48-48. This classifies the irons into several groups designated by numbers that correspond with the tensile strength in thousands of pounds. These run from group 20, with a tensile strength of 20,000 lb, to group 60, with a tensile of 60,000 lb. Not only are the lower-strength irons cheaper, but also they cast better, especially in thin sections, and are easier to machine. Thus the lowest group that will give satisfactory strength is usually specified.

Malleable iron is much tougher and less brittle than gray iron. It machines well, and is much used for parts requiring a tensile strength greater than that of gray iron. It is considerably more expensive than gray iron, but may replace the much more expensive steel forgings in some applications. Malleable iron castings are made in the same way as gray iron, and the castings, as they come from the mold, are a very hard, brittle, white cast iron. This is converted to malleable iron by an annealing process that involves heating and slow cooling under carefully controlled conditions of temperature and time. The time for this process may run to several days.

Two types of malleable iron are in general use: the *standard*, which is the one most commonly used, and the *pearlitic*, which is more expensive and has higher physical characteristics. The tensile strength of standard malleable iron is from 50,000 to 53,000 pounds per square inch (psi), while that of the pearlitic type runs from 60,000 psi to 90,000 psi, according to the grade. In comparing the cost of gray iron and of malleable castings, it should be remembered that it is often possible to redesign a part for reduced weight because of the higher strength, the greater toughness, and the greater ductility of the malleable material.

Malleable iron castings are used widely in the automotive industry, in agricultural implements, and in military equipment.

Various steel and stainless steel alloys can be cast, each having its particular virtues and applications. In addition to low carbon steels containing roughly 0.05 percent to 0.3 percent carbon, medium carbon steels with 0.3 percent to 0.7 percent carbon, and high carbon steels with 0.7 percent to 1.5 percent carbon, many alloys are available. These are quite similar to the alloys used for rolled or wrought steel shapes, although, as a rule, more silicon and manganese are used to improve the casting properties. The principal elements used in alloy steels, together with a very general indication of their usefulness, are as follows:

Chromium adds hardness, stiffness, and toughness, and is used in highly stressed castings; *manganese,* in small percentages, makes the steel very brittle, but larger amounts give a steel that is very hard but ductile when properly heat-treated; *molybdenum* is used more in high-speed tool steels than in casting alloys; *tungsten* also is used in high-speed tool steels and for permanent magnets. (Both tungsten and molybdenum steels can be hardened by heating and cooling in air instead of being quenched in water or oil, as other steels require.) *Nickel* adds hardness and, in some alloys, heat and corrosion resistance; *vanadium* increases the tensile strength and the elastic limit and is used for parts subjected to vibrational stresses.

Most alloy steels contain several alloying elements to give the desired properties and to make them respond in the desired manner to heat treatment. The tensile strength of carbon cast steels runs from 70,000 psi to 100,000 psi, according to the carbon content. Some of the alloy cast steels, properly heat-treated, go as high as 200,000 tensile.

Stainless steel casting alloys are available in a variety of compositions. The alloying elements are primarily nickel and chromium, with other elements added to give various combinations of strength, heat and corrosion resistance, and machinability. The cost is quite high, especially in the high chrome-nickel alloys, where these elements may form more than 50 percent of the total, but they have found wide use in such industries as food processing, aircraft, chemicals, oil refining, and paper and pulp.

Several iron alloys with characteristics intermediate between iron and steel are excellent for certain uses. Among these are Meehanite, Duriron, Ni-Resist, Semi-steel, and Nodular or Ductile Iron.

Meehanite metals are a group of 24 alloys produced under license for specific purposes and combinations of characteristics. They are classified as general purpose, heat-resisting, wear-resisting, and corrosion-resisting. The process has been worked out to control not only the composition of the metal but also the conditions under which it is melted, poured, and cooled to give desirable and uniform grain structure to the final casting. The result is elimination of much of the brittleness and the local weaknesses of gray iron castings and the production of parts comparable in many respects with malleable iron and steel castings. Although Meehanite castings cost somewhat more than gray iron, they are used widely for load-carrying parts of machinery of all types.

Duriron is a corrosion-resistant alloy which is extremely hard and difficult to machine. Other corrosion- and heat-resistant iron alloys under trade names such as *Durco* and *Ni-Resist* have a fairly high nickel content and are available in several grades for different applications. They are used for valves, pipes, pumps, tank fittings, and similar applications where corrosive materials are handled.

Semi-steel is cast iron containing about 20 percent of steel scrap. This reduces the carbon content and improves the ductility and the grain structure. It is often used for gears and tables of machine tools. The appearance of the machined surface is much superior to that of plain cast iron.

Nodular or Ductile Iron is a relatively new development, having been introduced first in 1948. It is basically gray iron with the addition of a small and closely controlled amount of magnesium, which causes the graphite particles, which are present in all iron, to form in spheroidal shape instead of in flake form as in gray iron. The result is much greater toughness and ductility than are found in gray iron. Test bars of nodular iron can be twisted and bent almost like steel. Tensile strengths of from 85,000 psi to 105,000 psi are reported in the "as cast" condition, and over 150,000 psi with proper heat treatment. Nodular iron also can be hardened to 400 or 450 Brinell, for superior abrasion resistance. While the cost is somewhat more than that of gray iron, its characteristics may make it a satisfactory substitute for steel and malleable castings in some applications at considerably lower cost. It can be machined at higher speeds than gray iron, which makes for further savings. Nodular iron seems certain to come into much more general use, and some of its advocates believe that soon it will be second only to gray iron in tonnage of castings produced.

Many aluminum and magnesium alloys are castable and used

widely where light weight and corrosion resistance offset their higher cost. The principal alloying elements with aluminum are as follows:

1. *Silicon,* which improves the casting qualities, making the metal flow better into intricate molds and thin cross sections.

2. *Copper,* which reduces shrinkage and improves casting qualities but also reduces corrosion resistance.

3. *Magnesium,* which makes the alloy heat-treatable when more than 6 percent is used or where it is combined with other elements.

4. *Zinc,* which improves mechanical properties, and, when it is used to the extent of 5 percent to 7 percent, is the basis for the "self-aging" alloys. After an aging period of a few weeks, these develop characteristics almost equivalent to those of the heat-treated alloys. Parts can be made from these alloys that would not be practical to heat-treat because of strains and distortion.

5. *Nickel,* which adds dimensional stability and heat resistance.

6. *Titanium,* which refines the grain size and improves mechanical properties.

Most aluminum casting alloys contain several or all of these elements in varying proportions, according to the qualities desired and the method of casting.

A wide variety of brass and bronze alloys is also available for applications requiring corrosion resistance, pleasing appearance, and antifriction properties. Some of the bronze alloys, such as manganese bronze and aluminum bronze, have a strength comparable with that of steel castings. The cost is fairly high, but for many purposes they are an economical material because of their excellent characteristics. Bronze and brass alloys consist primarily of various proportions of copper, tin, zinc, and lead. In some alloys, nickel, phosphorus, aluminum, antimony, silicon, and manganese are added.

Magnesium is coming into much more common use as its availability increases and its uses are understood better. It weighs about two thirds as much as aluminum, and this is an important factor in aircraft uses and in hand tools.

In an effort to overcome the disadvantages of rough finish and lack of accuracy of sand castings, several other casting methods have been developed and are rapidly coming into more general use.

SHELL MOLD CASTING

Shell mold casting was originated in Germany prior to World War II; it is now being developed into a mechanized process of considerable importance.

Figures 15 to 24 show the steps in shell molding. A metal pattern, the shape of the desired piece, is required. This is usually in two halves, as in sand casting, although sometimes more than two parts are required in intricate shapes. Each section of the pattern is mounted on a flat metal plate. The pattern and the plate are heated to a temperature of 375 F to 600 F, either by means of built-in electric heating elements or from an external source of heat, such as an oven or a radiant heater. The plate is then clamped, with the pattern facing in, to the open side of a box containing a mixture of fine sand and a thermosetting plastic resin, usually of the phenolic type. The box is inverted so that the sand-resin mixture rests on top of the heated pattern and plate. Within 5 to 15 sec, a shell about ¼ in. thick has formed around the hot pattern; the box is reversed, so that the remaining quantity of sand-resin mixture falls back to the bottom of the box; and the plate and the pattern, with the shell on it, are removed from the box. The shell at this stage is only partially cured and would fall apart if it were removed from the pattern, so the entire plate and shell are placed in an oven or under a radiant heater and further cured for a period of 15 sec to 3 min. The shell can now be removed from the pattern by means of ejector pins which are built into the pattern and the plate. To facilitate this removal, the pattern is coated with a release agent prior to the forming of the shell.

The two or more sections of the shell are clamped or cemented together to form a complete mold with a cavity the shape of the piece to be cast. Provision is made on the original pattern for a gate to pour the metal, and this is usually between the halves of the mold. If the pieces are small, often several of the patterns are mounted on each plate with provision for the metal to flow properly to each cavity in the mold. If cores are required, they can be made of baked sand or of the sand-resin mixture, and are supported in recesses in the mold just as in sand casting. The sand-resin cores give a much better finish and closer tolerances to the recesses in the piece.

In contrast with usual foundry practice, the parting line of the shell mold is usually vertical during the pouring. In most cases, the shells require some support to prevent them from spreading under the weight of the molten metal that is poured into them. Usually this support is obtained by placing the shell mold in a metal box and pouring in iron shot, coarse sand, or crushed rock around it.

The metal is then poured, and, after cooling, the shell is broken away, the gating is cut off, and the parts cleaned by sand blasting or tumbling. While it is possible to recover the sand from the shells by burning out the plastic resin, usually this is not economical unless the production rate is very high.

The castings obtained by shell molding are characterized by sharp reproduction of the details of the original pattern, a smooth surface finish, of the order of 125 microinches (μin.) (see Chap. 18), and good accuracy. Tolerances of 0.003 in. to 0.005 in. per inch of dimension can be held, except across the parting line, where an additional 0.010 in. usually is allowed. Practically all castable alloys, both ferrous and nonferrous, can be shell-molded with good results. Because the mold is permeable, it allows the escape of air and gases and the castings are exceptionally sound.

The process is being used at the present time principally for small- and medium-size castings weighing up to 20 lb or so. However, some foundries are making shell moldings weighing up to 200 lb or more, and there is no doubt that this weight will be increased as the process is developed. Usually the patterns are made of alloyed iron or mild steel, although some bronzes have been used; aluminum is not very satisfactory. They must be finished smoothly to insure easy removal of the shells. The pattern cost, therefore, is considerably more than for sand casting, which means that the process is not usually economical for very small-quantity runs. In general, the piece cost is also somewhat higher than that of sand castings, so the better finish, the closer tolerances, or the saving in machining or finishing time must be counted on to offset this. Figures 25 to 28 show four cases where substantial savings were made by the use of shell mold casting.

The shell-molding process is basically better adapted to mechanization than sand casting, and several companies are now making equipment for this purpose (see Fig. 29). When this type of equipment comes into general use, it is quite possible that small castings such as gears, sprockets, brackets, chain links, and similar parts that run in large quantities can be produced better and at a lower cost as shell moldings than as sand castings.

PLASTER MOLD CASTING

Small castings in nonferrous metals (aluminum, brass, bronze) can be produced in plaster molds with a surface finish as fine as 90 μin. to 125 μin. and an accuracy as close as ±0.005 in. on small dimensions with an additional 0.002 in. per inch on larger dimensions. From 0.005 in. to 0.015 in. more is usually required across the parting line. Molds are made of a special plaster. The pattern and the piece cost are considerably higher than for sand castings, but this is often justifiable because of the better finish and the elimination of machining. Thin wall sections and fine details can be produced.

A split metal pattern is used, mounted on plates and so designed that it can be removed in two halves from the mold, as described above under shell mold casting. The plaster is poured around this pattern and allowed to harden. Then the pattern is removed and the two halves of the mold are baked in an oven to harden them further and to dry out all moisture. Cores, for holes and recesses, also can be made of the plaster composition. The size of parts usually made in plaster molds ranges from a small fraction of an ounce to 10 lb, but pieces weighing over 200 lb have been made by special techniques. The plaster causes slower cooling of the casting than would occur in sand molds, and this has a tendency to improve the characteristics of bronze castings, but it is a disadvantage with aluminum, giving properties that are somewhat lower than sand or shell mold castings.

Similar in general nature to the plaster mold process, but differing greatly in the results obtained, are two relatively new processes.

One, known as the Antioch process, is limited to nonferrous metals and is used primarily for aluminum. It involves a combination of techniques including mold material, which is a mixture of sand and plaster, use of metal chills at critical points, and close control of all steps in the mixing and the pouring of the plaster composition and of the mold hardening. As a result, large and complex pieces, such as wave guides for the electronics industry, tire molds and torque converters for the transportation industry, and many aircraft parts, are made with very fine finish and high accuracy (see

Figs. 38, 39). The processed mold has a high degree of permeability, and, because of the sand content, furnishes a good heat sink. In addition, extensive use is made of chills to get maximum properties in critical areas.

The other is known by the name Ceramicast® and is used for casting ferrous alloys, especially carbon, alloy, and stainless steels. Patterns of wood, plastic, or metal can be used, and pieces weighing up to several hundred pounds can be cast. The mold is made of a special ceramic material which is poured over the pattern in the form of a liquid slurry, which sets very quickly. The tolerances and the finish obtained are comparable with those of the plaster mold process, but the use of steel in the castings opens many new fields, such as turbine blades, pump impellers, and other aircraft and mechanical parts, where nonferrous metals would not be suitable. Photographs illustrating this process, and parts produced by it, are shown in Figs. 40, 41, and 42.

PERMANENT MOLD CASTING

Molten metal can be poured into metal molds to form castings of high accuracy, fine finish, and superior physical characteristics. The process generally is used for lower melting point alloys such as aluminum, magnesium, zinc, tin, or lead, and occasionally for some of the copper base alloys.

Permanent mold castings of iron and steel are made also by coating the molds with a heavy layer of lampblack or other heat-insulating material, but this, of course, decreases the accuracy and the surface finish that are the principal advantages of the process.

The design of parts for permanent mold casting is more restricted than for sand casting, since they must be removed directly from the mold without destroying the mold as in sand casting or shell or plaster molding. Cores also are made of metal, and these, also, must be shaped so that they can be withdrawn from the finished piece.

The mold cost is considerably higher than the pattern cost for sand castings, but the process can be mechanized so that the piece cost in quantities may be considerably less. Therefore, the process is adapted best to medium or large quantities of small- or medium-sized parts. Accuracies of the order of 0.0015 in. to 0.003 in. per inch can often be maintained, and a surface finish of 100 μin. to 125 μin. is possible.

Semipermanent mold castings are made also in metal molds, but with sand cores instead of metal cores. This results in greater latitude in design, since the cores can be broken out of internal cavities and recesses, but the finish of the cored recesses and openings is no better than sand castings. The mold cost would be reduced somewhat, but the production speed using sand cores is considerably lower, with resultant higher piece cost.

Slush molding is a variation of permanent mold casting, usually used with zinc, lead, or tin alloys. The molten metal is poured into a split metal mold and is left just long enough for a shell of the metal to form on the inside of the mold. The still melted metal in the center is then poured out, leaving a hollow casting to be removed from the mold. This process is used mostly for small toys and novelties where accuracy and strength are not required.

CENTRIFUGAL CASTING

Centrifugal castings are tubular or cylindrical parts cast in whirling metal molds. Centrifugal force presses the metal against the inside wall of the mold, leaving a straight, cylindrical hole in the center. The outer surface of centrifugal castings can have a very fine, smooth finish and slightly greater density than gravity castings. In some alloys, such as leaded bronzes, the lead tends to concentrate in the outer layers, due to its greater weight; this is a disadvantage in certain applications, such as bearings, where the lead is needed most on the inner surfaces. The cost of centrifugal castings may be less than that of sand castings, due to the smaller waste of metal in gates and risers. Cast iron and aluminum pipe and hollow bronze bars are often made by centrifugal casting.

In *semicentrifugal castings*, the molten metal is forced to the outside of the mold centrifugally, but the mold is filled completely so that no center hole, or, if desired, a cored center hole, is left. Sometimes this is used for such parts as pulleys and sprockets.

INVESTMENT CASTING

Investment casting, sometimes called lost wax or precision casting, is used mostly for small, intricate parts requiring high accuracy and fine finish. When compared with sand or permanent mold methods, this is a relatively expensive casting process, but the saving of machining often makes it economical. Certain complex parts can be made by no other method. The method is also adapted to fairly short runs where the die cost of permanent mold or die castings would be excessive. Almost all metals can be cast by this process, including some of the very hard alloys (such as Stellite) that are extremely difficult to machine.

A mold or die is made, usually of metal, which is the reverse of the desired part. Patterns of wax or thermoplastic resins such as polystyrene (see Chap. 14) are cast in this die, under pressure, and these patterns are used to form the cavities in the final mold. In very intricate parts, the pattern may be made of several pieces of wax or plastic cemented together.

If the wax patterns are small, a number of them are cemented together by means of heat into the form of a "tree" with a center trunk of wax and wax branches that support the individual patterns. This "tree" is then dipped in a slurry of a very fine powder of refractory material and a binder which forms a thin shell around the wax and insures a smooth finish on the final castings. The coated "tree" is placed in a metal cylinder or flask and a thick mixture of the refractory "investment" material is poured around it, filling the flask but leaving the base of the center trunk exposed at one end. During this filling process, the unit is vibrated to remove air bubbles and to insure complete filling of the flask.

After the investment material has hardened, the flask is placed in an oven at high temperature for a considerable length of time. The heat not only cures the investment to a hard, dry material with just enough porosity to insure proper venting and sound castings, it also melts out the wax or plastic patterns. This leaves a central opening where the trunk was, with branch passages leading to each cavity, which is an exact reproduction of the wax pattern.

While the mold is still hot, the molten metal is poured in, sometimes by gravity but usually by centrifugal force or gas pressure, to force it into every part of the cavities. A vacuum is also often used around the mold to insure complete filling.

After cooling, the investment material is broken from the flask and the castings; the gate and the feeder sprues are cut and ground off, leaving the finished castings. These usually are cleaned by sand blasting or tumbling to make them ready for use.

Parts having intricate internal cavities and small cored holes can be made more accurately by this method than by any other casting process. Highly complex parts, having difficult or impossible to machine contours, such as turbine blades, can be made of all castable alloys including the very hard, high-temperature alloys such as Stellite. Extremely fine detail can be reproduced with a surface finish of 60 μin. to 90 μin. and tolerances of 0.003 in. to 0.005 in. per inch. Although the process is used mostly for small parts weighing up to 2 or 3 lb, a few companies are now producing investment castings weighing up to 35 lb in steel or bronze. However, these larger castings are seldom economical from a cost standpoint, unless considerable machining can be saved.

A variation of the investment casting process uses frozen mercury instead of wax or plastic for the pattern. The liquid mercury is poured into the metal die, which is split for easy removal and is equipped with any necessary metal cores. The filled mold or die is then immersed in a freezing mixture and the temperature reduced to about -100 F. This freezes the mercury so that it can be removed from the die as a solid metal pattern. If the piece is complicated, several pieces of the frozen mercury pattern can be joined together by simple surface contact, which causes the mercury to adhere or weld together into an integral unit. The complete mercury pattern is then dipped repeatedly into a ceramic slurry which builds up a shell, $\frac{1}{16}$ in. to $\frac{1}{8}$ in. thick, around the pattern. After this shell has hardened, the mercury is allowed to melt out, which it will do at room temperature. The ceramic shell is then fired to harden it and this forms the final mold for the casting. Figures 54 and 55 show two examples of the large, precision castings made by the frozen mercury process. Both require close tolerances, soundness, and exceptional physical characteristics.

Frozen mercury investment castings can be made much larger than the lost wax type. They have been made with dimensions of over 42 in. and a weight of over 300 lb. They can be made also in extremely intricate shapes and with very fine finish and close tolerances. However, both the tool cost and the piece cost are very high, so the process is used primarily for parts that cannot be produced satisfactorily by any other method.

DIE (PRESSURE) CASTING

Die, or pressure, casting has become one of the most important of all mass-production processes. Molten metal (aluminum, zinc, or magnesium) is forced under pressure into a metal die or mold, and the pressure is maintained until the part has hardened. The mold is then opened, the part ejected, and the cycle repeated. The process is done in automatic machines at high production rates, and the piece cost of parts adapted to the process is usually less than by any of the other casting processes. An excellent surface finish (70 μin. to 90 μin.) of high density is obtained with good accuracy, of the order of 0.003 in. to 0.005 in. per inch.

The die must be made accurately of good steel, properly heat-treated, so the die cost is high. For this reason, and because of the setup time of the machines, die casting is a quantity process and is not adapted to short runs. Usually the minimum economical quantity is 2000 to 5000 pieces, although shorter runs are often made under special circumstances. Brass is sometimes die-cast, but the die life is quite short because of the high melting point of the metal. As higher temperature alloys are developed for dies, brass and bronze die casting will no doubt assume much greater importance.

The design of the parts for die casting is more limited than that for sand casting because of the nature of the mold, but very intricate parts can be made by the use of several sections to the die and cores withdrawing in different directions. The wall thickness of die-cast parts can be less than that of sand castings because of the smoother and denser surface, so parts are usually lighter and use less metal for equivalent strength. In large, flat surfaces, a thin wall section usually is used with reinforcing ribs.

The flash that is always present around the parting line of the dies and the cores can be minimized by careful design and die construction. The cost of removing this flash should be considered since it is often a substantial part of the total piece cost.

The size of die castings runs from extremely small pieces weighing only about $\frac{1}{250}$ oz to pieces weighing 35 lb or more in zinc and up to 20 lb in aluminum.

Die-casting machines are divided into two general types, according to the method of injecting the molten metal into the die. The earlier type is known as the *hot chamber machine,* and in this the plunger, which forces the metal into the die, operates in the pot of molten metal (see Figs. 57, 58). This plunger is operated mechanically or by air or hydraulic pressure, and forces the metal up through a gooseneck tube into the die cavity. In some cases, the plunger is dispensed with and air pressure operates directly on the molten metal to accomplish the same result. The hot chamber machine is used usually for the lower melting point metals, such as zinc, tin, and lead. The direct air pressure types can be used for aluminum, but the injection pressure is not sufficient to form really good, dense castings in this material.

The *cold chamber type* of die-casting machine (Fig. 56) has been developed especially for use with the higher melting point alloys such as aluminum, magnesium, and brass. The portion of the machine carrying the dies and the die-closing mechanism is exactly the same as in the hot chamber type, but the melting pot is not a part of the machine itself and at each stroke the required amount of molten metal is poured from a ladle into a slot in the top of the injection cylinder. As the plunger advances, it carries this charge of metal into the die chamber and forces it in under high pressure. The ladling may be done by hand, or, in some of the newer machines, automatically. The pressures used on the metal in the cold chamber machines may run from around 2,000 psi up to 30,000 psi, or, in special applications, as much as 100,000 psi. The high pressures are obtained with smaller cylinders which limit the weight of metal that can be handled at each stroke, and hence the size of castings produced.

The size of both types of machines is given by both the size of the die-mounting plates and the locking pressure that is applied to the closed dies. One of the larger size standard machines has die plates measuring 48 in. by 56 in. and a locking pressure of 750 tons. The smaller machines, in which most die castings are made, have a die space about 24 in. square and a locking pressure of 100 tons to 200 tons. Much smaller machines are made for high-speed automatic production of small parts, especially in zinc, and much larger special machines have been made making parts up to 84 in. in length.

The automotive industry uses large quantities of die castings, both large, for radiator grilles, instrument panels, transmission housings, etc., and small, for door handles, knobs, and ornamental trim. Windshield wipers, carburetors, fuel pumps, and other mechanical parts are also die-cast.

All types of home appliances make wide use of die castings, as do hand power tools, lawnmowers, business machines, electronic equipment, and innumerable other products. Even aluminum cylinder blocks weighing 50 lb have been cast experimentally on a new, 72 in. machine, weighing 250 tons and handling dies up to 50 tons in weight (see Figs. 71, 72). Work is being done on a still larger V-8 engine block weighing 70 lb to 75 lb, to be cast in aluminum on this same machine.

CONTINUOUS CASTING

Of all the casting processes described, the only one that even approaches the production man's ideal of a continuous process is the manufacture of die castings in an automatic machine. The others are definitely "batch" processes, although they may be mechanized to form a continuous series of batches.

For many years, efforts have been made to develop a truly continuous casting process for the forming of steel billets and other shapes of uniform cross section, such as iron pipe. Although progress has been made in this direction and experimental setups are in operation, continuous casting of ferrous metals is not yet being done in significant quantities.

However, the continuous casting of nonferrous metals is being done commercially with excellent results. Both solid and hollow bars of uniform cross section, similar to extrusions (see Chap. 3) are formed directly from the molten metal in several bronze alloys. The process is illustrated and described in Figs. 74, 75, and 76. The dies are made of graphite, and, as the molten metal flows through the die, it is cooled at a controlled rate, giving fine grain structure and excellent physical characteristics. Shapes from $\frac{1}{2}$ in. to 9 in. in diameter and up to 105 in. long are being produced.

Fig. 1. A pump casing sand-cast from gray iron which is typical of the thousands of machine parts cast from this versatile material. (Courtesy, Gray Iron Founders' Society, Inc.)

Fig. 2. A section of a large drilling machine base, sand-cast of gray iron. The reinforcing ribs provide stiffness without excessive weight. (Courtesy, Gray Iron Founders' Society, Inc.)

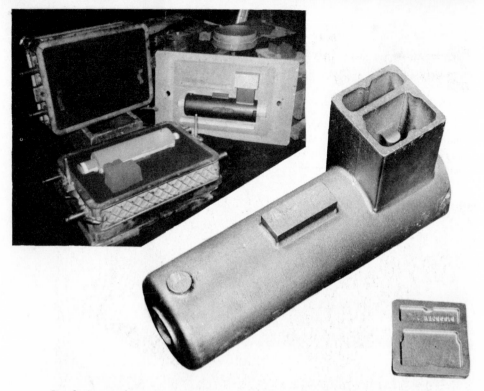

Fig. 3. A typical gray iron casting requiring cores to form the hollow center and the openings in the rectangular projection. The insert shows the sand mold in its flask ready for closing. The "drag," or bottom part, has the lighter-color sand cores in place. At the right is the pattern used to form this mold. (Courtesy, Reading Gray Iron Castings, Inc.)

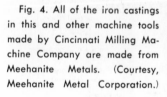

Fig. 4. All of the iron castings in this and other machine tools made by Cincinnati Milling Machine Company are made from Meehanite Metals. (Courtesy, Meehanite Metal Corporation.)

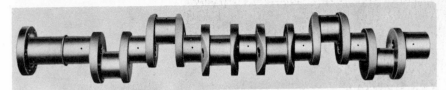

Fig. 5. Crankshafts, such as this, for internal combustion engines, especially of the large Diesel type, are often made from Meehanite metals. Close control of all steps in the casting process is necessary for highly stressed parts of this kind. (Courtesy, Meehanite Metal Corporation.)

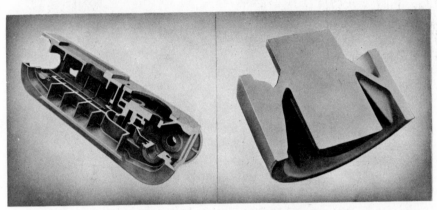

Fig. 6. Two cross-sectioned Meehanite castings showing the uniform density and the absence of porosity obtainable even in complex shapes of varying wall thickness. (Courtesy, Meehanite Metal Corporation.)

Fig. 7

Figs. 7–8. To avoid complex coring, the two halves of this rolling mill pinion housing were made as separate steel castings and then welded together to form a piece weighing over 6000 lb. (Courtesy, Steel Founders' Society of America.)

Fig. 8

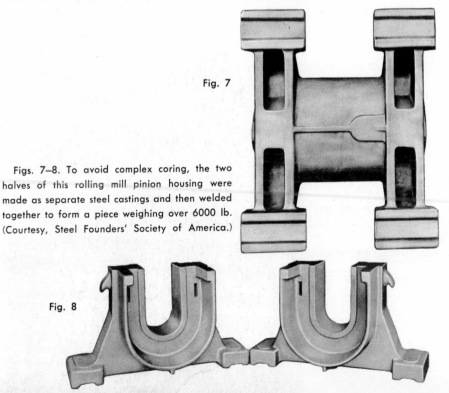

Fig. 9. Rolls for use in steel mills made from "Magaloy" nodular iron show better wear and less breakage than the alloy iron rolls previously used. Casting and machining qualities are superior to those of steel rolls, and the cost is less. (Courtesy, The Aetna-Standard Engineering Company.)

Fig. 10. Large screws cast from nodular or Ductile iron being machined on the lathe in the background. Finished products are shown in the foreground. High strength and good machining properties of nodular iron are important here. (Courtesy, The Aetna-Standard Engineering Company.)

Fig. 11. A group of nodular iron castings used in farm implements. The superior physical properties of the new material were appreciated quickly in this field. (Courtesy, International Harvester Company.)

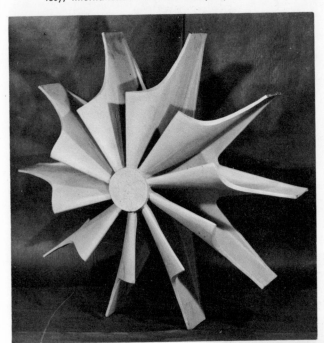

Fig. 12. Sand-cast aluminum impeller, 40 in. in diameter and weighing 200 lb, used in ventilating equipment. (Courtesy, Aluminum Company of America.)

Fig. 13. Sand-cast aluminum flywheel housing used on heavy-duty highway trucks to save weight. (Courtesy, Aluminum Company of America.)

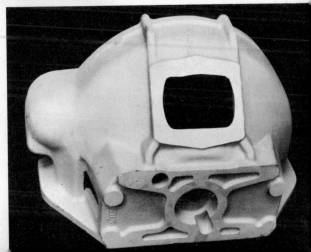

Fig. 14. A typical group of nonferrous sand castings in aluminum, brass, and bronze.
(Courtesy, Bronze Bearings, Inc.)

Fig. 15. The heated pattern for a shell mold casting is sprayed with a release agent.
(Courtesy Bakelite Company.)

Fig. 16. The pattern is clamped to the shell machine which is filled partially with the sand-resin mixture. (Courtesy, Bakelite Company.)

Fig. 17. The machine is inverted, covering the pattern with the sand-resin. (Courtesy, Bakelite Company.)

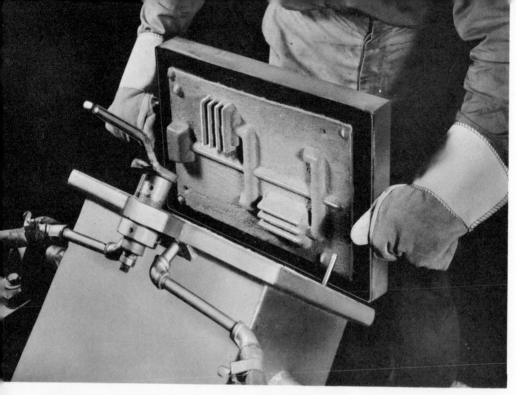

Fig. 18. The machine is turned up again and the pattern with an adhering shell of sand-resin is removed and placed in an oven for further curing. (Courtesy, Bakelite Company.)

Fig. 19. The cured shell is removed from the pattern by means of the ejector pins. (Courtesy, Bakelite Company.)

Fig. 20

Figs. 20–21. The two halves of the shell are placed together and clamped (Fig. 21) to form the complete mold. (Courtesy, Bakelite Company.)

Fig. 21

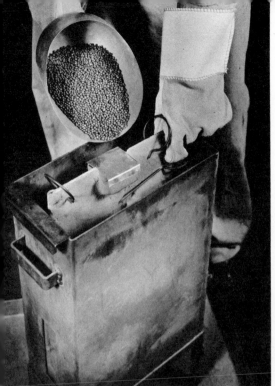

Fig. 22. The mold is placed in a flask and backed up with iron shot or grit. (Courtesy, Bakelite Company.)

Fig. 23

Figs. 23–24. The metal is poured. After cooling, the shell is broken off, leaving the completed casting, in this case four pieces, ready to have the gating cut off (Fig. 24). (Courtesy, Bakelite Company.)

Fig. 24

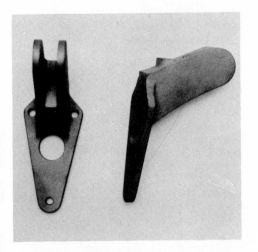

Fig. 25. A lubricator bracket produced as a shell mold casting in both gray and malleable iron. A saving of 30 percent in weight and 70 percent in machining over sand casting was realized, in addition to a much better surface finish. Hole centers were held within ±0.005 in. (Courtesy, Emmaus Foundry & Machine Company, Inc.)

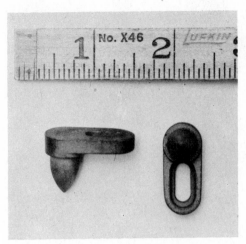

Fig. 26. An indexing lug for a textile machine. Brass sand castings originally used required excessive machining; die castings were then tried but the material was too soft. Now shell-molded in gray iron at less cost and with four to five times the life. (Courtesy, Emmaus Foundry & Machine Company, Inc.)

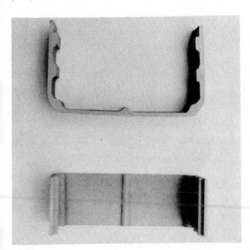

Fig. 27. An electronic part in aluminum. The wall thickness of 0.080 in. was too thin for sand casting. The part could be made as a die casting but the tool cost was four times as high and ductility not so good as the shell mold piece. (Courtesy, Emmaus Foundry & Machine Company, Inc.)

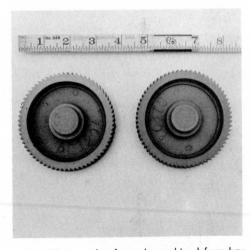

Fig. 28. A ratchet formerly machined from bar stock but now shell mold cast from gray iron. A saving of 30 percent in weight and $4.80 in machining cost resulted from the change. (Courtesy, Emmaus Foundry & Machine Company, Inc.)

Fig. 29. This four-station shell mold machine (*right*) and shell closing machine (*left*) are the heart of a completely mechanized shell mold casting system. Here it is being used to produce malleable iron sprockets in large quantity. (Courtesy, Link-Belt Company.)

Fig. 30. One half of the shell mold and a group of 14 sprockets cast at one time. (Courtesy, Link-Belt Company.)

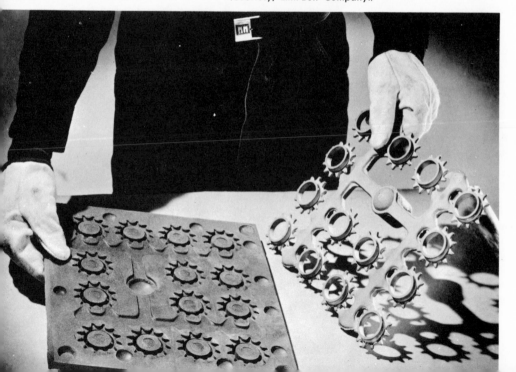

Fig. 31. The finished sprockets. Cutting of the thread is the only machining operation required. (Courtesy, Link-Belt Company.)

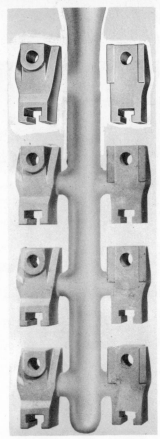

Fig. 32. A "tree" of stainless steel valve wedges after the shell mold is broken off. The two top wedges have been cut loose to show the individual pieces. (Courtesy, Investment Casting Company.)

Fig. 33. A group of small shell mold castings in bronze, aluminum, steel, and stainless steel. (Courtesy, Investment Casting Company.)

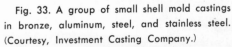

Fig. 34   Fig. 35

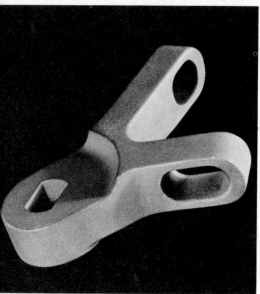

Figs. 34–35. Typical parts produced in aluminum by the plaster mold process showing the sharp detail and the good finish obtainable. (Courtesy, Ohio Precision Castings, Inc.)

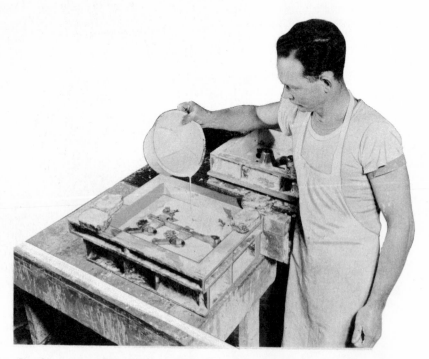

Fig. 36. Pouring the plaster over the pattern for a plaster mold casting. (Courtesy, Ohio Precision Castings, Inc.)

Fig. 38. A 130-lb diffuser made of aluminum by the Antioch process. The smooth filleted blades required no finishing. (Courtesy, Morris Bean & Company.)

Fig. 37. Removing the pattern from the hardened plaster mold. (Courtesy, Ohio Precision Castings, Inc.)

Fig. 39. A large aluminum tire mold, cast by the Antioch process, weighing 2000 lb with the 9-ft diameter held to ±0.060. The tread surface is used as cast and must be free from all porosity. (Courtesy, Morris Bean & Company.)

Fig. 40. A group of steel castings produced by the Ceramicast ® process, showing sharp detail and smooth surfaces. (Courtesy, Lebanon Steel Foundry.)

Fig. 41. Pouring the ceramic slurry over the pattern for a Ceramicast ® mold. (Courtesy, Lebanon Steel Foundry.)

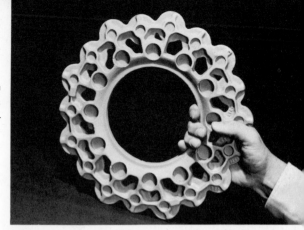

Fig. 42. The steel casting from the pattern shown in Fig. 41. (Courtesy, Lebanon Steel Foundry.)

Fig. 43. Permanent mold-cast aluminum pistons such as these are used in most automobiles, trucks, buses, and aircraft. (Courtesy, Aluminum Company of America.)

Fig. 44. Permanent mold-cast aluminum washing-machine agitators are light in weight and resist corrosion. (Courtesy, Aluminum Company of America.)

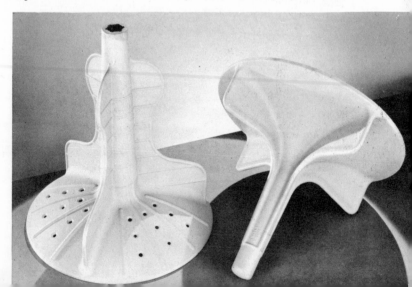

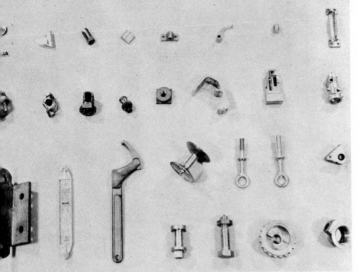

Fig. 45. A group of permanent mold castings made of aluminum bronze. Excellent physical characteristics and grain structure are obtained in these parts. (Courtesy, Alcaloy, Inc.)

Fig. 46. A chain and shackles cast entirely of aluminum bronze in permanent metal molds. Alternate links are cast individually and these are held in the mold while the connecting links are cast around them. It is used where the unit must be nonmagnetic and nonsparking, yet have good strength. (Courtesy, Alcaloy, Inc.)

Fig. 47. This stainless steel pipe was cast centrifugally, then turned and bored. It is 12 in. in diameter with 1.17-in. wall thickness, and is for use in a chemical plant where strength and corrosion resistance are required. (Courtesy, United States Pipe and Foundry Company.)

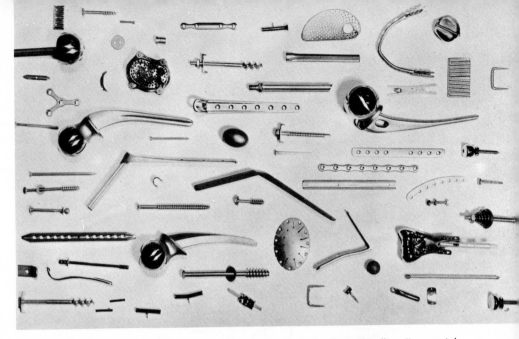

Fig. 48. A group of surgical appliances investment cast from "Vitallium," a special cobalt-chromium alloy developed especially for this purpose. The parts shown are used to repair fractures, replace bone sections and joints, and for similar uses. (Courtesy, Austenal Laboratories, Inc.)

Fig. 49. A group of typical investment castings in a variety of metals. (Courtesy, Investment Casting Company.)

Fig. 50. Wax patterns for investment castings being mounted in the form of a tree. (Courtesy, Investment Casting Company.)

Fig. 51. The "tree" of wax patterns is placed in the cylindrical flask and the investment material is poured around it. Vibration and a vacuum insure complete filling. (Courtesy, Investment Casting Company.)

Fig. 52. After casting, the investment material is broken away, leaving a "tree" of castings which are exact duplicates of the wax originals. (Courtesy, Investment Casting Company.)

Fig. 53. These turbine blades with their complex contours would be very difficult to machine. They are made in large quantities by investment casting in various heat- and corrosion-resistant alloys. (Courtesy, Austenal Laboratories, Inc.)

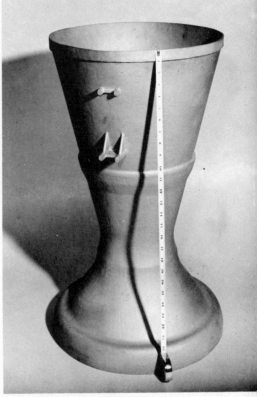

Fig. 54. A missile booster nozzle precision cast by the frozen mercury process, 30 in. long and weighing 150 lb. (Courtesy, Kolcast Industries, Inc.)

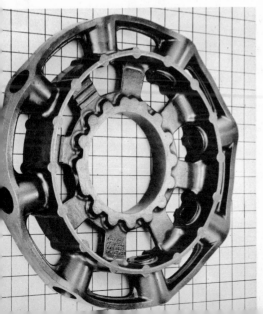

Fig. 55. A jet engine bearing support 15 in. in diameter, weighing 30 lb, made as a frozen mercury casting. (Courtesy, Kolcast Industries, Inc.)

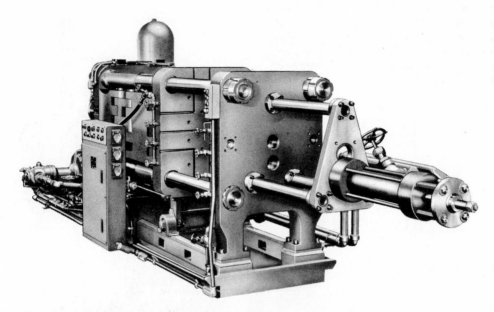

Fig. 56. A typical cold chamber die-casting machine for aluminum, magnesium, or brass. The melting pot is separate, and just enough metal for one casting is ladled into a slot in the injection cylinder at each stroke. The average production for a machine of this type is 150 castings per hour. The die-mounting plates are 36 in. by 40 in. and the locking pressure is 500 tons. (Courtesy, Cast-Master, Inc.)

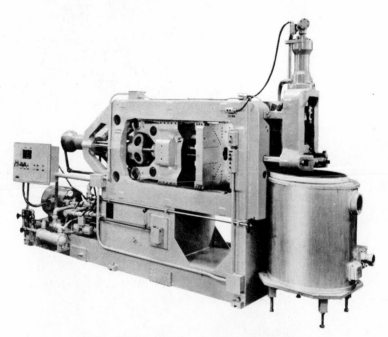

Fig. 57. A typical hot chamber die-casting machine for use with zinc, lead, or tin. (Courtesy, Lester-Phoenix, Incorporated.)

Fig. 58. A cross-sectional drawing of the same machine as that shown in Fig. 57. The melting pot is integral with the machine and the plunger is submerged in the molten metal. Action of the plunger forces the metal up through the gooseneck tube into the die cavity. (Courtesy, Lester-Phoenix, Incorporated.)

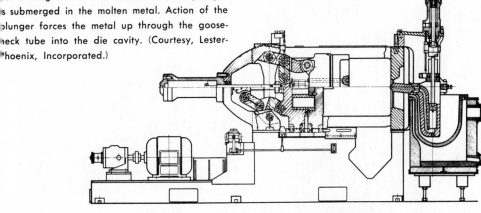

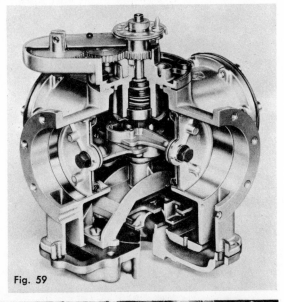

Figs. 59–60. The complex body of this A. O. Smith gasoline meter pump is made as an aluminum die casting in the intricate die shown in Fig. 60. Eight slides are required, four for the circular cores and four for the side pulls. (Courtesy, American Die Casting Institute, Inc.)

Fig. 59

Fig. 60

Fig. 61

Figs. 61–62. The housing of this Jack & Heintz aircraft inverter was changed from a machined sand casting to a magnesium die casting with a 54 percent saving in cost. The complex die for making this large part is shown in Fig. 62 (below). In spite of the cost of a die such as this, it was amortized in the first 1500 to 1800 pieces. (Courtesy, American Die Casting Institute, Inc.)

Fig. 62

Fig. 63. The housing of this attractive portable radio combines molded polystyrene (see Chap. 14) with zinc die castings. (Courtesy, American Die Casting Institute, Inc.)

Fig. 64 (below). The die-cast frame, base, and dial of the radio illustrated in Fig. 63. The smooth surface is finished with a brass satin lacquer and the molded-in name and dial markings are filled with black. (Courtesy, American Die Casting Institute, Inc.)

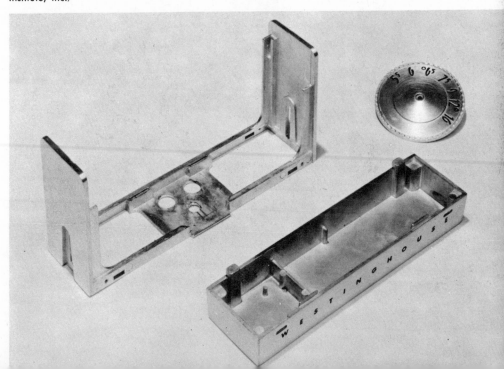

Fig. 65

Fig. 66

Fig. 67

Figs. 65–67. This Singer sew
ing machine was changed
from the old style (Fig. 65) (top)
which used mostly iron sand cast
ings, requiring considerable ma
chining, to the new design (Fig
66) (center). Reduced weight, im
proved appearance, and lowe
cost were made possible by the
two complex die castings shown
in Fig. 67 (bottom). (Courtesy
American Die Casting Institute
Inc.)

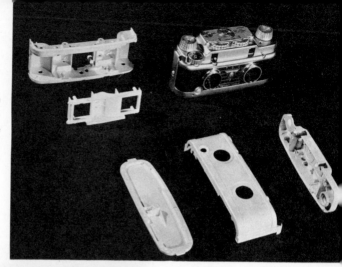

Fig. 68. These five aluminum die castings make up most of the stereo camera shown. The five parts together weigh only 0.681 lb. (Courtesy, Aluminum Company of America.)

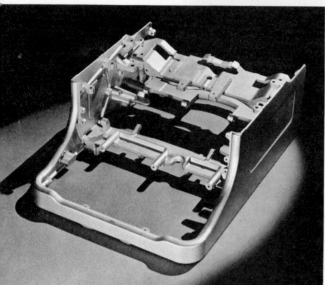

Fig. 69. Six aluminum-silicon alloy die castings make up this intricate but easily assembled typewriter frame. (Courtesy, Aluminum Company of America.)

Fig. 70. A group of tiny zinc die castings produced in large quantities by special techniques that permit close tolerances and turn out finished parts at low cost. The pencil point gives an idea of size. (Courtesy, Gries Reproducer Corp.)

Fig. 71

Figs. 71–72. This 72-in. die-casting machine, weighing 250 tons, is said to be the world's largest. It opens new fields for large die castings, such as the 50-lb, 6-cylinder automobile engine block shown in Fig. 72. The same block in gray iron would weigh about 175 lb and would cost about 10 percent more. The superior heat conductivity of aluminum is also an advantage here. The production rate from the one machine is 30 to 35 pieces per hour. (Courtesy, Doehler-Jarvis Div., National Lead Company.)

Fig. 72

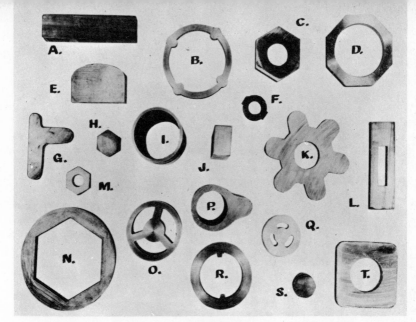

Fig. 73. A group of continuous cast bronze shapes that are formed in bars up to 105 in. long. They are as follows: (A) Sliding way for ATF printing press; (B) shape designed for use in Naval Ordnance; (C) nut stock; (D) octagon nut shape; (E) sliding way in a dam gate; (F) special nut stock; (G) pistol shape used in the thread guide of a textile machine; (H) nut stock; (I) bushing; (J) key stock; (K) six-tooth gear blank; (L) slide valve bushing for air brake; (M) nut stock; (N) shaft bushing; (O) valve seat; (P) connecting rod; (Q) valve seat; (R) seat ring; (S) rod; and (T) bearing used on hospital bed. (Courtesy, American Smelting & Refining Co.)

Fig. 74. A cross-sectional drawing of the vertical production line used in continuous casting of bronze shapes. From the furnace at the top, the metal flows through water-cooled graphite dies to the roll drive on the floor below. The movement of the now solidified metal is controlled by the roll drive on the floor below. They are then cut to length and carried away on conveyors on the lower floor. (Courtesy, American Smelting & Refining Co.)

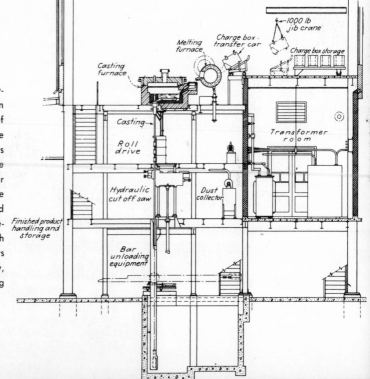

Fig. 75. The roll drive that controls the continuous casting process. (Courtesy, American Smelting & Refining Co.)

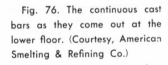

Fig. 76. The continuous cast bars as they come out at the lower floor. (Courtesy, American Smelting & Refining Co.)

2

Stamping and Forming Processes

All of these processes are based on various methods of cutting and forming metal that previously has been rolled at the mill into sheets, plates, or strips. Although the processes are basically the same, the size and the power of the presses used vary tremendously, since the raw material may be anything from a fragile aluminum foil to armor plate several inches thick! All sheet metals can be stamped, but some will stand much more severe bending and forming than others. The processes themselves range from simple shearing to extremely complex forming operations on automatic, multiple-slide machines. Along with castings, stampings are the most widely used components of the mechanical devices that are so familiar in our everyday lives. The cost is very low, especially if the quantities are large enough to justify fairly elaborate tooling. On parts that can be adapted to the requirements of stampings, this is without doubt the most economical production process.

PUNCH PRESS WORK

Stamping operations are performed on various sizes and types of punch presses, and, while the presses themselves are simple machines, great skill and ingenuity go into the design and the building of the dies that do the actual work in them.

The complete die usually consists of a movable part, or punch, carried by the ram of the press, and a stationary part, or die block, mounted in the bed of the press. (The word "die" is often used somewhat confusingly, both for the complete set, consisting of punch and die block, and also for the stationary member of the pair, herein called the die block.) The material to be worked is placed between these. The ram may be driven by mechanical power from a crankshaft which usually is assisted, during the working part of the stroke, by the power stored in a flywheel, or it may be driven by hydraulic power. The size of presses varies, from those that form a whole automobile body top at one stroke to tiny high-speed automatic units for stamping out little washers and lugs. Other types of heavy presses form material up to ¾ in. thick cold or up to 3½ in. hot. However, most stampings are made from sheet stock less than ⅜ in. thick. Almost all sheet metals can be formed by punch-press operations. Those most commonly used are steel, including many alloy and stainless types; brass and other copper base alloys; and various aluminum alloys. Magnesium usually has to be formed hot. For deep-drawn parts, special alloys are available to stand the severe cold working involved.

Dies may be divided roughly into those with a cutting action (such as perforating, blanking, and shearing dies) and those that do bending and forming operations. Many combination dies perform both operations at a single stroke.

Perforating dies punch holes of various sizes and shapes in the workpiece, and the slugs that are punched out drop through the die block and usually are scrapped. A blanking die, on the other hand, trims the outer edges of the workpiece to the desired shape, and the part trimmed off from the edges is. the scrap. Perforating dies may punch a single hole, a group of holes, or all of the holes in a large and complicated piece. The quantity required will determine whether a piece should be perforated by single dies in a series of operations or whether the cost of a multiple die will be justified. For any irregular shape, a blanking die is usually necessary in any case.

Dies are classified according to the service expected of them and the quantities of parts that are likely to be required. Considerable savings can be made by not building dies that are much better than required. *Carbide* dies are the most durable and expensive type of stamping tools and are seldom economical unless a production quantity of 5 million pieces or more is anticipated. *Class A* dies are the highest quality of tool steel dies and are good for production of over 1 million pieces. *Class B* dies usually are specified for quantities of ½ million to 1 million pieces. They are made of less expensive steels and thinner materials and cost about one half as much as the Class A dies.

For runs of less than ½ million pieces, often various forms of short-run tooling can be used to advantage. These are made of thinner material than conventional dies, sometimes as thin as $\frac{1}{16}$ in., backed up by standard backing plates. The cost of these short-run dies is often one fifth to one tenth that of Class A dies, and, where the quantity of parts required is within their normal life, they do a perfectly adequate job.

In stamping relatively soft or thin metals, especially where the quantities are not large, one part of the die may often be a rubber pad, with a considerable saving in die cost. A flat rubber pad, properly supported, can be used in place of the punch on perforating and blanking operations. In forming, either the punch or the die may be of rubber, according to the shape to be formed. Some shapes with internal bulges or recesses can be formed with rubber pads that would be difficult or impossible to form by any other method. Selection of the proper grade of rubber, and the proper method of mounting and supporting it, is very important in applying this method, but good results are being obtained in regular production. The aircraft industry has made good use of this method (see Figs. 103, 104).

Some companies make a large variety of standard stock dies in round, square, oval, and rectangular shapes, as well as certain frequently used combination perforating dies. Where a stock of these dies is maintained and parts are designed with their use in view, often short runs can be made without tool cost or with very low tool cost. The use of these dies usually requires a series of operations for a part that a special die could do at one stroke, so each part should be examined carefully to determine the proper balance between tool cost and production labor. Multiple perforating dies for moderate runs are often assembled from these standard punches and die blocks mounted on standard beds or plates. Many types of parts with a number of holes can be made very economically by the use of these standard die sets (see Figs. 106, 107).

For forming and drawing dies in the lighter gage metals, especially where the quantities are not too large, dies of a zinc alloy known as Kirksite are often used to good advantage. This material can be cast easily and worked to final form so that the cost is much less than steel dies. Its self-lubricating qualities prevent scratching and scoring the work.

With the improvement in plastic materials, the use of plastic forming dies is expanding rapidly (see Figs. 108–111). Both epoxy and phenolic resins (see Chap. 14) are used for this, with or without fillers or reinforcements of metal powders or glass fibers. They are made economically by casting or building up over forms of metal or even wood, and for light-gage metal and moderate runs they have proved entirely satisfactory.

Another economical method of making multiple perforating dies is by the use of a special low melting point alloy known as Cerromatrix® (see Figs. 112–114). A female die plate is made having the necessary holes machined in it. For short-run work, this may be a relatively thin plate of tool steel with the holes simply drilled and reamed. This plate is used as a template to locate the punches which are positioned by it on a standard flat plate or in oversize holes in such a plate, and the melted Cerromatrix poured around them. This alloy has the property of expanding when it cools so that the punches are locked firmly in position.

Shearing dies are used for straight cuts such as cutting rectangular blanks or strips out of sheet stock. Shearing dies may be used in a punch press, but most shearing is done in special shears having long straight blades. These are made in a wide variety of sizes up to gigantic machines with blades 20 ft or more long that will cut 1½-in. steel plate.

In the same way, simple straight bends usually are made in special "brakes" having long, straight dies that fold the sheet metal to the desired angle, and with the desired radius. More complicated bends are made in quantity on special forming dies used either in these brakes or in punch presses. Brakes can be used also with special blanking or perforating dies for certain types of stamping operations, especially on large, flat pieces.

When complicated pieces are to be made in large quantities, progressive dies may be made and the raw material purchased in the form of long strips of the desired width. This strip stock may be fed automatically through the various stages of the progressive die (see Fig. 93) which performs the necessary perforating and forming operations before the piece finally is blanked out. Dies of this type are expensive, but the production rates from them are very high and the piece cost correspondingly low.

Complicated small pieces, made of wire or narrow strip, can be formed in large quantities on multiple-slide machines which are completely automatic and have a very high production rate. However, the tooling and the setup of these presses is expensive, and is justified only on long runs.

Irregularly shaped pieces or holes can be cut in small quantities on "nibbling" or circular shearing machines. These work from a sheet-metal template or can be guided by hand to cut out the desired pieces, one at a time. They are very useful for sample work (see Figs. 115–117).

Another special press for perforating small and medium quantities is a turret press (see Fig. 94), where a number of various size punches and die blocks are mounted on a pair of disks or turrets which can be rotated by hand to bring the desired die set into the operating position. This saves the time that otherwise would be required to set up each individual die in a standard press.

In the design of stampings, it is good practice to have the diameter of the smallest holes no less than the thickness of the material being punched, and no closer to the edge or to another hole than the material thickness. The tolerance on all dimensions should be as liberal as possible, $\pm \frac{1}{64}$ in. being common where holes are punched in a series of operations. Much closer tolerances can be held between the holes in a multiple die. Where holes are located on opposite sides of a bend, close tolerances are very difficult to hold, and, if possible, one of the holes should be slotted so that a slight variation in dimensions will not interfere with later assembly operations.

DRAWING

Deep-drawn pieces, such as metal cans or cups, are formed from flat stock in a series of operations in which each die draws the piece nearer to its final form. Since severe forming makes the metal hard and brittle, it is sometimes necessary, between the operations, to anneal the pieces by heating to prevent cracks from developing. These deep-drawn parts usually are formed in hydraulic presses, since a slow steady pressure at a controlled rate is desired rather than a sharp blow.

A form of deep drawing or forming has been developed recently known as Hydroforming (see Figs. 121–124). Hydraulic pressure acting against a rubber diaphragm forms the female half of the die so that only the male half or punch is required. The blank of sheet metal is clamped to a ring with the diaphragm over it. Hydraulic pressure is applied to a chamber above the diaphragm, and the punch, which is formed to the desired shape, is forced up against the blank. As the punch moves up, the hydraulic pressure, working against the diaphragm, forms the metal into the shape of the punch. In light-gage metals, deep draws can be formed by this method with half or less of the tool cost of regular drawing dies.

ROLL FORMING AND BENDING

Strips of sheet metal can be formed into angles, channels, tubes, or complex irregular shapes by passing them between a series of rolls, so formed that they work the material gradually into the desired form (see Figs. 125–128). This is a very economical way of producing shaped moldings and tubing in large quantities, since the production rate is very rapid, as high as 300 feet per minute (fpm), and the finished work very smooth. Material from thin strips to bars ¾ in. thick can be worked in this way. A simple version of roll forming is used by sheet-metal workers for forming the lock seams in heating and air-conditioning ducts and similar work.

Roll-forming machines are relatively inexpensive and they are practical for use in many small shops having this type of work to do. Roll-formed parts are often competitive with standard structural steel shapes and with extrusions. They are lighter in weight, and offer a wider variety of shapes than the hot rolled steel shapes, and have a much smoother surface, which often reduces finishing costs. (For a comparison with extrusions, see the section on this process in Chap. 3.)

Wide sheet can be roll-formed with corrugations, with ribs, or in special shapes that often simplify the forming of such structures as refrigeration cabinets and bus bodies.

Roll bending consists of passing sheets or bars of flat stock through three flat rolls, so spaced that they bend the material into a ring or curve of predetermined radius. The radius is determined by the roll spacing. Rings or hoops often are formed by this method, with the ends welded together after forming. Structural steel beams can be bent to a given radius by means of rolls shaped to fit the beams. Heavy steel plates for ships' hulls are bent to shape by bending rolls, some of which are heavy enough to handle armor plate up to a thickness of several inches.

SPINNING

Disks of flat material can be formed by spinning into simple or complex round shapes similar in some cases to those formed by drawing. The blank is clamped against a wood, plastic, or metal pattern, and both are rotated in a lathe. The metal gradually is worked into shape against the pattern by means of simple hand tools or rollers which are pressed against the rotating workpiece, or by means of automatically operated tools in special lathes. The patterns cost much less than dies for drawing and, while the piece cost is much more than for stamped or drawn parts, it is not excessive; spinning is often the most economical method where the quantities do not justify drawing dies. Ornamental bases and trim for lamps and lighting fixtures are often spun, as well as metal reflectors and kitchenware. While spinning usually is thought of in connection with small parts of light-gage metal, it is by no means limited to this field. Curved heads for large tanks are regularly spun out of steel plates up to 1¼ in. thick and in diameters up to 20 ft in special heavy lathes built for this purpose. By hot spinning, thicknesses up to 6 in. can be formed.

A highly refined development of the spinning process is known as Floturning or Hydrospinning (see Figs. 138–142). It is actually a cold extrusion process (see Chap. 3), since the thickness of the metal in the original blank is reduced considerably in the forming. In a typical case, a flat disk is clamped at the small end of a cone-shaped steel mandrel in a very heavy lathe. The two are rotated while two polished rollers of hardened steel are forced under tremendous pressure against opposite sides of the work and press it against the mandrel or form, moving gradually to the large end of the cone as the work progresses. The angle of the rollers and the pressures involved cause a reduction in thickness, often to less than half that of the original blank. Close tolerances can be held and the cold working improves the characteristics of the metal. Compared with deep drawing, the process is expensive, although the tool cost is lower. Compared with the cost of machining the parts from solid stock or from a forged blank, it may show substantial savings and result in a considerable reduction in the weight of the finished part.

PERFORATED METALS

The use of perforated metal sheets or coils often saves considerable special tooling and press work. Perforated metal, as the name implies, is simply sheet metal that has been perforated by a pattern of holes. The entire area can be perforated, or, for special applications, margins and certain areas may remain unperforated. A great variety of perforated patterns is available with varying sizes and arrangements of holes for different purposes. A few uses are: architectural enclosures; screening for mining, rock products, food processing, and chemical industries; automobile grilles; sound abatement; machine guards; air vents in cabinets and enclosures of all kinds. Steel, other metals, and nonmetallic sheeting can be perforated economically with standard dies.

EXPANDED METALS

An ingenious process that eliminates the waste of metal when holes are punched in it is used in producing expanded metal. A sheet of solid metal is pierced with a series of slits that cut through the sheet but do not remove any metal. The sheet is then gripped at its two sides, that are parallel with the slits, and is stretched to several times its original length, thus opening the slits into diamond-shaped openings. The surface of the sheet is left irregular with sharp edges, but, in this form, it is suitable for certain uses such as metal lath for use under plaster and for factory partitions and the like. For other uses where a smooth, flat surface is required, the sheets are flattened to resemble the perforated products. In this form, it is used for many of the same applications as perforated metal. It is considerably less expensive, but does not have the variety of patterns available in the perforated product.

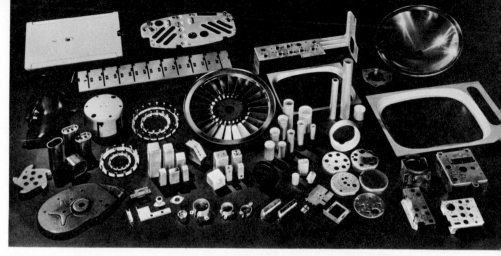

Fig. 77. A group of small stampings produced for the electronics industry. The television tube mask at the right center was formed by the unconventional procedure of blanking the large center hole first to salvage 2 lb of usable steel. The throat is then drawn to the contour of the tube with a tolerance of ±0.002 in. This part was produced at the rate of 20,000 per week. (Courtesy, Paul & Beekman, Inc.)

Fig. 78. A group of automobile radio chassis produced in large quantity by progressive dies. Some of these are made from terne plate (see Chap. 16) to avoid the need for a plating operation. (Courtesy, Paul & Beekman, Inc.)

Fig. 79. These two lawn-mower stampings, spot welded together, replaced a casting at about one half the cost, due to large-volume production. (Courtesy, Paul & Beekman, Inc.)

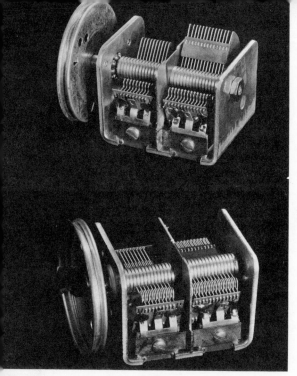

Fig. 80. A variable condenser of the type used in all radio receivers is made almost entirely of stampings except for the shaft, which is a screw machine part. These units are made in large quantities by automatic equipment at very low cost. (Courtesy, Paul & Beekman, Inc.)

Fig. 81. This modern-type shear and press brake form an excellent team for a wide variety of straight cutting and forming operations on material up to ½ in. mild steel. In combination with the two heavy presses in the background, a shop would be equipped to handle most of the usual blanking, perforating, and forming operations on medium-size work. (Courtesy, Niagara Machine & Tool Works.)

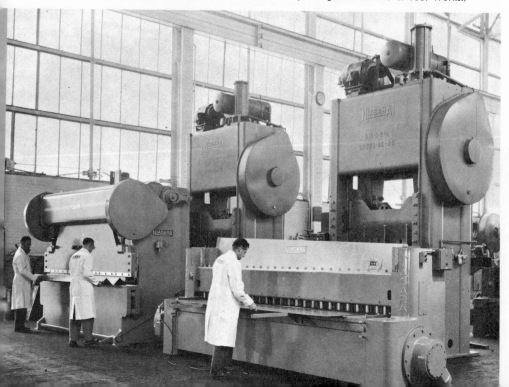

Fig. 82. The press brake, when equipped with special work area features, can be adapted to a wide variety of standard and special bending, punching, and drawing operations. This one has been fitted with a flanged bed and ram for use on a multiple step perforating and notching operation. (Courtesy, Niagara Machine & Tool Works.)

Fig. 83. A deep throat punch press made with either 18-in. or 24-in. throat depth especially for perforating large size sheets. A variety of standard punches and dies in round, square, hexagonal, rectangular, and other shapes is available at low cost for use in such presses. (Courtesy, Whitney Metal Tool Company.)

Fig. 84. One of the heaviest standard shears made. It will cut mild steel up to 1½ in. thick, 12 ft long. (Courtesy, The Cincinnati Shaper Co.)

Fig. 85. The press brake used for perforating corrugated sheets of galvanized iron for a corn crib. On light operations such as this, wide extensions can be used on the ram and bed. All of the holes are punched in one operation. (Courtesy, The Cincinnati Shaper Co.)

Fig. 86. Adjustable dies used in a press brake to perforate a large sheet. (Courtesy, The Cincinnati Shaper Co.)

Fig. 87. A large press brake with special dies used to form long sections of complex shape. (Courtesy, The Cincinnati Shaper Co.)

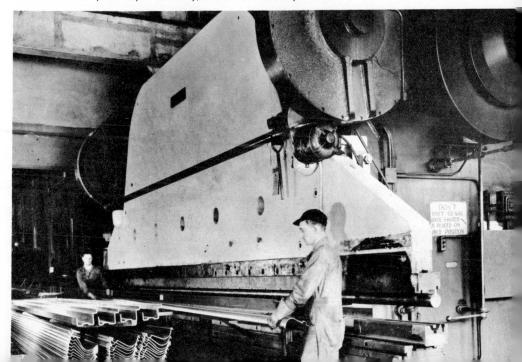

Fig. 88. These water cooler housings were perforated and formed on a press brake using interchangeable dies. (Courtesy, The Cincinnati Shaper Co.)

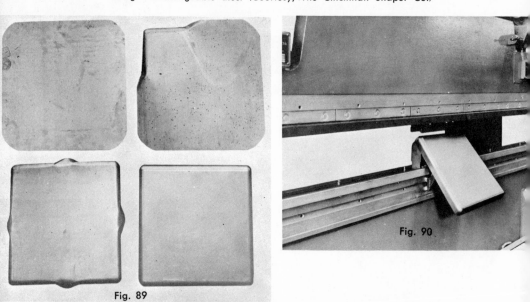

Fig. 89

Fig. 90

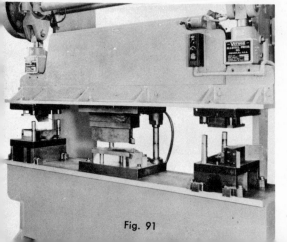

Fig. 91

Figs. 89–91. An ingenious method of producing a drawn furnace cover with simple dies on a press brake. The flat blank is shown (top left). The corners are formed, one at a time (top right and bottom left). The sides are then finish formed (bottom right and Fig. 90). Fig. 91 shows the die setup in a medium-size brake. Operations are from right to left: trim corners of blank, draw corners, and trim surplus stock after draw. (Courtesy, Verson Allsteel Press Company.)

Fig. 92. An unusual application of the press brake to form conical sections with standard dies. (Courtesy, The Cincinnati Shaper Co.)

Fig. 93. This set of progressive dies forms the automobile part in the foreground, by a series of 14 stages. The workpiece in the center shows the various steps from the flat strip at the bottom to the finished piece at the top. The work is moved up one step automatically at each stroke of the press. (Courtesy, Paul & Beekman, Inc.)

Fig. 94. A large turret punch press with a direct measuring table for locating the work under the punch and an electronic control by means of which the operator can select any desired die set easily and rapidly. In the simpler turret presses, these operations are performed manually. (Courtesy, Wiedemann Machine Company.)

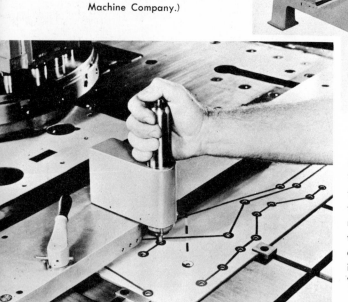

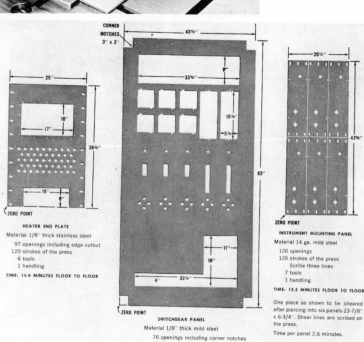

Fig. 95. A template attachment on the turret punch press. The operator moves the plunger from one position to another on the template and the work is moved to a corresponding position. The punch trips automatically when the plunger drops into the template hole. (Courtesy, Wiedemann Machine Company.)

CORNER NOTCHES 3" x 3"

43¾"

25"

10"

17"

36¾"

15"

6"

ZERO POINT

HEATER END PLATE
Material 1/8" thick stainless steel
97 openings including edge cutout
120 strokes of the press
6 tools
1 handling
TIME: 14.9 MINUTES FLOOR TO FLOOR

33¾"

8"

15½"

5½"

63"

11"

16"

4"   33¾"

ZERO POINT

SWITCHGEAR PANEL
Material 1/8" thick mild steel
76 openings including corner notches
126 strokes of the press
8 tools
1 handling
TIME: 21.8 MINUTES FLOOR TO FLOOR

20¼"

47¾"

ZERO POINT

INSTRUMENT MOUNTING PANEL
Material 14 ga. mild steel
126 openings
126 strokes of the press
Scribe three lines
7 tools
1 handling
TIME: 15.5 MINUTES FLOOR TO FLOOR

One piece as shown to be sheared after piercing into six panels 23-7/8" x 6-3/4". Shear lines are scribed on the press.
Time per panel 2.6 minutes.

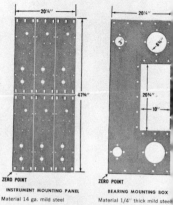

20¼"

6½"

20¼"

10"

ZERO POINT

BEARING MOUNTING BOX
Material 1/4" thick mild steel
38 openings including edge
52 strokes of the press
5 tools
1 handling
TIME: 9.2 MINUTES FLOOR TO

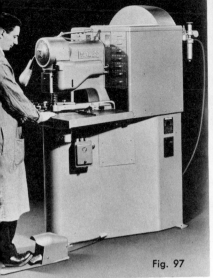

Fig. 97

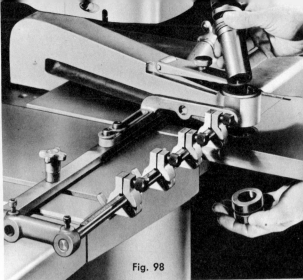

Fig. 98

Fig. 99

Figs. 97–100. A versatile sheet-metal fabricating machine (Fig. 97) uses quickly interchangeable punches and dies with individual strippers (Fig. 98) kept in the cabinet at the rear. Adjustable stops (Fig. 99) locate the work on the table. A nibbling punch can be used for cutting circles and large holes. Short-run perforating and notching can be done economically with standard dies. Typical work is shown in Fig. 100. (Courtesy, Wales-Strippit Corporation.)

Fig. 96. Typical work done the press shown in Fig. 94 h a 32-station turret. Pro-ction operations and time are o shown. (Courtesy, Wiede-nn Machine Company.)

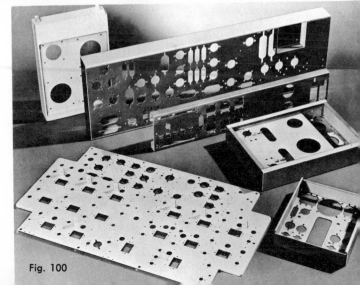

Fig. 100

Fig. 101. A "Multi-Slide" ® forming machine for making intricate small parts of wire or strip in large quantities. (Courtesy, U.S. Tool Company, Inc.)

Fig. 102. A group of parts made on the "Multi-Slide" ® machine. (Courtesy, U.S. Tool Company, Inc.)

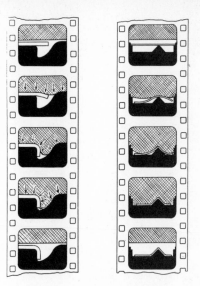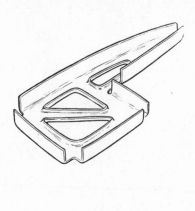

Fig. 103. A series of drawings showing the action of a rubber pad used in a forming die. The rubber pad is cross-hatched; the metal die is solid black with the workpiece between them. (Courtesy, Clearing Machine Corporation.)

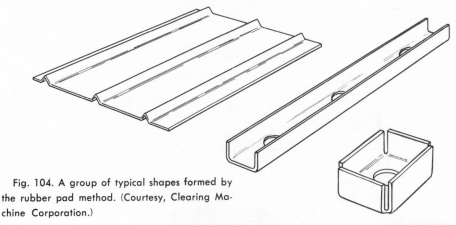

Fig. 104. A group of typical shapes formed by the rubber pad method. (Courtesy, Clearing Machine Corporation.)

Fig. 105. These air-conditioner parts were produced almost entirely with standard dies, from steel sheet that was preplated with zinc. Since there was very little scrap loss on these pieces, this proved more economical than a later finishing operation. (Courtesy, Paul & Beekman, Inc.)

Fig. 106. A typical setup of adjustable perforating dies with the finished workpiece in the foreground. Any combination of these dies can be set up on the standard base plates by means of the tee slots. The dies can be reused in a new setup after the job is done. This is especially good for runs of a few thousand pieces where the same piece is not rerun often. (Courtesy, S. B. Whistler & Sons, Inc.)

Fig. 107. Another type of adjustable perforating die where the dies are held to the base plate by means of permanent magnets in each retainer unit. The punches and dies are located by a $\frac{3}{16}$-in. thick template. These templates can be stored for a rerun of the same job and a very quick setup is possible. This makes a flexible arrangement where a variety of perforating jobs is run and repeated in moderate quantities from time to time. (Courtesy, S. B. Whistler & Sons, Inc.)

Fig. 108. This large drop hammer die at Lockheed Aircraft is made of modified Ciba Araldite epoxy resin. The cores of the punch and the die are made of Kirksite metal with a ¼-in. to ⅜-in. facing of plastic. (Courtesy, Furane Plastics, Inc.)

Fig. 109. Typical draw die made of Rezolin Toolplastik with parts made from this and similar dies. A gray iron core was used for the die cavity with plastic face. The punch is solid plastic. The parts shown are made of cold rolled steel from 18 to 24 gage. (Courtesy, Modern Pattern & Plastics Co.)

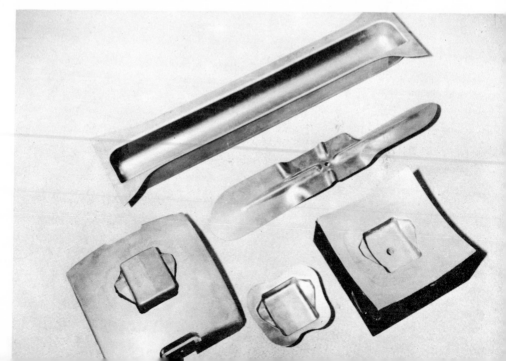

Fig. 110. A forming die using a combination of metal and Rezolin casting epoxy. A rubber pad is used above this and the forming is started by pressing the work against the metal die shown. Then the plastic wedge blocks are placed in position above the work and it is pressed to its final shape with sharp corners and accurate contours. Cost was about 50 percent of steel wedges. (Courtesy, North American Aviation, Inc.)

Fig. 111. A combination drawing and trimming die made by Shore Metal Products with interchangeable epoxy inserts for several designs. Some of the punches are of metal, some of plastic. The die shown had made 8000 of these hub caps without appreciable wear. Savings of approximately 40 percent on tool cost and 50 percent on procurement time were realized. (Courtesy, Rezolin, Inc.)

Fig. 112. The components of the complete perforating die made by the Cerro-matrix ® method: the die block D, the punches A, located by means of the die block, the punch plate B and the temporary assembly plate C. (Courtesy, Cerro de Pasco Corporation.)

Fig. 113. The low melting point alloy being poured around the punches to set them in the plate (Fig. 112). This metal expands on cooling, locking the punches tightly in place. (Courtesy, Cerro de Pasco Corporation.)

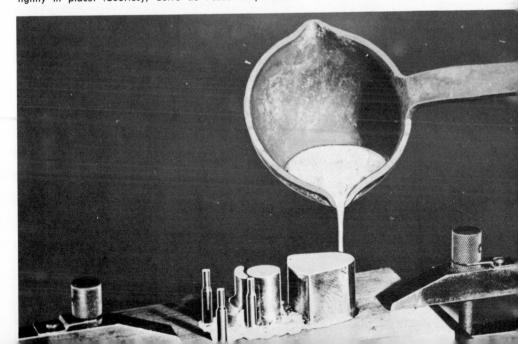

Fig. 114. The complete multiple punch (Fig. 112) ready for use. Savings of 50 percent or more are often realized when die sets are made by this method. (Courtesy, Cerro de Pasco Corporation.)

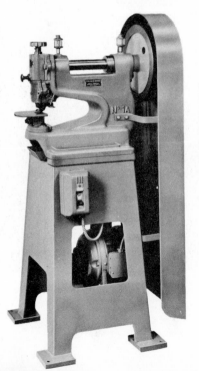

Fig. 115. A typical nibbling machine for sample and short-run cutting of irregular shapes in sheet metal. The machine shown will cut up to $\frac{3}{16}$-in. thick mild steel. Other sizes will handle up to $\frac{1}{2}$-in. plate. (Courtesy, Campbell Machine Div., American Chain & Cable Company, Inc.)

Fig. 116. The punch and die used in a nibbling machine. The rapidly moving punch takes a small crescent-shaped cut at each stroke, and cuts equally well in any direction. (Courtesy, Campbell Machine Div., American Chain & Cable Company, Inc.)

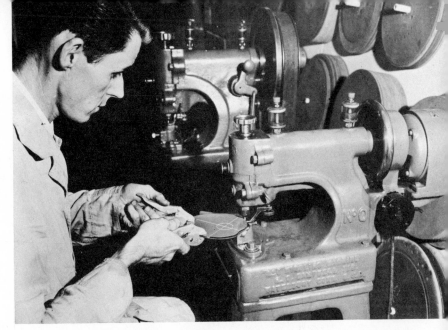

Fig. 117. A simple template, cut by hand from thin sheet metal, guides the nibbling machine in cutting irregular shapes such as this cam. (Courtesy, Campbell Machine Div., American Chain & Cable Company, Inc.)

Fig. 118. The deep drawing of a stainless steel sink bowl on a 500-ton hydraulic press. Two stages of drawing are used with different dies in the same press. The first draw is 5¾ in. deep, the second 6¾ in. The blank holding pressure is unusually high, 300 tons, although the actual draw requires only 100 tons. (Courtesy, Clearing Machine Corporation.)

Fig. 119. The bowl (Fig. 118) being removed from the press before trimming of the flange. (Courtesy, Clearing Machine Corporation.)

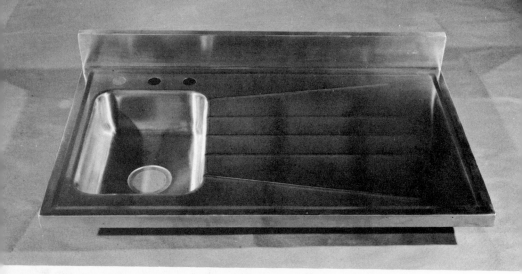

Fig. 120. The completed sink in which the bowl (Fig. 119) is used. (Courtesy, Clearing Machine Corporation.)

Fig. 121. A 19-in. Hydroform machine. (Courtesy, The Cincinnati Milling Machine Co.)

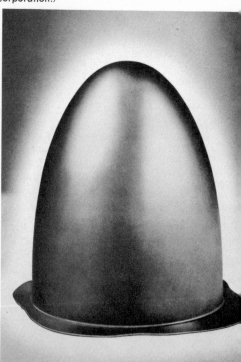

Fig. 122. A 6-in. diameter housing 6¾ in. high Hydroformed from 0.037-in. cold rolled steel at one operation. (Courtesy, The Cincinnati Milling Machine Co.)

Fig. 123. A bezel for an automotive tail light. Sixty pieces were required for model approval and Hydroforming showed a saving of 6 to 8 weeks' time and 85 percent tool cost. (Courtesy, The Cincinnati Milling Machine Co.)

Fig. 124. Three parts required in limited quantities on a rush project. Three months' time and $30,000 of tooling were saved by Hydroforming over conventional deep drawing. (Courtesy, The Cincinnati Milling Machine Co.)

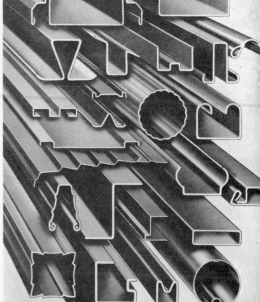

Fig. 125. A group of typical roll-formed shapes showing the wide variety and the complex contours that can be formed economically by this method. (Courtesy, The Yoder Company.)

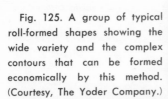

Fig. 126. A roll-forming machine. The flat strip enters the machine at the end in the background and is formed by passing through the various rolls into the finished shape coming out in the foreground. (Courtesy, The Yoder Company.)

Fig. 127. Special attachments for the roll-forming machine perform such operations as perforating, notching, and cutting to length, continuously, as the shaped strip emerges from the forming rolls. (Courtesy, Roll Formed Products Company.)

Fig. 128. Another roll-forming attachment forms the material into complete rings after the perforating and the notching. (Courtesy, Roll Formed Products Company.)

Fig. 129. A roll-bending machine for sheet and plate stock. This one has 6-in. diameter rolls and a capacity up to ¼-in. mild steel. (Courtesy, Niagara Machine & Tool Works.)

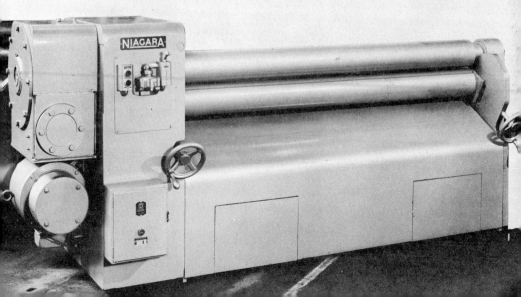

Fig. 130

Figs. 130–131. Two steps in spinning a propeller cap from a flat sheet to the finished piece, using hand tools on a spinning lathe with a wood form. (Courtesy, Spincraft, Inc.)

Fig. 131

Fig. 132. Automatic spinning on a metal form. On quantities up to several thousand pieces, spinning is often more economical than drawing or stamping because of the lower tool cost. (Courtesy, Spincraft, Inc.)

Fig. 133. A large piece being formed by manual spinning. Parts up 12 ft or more in diameter and up to ¼ in. thick in soft metals or ³⁄₁₆ in. in mild steel can be formed by this method. Still heavier work is done on special power-driven equipment. (Courtesy, Spincraft, Inc.)

Fig. 134

Fig. 135

Figs. 134–136. Typical parts produced by manual and automatic spinning. (Courtesy, Spincraft, Inc.)

Fig. 136

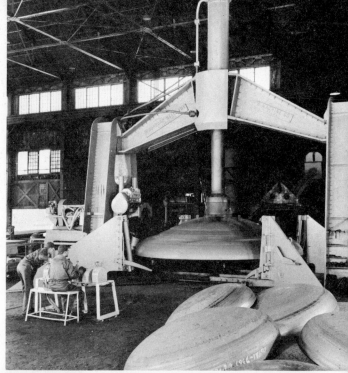

Fig. 137. This huge machine spins flanged and dished heads in carbon, alloy, and stainless clad steel or in nonferrous metals. Sizes range from 9 in. to 19 ft in diameter, $\frac{3}{16}$ in. to 6 in. thick. (Courtesy, The Colorado Fuel and Iron Corporation.)

Fig. 138 A Floturn lathe in operation. (Courtesy, The Lodge & Shipley Company.)

Fig. 139. A group of pieces produced by the Floturn process. (Courtesy, The Lodge & Shipley Company.)

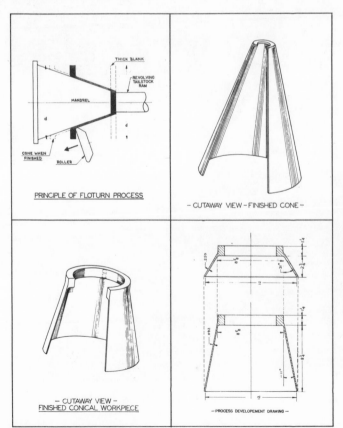

PRINCIPLE OF FLOTURN PROCESS

– CUTAWAY VIEW – FINISHED CONE –

– CUTAWAY VIEW –
FINISHED CONICAL WORKPIECE

– PROCESS DEVELOPEMENT DRAWING –

Fig. 140. Cross-sectional views of Floturn parts showing how the wall thickness is reduced by the operations, making this a cold extrusion rather than a spinning process. Production rate on the cone at the upper right was 6 per hour; on the piece at the lower left, 12 per hour. (Courtesy, The Lodge & Shipley Company.)

Fig. 141. One of the heaviest parts produced by Hydrospinning is this alloy turbine shaft. (Courtesy, The Cincinnati Milling Machine Co.)

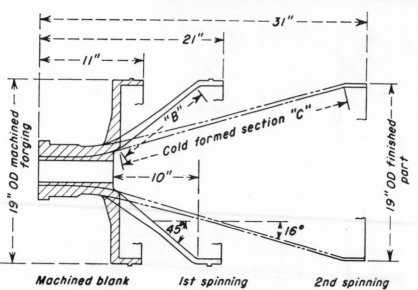

Fig. 142. The part shown in Fig. 141 is spun in two operations from a forged and machined blank. (Courtesy, The Cincinnati Milling Machine Co.)

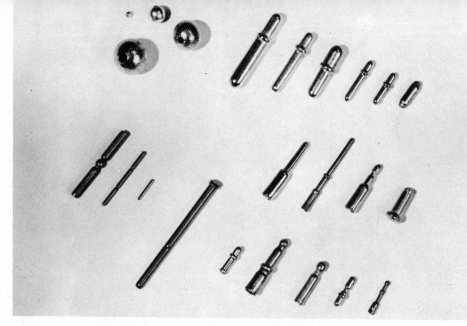

Fig. 143. A group of small parts made by a process known as "Multi-Swage" which forms flat strip stock in tubular or cylindrical shapes with tightly closed seams. The process is done automatically at high speeds and is very economical for large production runs. Maximum size is ¼ in. in diameter and 1½ in. in length. Many millions of these parts are used for such purposes as radio tube base pins, bead chains for electric sockets, and similar applications. (Courtesy, The Bead Chain Manufacturing Co.)

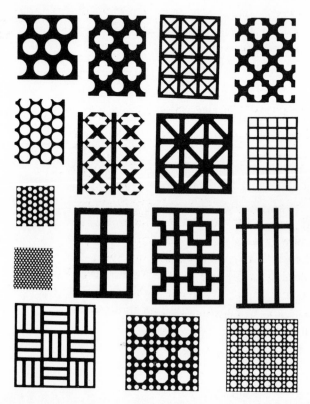

Fig. 144. A few of the thousands of patterns available in perforated metal. Steel sheets in various gages of patterns such as these are stock items and have many decorative and functional applications. (Courtesy, Harrington and King Perforating Co.)

3

Forging and Extrusion Processes

FORGING

Forging is the process of working heated (but not melted) metal into shape by means of pressure, usually with a hammering action. Its simplest form is represented by the method of the old-time blacksmith with his forge and anvil. Most forging is now done by mechanically operated presses, but it is still the best method that has been found for developing the greatest strength and toughness from steel, bronze, brass, copper, aluminum, and magnesium. Forgings are generally more expensive than castings, but there are many applications where no other process would give satisfactory results. In addition to various hot forging methods, much "forging" is now being done cold, tremendous pressure causing the solid metal to flow into the desired shape.

Open-Die Forging

The simplest forging method, after the hand hammer of the blacksmith, is open-die or smith forging (see Figs. 145–148). This is really just a mechanically operated hammer under which the hot metal is manipulated by the operator in such a way as to form it into the desired bars, rings, or other simple shapes. Although a skilled operator can do remarkably good work with one of these hammers, the resulting pieces naturally cannot be held to any close tolerance and are usually just rough blanks for further machining or closed-die forging. Forged shafts, die blanks, and gear blanks are examples of open-die forgings. In addition to forming the steel roughly to shape, improvement in grain structure and strength is an important reason for the use of open-die forgings.

Drop Forging

Drop forging is a refinement of the open-die process that produces parts of fairly close tolerance and more complex shape with the strength and the toughness that are developed only by forging. Drop forgings vary in size from an ounce or less to several tons. By far the greatest tonnage of forgings is produced by this method. In drop forging, the flat hammer and anvil of the open-die method are replaced by a pair of heavy steel dies having a cavity the shape of the desired piece. The hot blank, which often is preformed to an approximate shape, is placed between these dies, and the hammering action completes the forming. Often several cavities are required to form the piece progressively into its final shape (see Fig. 149). The dies must be so formed as to work the metal gradually into shape and to control its flow to develop the maximum strength where it is most needed. To assure complete filling of the die, some surplus metal is allowed which forms a thin flash around the parting line of the dies. This flash is removed later by a trimming operation. Then the forging is cleaned by pickling in an acid solution or by sand blasting. The dies for drop forging are, of course, expensive, so it is primarily a quantity process. Steel drop forgings are used extensively in automobiles and tractors for such parts as steering knuckles and spring shackles, connecting rods and crankshafts, all requiring high strength with minimum bulk. In the aircraft industry, aluminum and magnesium forgings are used very generally for highly stressed parts.

The machines used for forming drop forgings are called drop hammers, and may be of several types. In the gravity type, the ram, which carries the upper portion of the die, is raised either mechanically, by rollers working against the sides of a wooden board, or by air pressure, to a fixed height and then falls by gravity against the workpiece in the lower die. The force of the blow depends on the weight of the ram and the height from which it is dropped.

Gravity forging hammers (Fig. 152) are rated by the weight of the falling ram, which in standard machines ranges from 200 lb to 10,000 lb. The normal falling velocity is about 14 feet per second (fps). In general, gravity hammers are used for the lighter and thinner types of forgings.

In the steam or air hammers, the movement of the ram, both rising and falling, is controlled by the steam or air pressure. This gives better control of the action so that the operator can regulate the strength of the blows. The steam or air hammers (Fig. 154) are made in sizes from 1,000 lb to 35,000 lb falling weight. Since the rate of fall is accelerated by the pressure in the cylinder, the velocity is greater, being approximately 30 fps, maximum. These hammers are used generally for larger and heavier forgings.

Both low and high carbon steels are used in forging, and also many of the alloy and stainless types. Among the nonferrous forging metals are copper, brass, several bronze alloys, aluminum, and magnesium. Producers of these materials can furnish comprehensive data on the characteristics, the uses, and the heat treatment of the various alloys. A comprehensive schedule of standard tolerances for drop forgings has been adopted as a standard by the Drop Forging Association and is available from them.

Upset or Machine Forgings

This process was used originally for forming heads on bolts, but has now been broadened to include many other applications. A heated rod is gripped between portions of the die, and another portion, containing a cavity of the desired shape, is forced against the protruding part of the rod. The action is one of squeezing pressure rather than hammering action. Several steps may be required to form the final shape, as in drop forging. The length of the original rod is reduced and the diameter is increased in the process. Machine forging can produce not only heads of various forms on the end of rods, but also flanges or projections along the length of the piece. Examples of products made by this process are cluster gear blanks, camshafts, and gear-shift levers. Parts weighing from a few ounces to several hundred pounds have been produced. As a rule, the dies for upset forging are fairly simple and not very expensive. It is therefore an economical method of forming medium or large quantities of parts. Often these may be used just as they are formed, or with very little machining. They not only form stronger parts due to the control of grain flow in the metal, but also save considerable material and machine work that would be needed if the part were machined from bar stock. The process is often used in connection with drop forging, either to preform the blank before further forming or to form a flange on the piece after forming.

The maximum length of stock that can be upset to form the head or flange is usually about three times the diameter of the rod. A variation of the machine forging process, known as "electric gathering" or "resistance upset," extends this greatly in certain applications up to 30 times the diameter or more. In this process, a heavy electric current is passed through the blank while the pressure is applied, which heats the material as it is being formed. This is being used where large-diameter heads or flanges are required, as in such parts as diesel-engine valves.

Press Forgings

Press forging is related to machine forging in that pressure rather than impact is used, but otherwise it is similar to drop forging. Closed dies are used to squeeze the hot metal into the desired form. It is often used in conjunction with drop forging, for the final sizing operations where close tolerances and smooth finish are required. Used in this way, it is sometimes called "coining" or "sizing."

Press forgings are made most commonly from brass or other copper base alloys, from aluminum, or from magnesium (see Fig. 159). They are used in preference to castings wherever superior toughness and strength are needed or where their more dense structure and lack of porosity offset their higher cost.

Very large and complex forgings of aluminum and magnesium for the aircraft industry are being produced in special hydraulic forging presses. The largest of these (Fig. 162), just put into use, will exert pressures up to 50,000 tons and will form whole sections of aircraft frames that otherwise would have to be fabricated of many pieces, riveted or welded together. Some civilian applications are also being found for these heavy presses, such as forged aluminum wheels for automobiles.

Rolling

The process of rolling hot metal billets into sheets and bars is related closely to the forging processes and is the basic forming method for most of the steel that is used in industry (Fig. 164). The forms are obtained by passing the hot billets through a series of heavy rolls which gradually work the material into the desired shape. It is used in the steel mills for forming most of the familiar angles, channels, and other standard shapes, as well as sheets, plates, bars, and rods of various cross section. The characteristics of rolled steel are intermediate between the forged parts and those formed by casting. The grain of the metal runs lengthwise of the bar or sheet, and this should be taken into consideration if maximum strength is required or if severe cold-forming of the material is necessary in further manufacturing processes. Such a wide variety of standard rolled forms is available that it is seldom necessary to go into special shapes. However, special shapes can be rolled by the mills if the quantity justifies it. After hot rolling, some sheets and bars are cleaned and given a cold rolling operation, which improves the surface finish and strength.

An extension of the rolling process, known as roll forging (Fig. 165), is used to produce such parts as tapered shafts, bars, and tubes. Examples are the tapered drive shafts and axles sometimes used in automobiles and farm machinery, and the tapered ends of leaf springs.

EXTRUSION

This is a process for producing long lengths of rod, tubing, or more intricate shapes from copper, brass, aluminum, or magnesium. A billet of hot (but not melted) metal is placed in the cylinder of an extruding press and forced through a die having an opening of the desired shape in one end of the cylinder, by means of tremendous hydraulic pressure applied to a plunger or ram at the other end. The plastic metal is squeezed out, much like toothpaste from a tube, and is supported on a conveyor until it has cooled. After extruding and cutting to length, a straightening operation is required, which usually is done by stretching. Some alloys also require a heat-treating operation to develop their maximum strength.

A number of aluminum alloys can be extruded. In general, those of lower strength can be extruded more easily and can be formed into more complex shapes. Thus, the lowest strength alloy that will give the necessary characteristics for a particular job should be used. Alloys regularly used for aluminum extrusions are as follows, with the lowest strength listed first and the highest strength last: EC, 1100 (2 S), 3003 (3 S), 6063 (63 S), 6061 (61 S), 6062 (62 S), 2024 (24 S), 2014 (14 S), and 7075 (75 S).

Very complex shapes can be produced economically by this process. It is used not only for such common mill products as brass and aluminum rods and tubes, but also for various structural and architectural shapes, moldings, and ornamental trim. Many of these shapes are standard, but the dies for special shapes are quite inexpensive and quantities as low as a few hundred feet are often economical.

The maximum size of extrusions has been limited by the presses available to sections that could fit within a 13-in. circle and having 19 sq in. cross-sectional area, weighing approximately 5 lb per ft in aluminum. A new 14,000-ton extruding press just put into operation extends this to a 23-in. circle, 60 sq in. cross section, and 22 lb per ft weight. These large extrusions are used mostly for aircraft work.

In addition to the softer metals, it is now possible to extrude both high and low carbon steels (see Fig. 167). A new process using glass powder as a lubricant on the hot steel has made this practical. Sections weighing up to 12 lb per ft can be produced at the present time, and this, no doubt, will be increased in the near future. The advantages of the extruded over the rolled sections are: (a) much lower tool cost, so that small quantities of special shapes (as low as 100 lb) can be produced economically and (b) more complex shapes can be produced.

There are many cases where question may arise as to whether a given shape can be produced most economically by extrusion or by roll forming (see Chap. 2). Usually an examination of the requirements will determine this. Extrusion permits variation in wall thickness to allow a better distribution of metal for the stresses involved. Roll-formed parts must have walls of uniform thickness. Dies for extrusion are much less expensive than rolls, so extrusions are more practical for short runs. On the other hand, the production rate is much higher and usually the cost per foot of rolled forms is considerably less. Also, the surface finish of the roll-formed parts is superior to that of extrusions, which often reduces the finishing cost (see Figs. 170–177, which show some typical aluminum extrusions compared with other methods of forming comparable parts).

Cold Extrusion and Cold Heading

It is easy to see how a molten metal will flow by gravity or under pressure into molds, as in the casting processes, or how a metal, softened by heating to a bright red or white heat, may be made to flow by hammering or by squeezing under high pressure as in the forging processes. It is more difficult to realize that a cold metal also may be made to flow by the application of sufficient pressure in properly designed dies. However, this is exactly what happens in the cold extrusion and cold heading processes.

In cold extrusion or impact extrusion (also called cold forging, extrusion pressing, or impact forging), a slug of metal is placed in the bottom of a die and subjected to tremendous pressure, causing it to flow upward into the narrow space between the punch and the die and to form a deep cup or shell (Fig. 178). The process was used originally to form collapsible tubes from tin or other soft metal and has been used for some time with aluminum, brass, bronze, and, more recently, steel. The dies, especially for the softer metals, are not unduly expensive, and it is often the most economical method of forming many types of deep, one-piece cans, cups, or similar shapes. Steel, of course, requires much heavier dies and presses (Fig. 187). Deep shells and tank sections weighing up to 100 lb are being produced in steel by this process. They do not have to be round in cross section but can be rectangular or fluted either inside or out. Die costs are moderately high, but can be amortized easily if any large quantity of pieces is involved. Accuracy and finish are good, and the controlled grain flow and compression of the metal make for excellent physical properties.

Cold heading uses the same principle to form an enlarged head or flange on rod or bar stock in the same way that upsetting or machine forging does on hot material. Where screws and similar parts are being turned out of bar stock, often great savings can be made by the use of smaller stock with the enlarged portion formed by cold heading. The enlarged portion does not have to be at the end of the bar, but can be at any point along its length. Most cold heading is done in automatic presses at high speed, and is a very fast and economical process where the quantities justify the setup. Production rates per machine run up to several hundred pieces per minute on small parts. The finish is excellent, with smooth contours and no burrs, and great savings in material and machine time are realized when compared with the cost of machining the parts from bar stock. The strength is also improved substantially by the cold working involved. While some cold heading is done on stock up to 1½ in. in diameter or more, usually these larger sizes are handled by hot machine forging, with most cold heading done on diameters of ¾ in. and less. The diameter of the upset portion should be kept, preferably, to no more than three or four times the diameter of the rod in steel, and seven or eight times in brass or aluminum. However, flanges several times this wide have been made in certain designs and with special techniques. Round flanges are the easiest to form and use the lowest cost dies, but square or irregular shapes can be made when necessary.

Cold Rolling

Another cold forming process that has long been used for such simple application as the forming of knurls and serrations on circular parts is now a very important method of forming screw threads, splines, and even gear teeth.

In thread rolling, the dies may be in the form of either flat bars or cylinders. In the flat type, two bars have the thread form cut in their inner surfaces in the form of straight grooves at a slight angle to the edges, as shown in Fig. 191. These dies are pressed against the round workpiece and are moved longitudinally so that the work is rolled between them to squeeze the thread form into the piece. The cylindrical dies do the same thing by rolling the work between three drums with the thread form cut into their surface, as shown in Fig. 193. Rolling is a very rapid and economical method of threading bolts, studs, and special parts in large quantity. The cold working gives threads that are stronger than cut threads and with better finish. Because of the displacement of metal to form the thread, the outside diameter of the thread is always greater than the original diameter of the rod, and this is a disadvantage in some applications.

The same method is just starting to be used for forming splines and gear teeth on both spur and helical gears (Fig. 197). The production rate is some 30 times faster than machining these parts by conventional methods.

Rotary Swaging

This is a cold working process that accomplishes just the opposite of cold heading; it reduces the diameter and increases the length of the original rod or tubing. This is done by a rotary hammering action which strikes rapid blows around the circumference of the workpiece (see Fig. 199). The machines are made in a variety of sizes, taking work from extremely small rods and tubes up to about 6-in. tubing or 4-in. solid rods. Rotary swaging is a high-production process and shows great economies on pieces adapted to it. The work has excellent physical characteristics, due to the hammering action, a fine finish, and tolerances as close as ±0.001 in.

Fig. 145. A smith or open-die forging hammer in operation. (Courtesy, Drop Forging Association.)

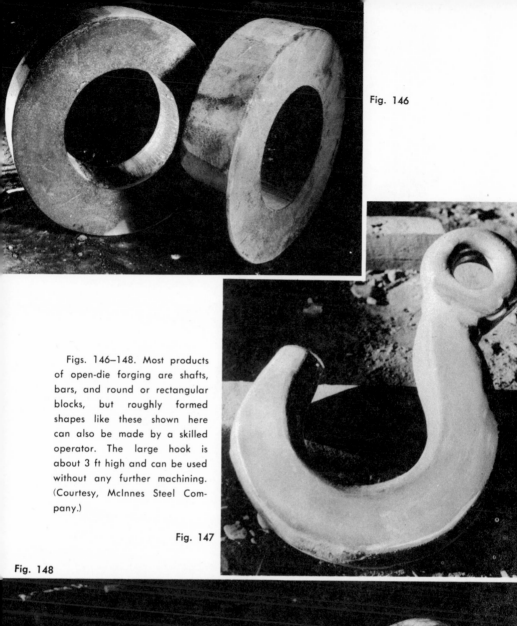

Fig. 146

Figs. 146–148. Most products of open-die forging are shafts, bars, and round or rectangular blocks, but roughly formed shapes like these shown here can also be made by a skilled operator. The large hook is about 3 ft high and can be used without any further machining. (Courtesy, McInnes Steel Company.)

Fig. 147

Fig. 148

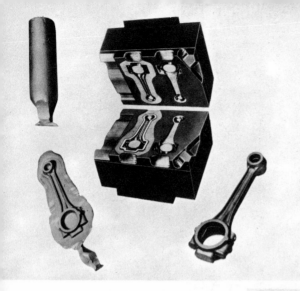

Fig. 149. A two-stage drop forging die for a connecting rod, showing the rough blank and the finished part, before and after trimming. (Courtesy, Drop Forging Association.)

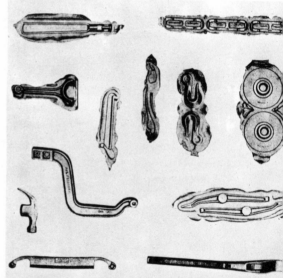

Fig. 150. A group of typical forgings made on the gravity drop hammer, some shown before and some after trimming of the flash. (Courtesy, Chambersburg Engineering Company.)

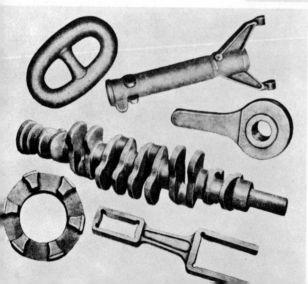

Fig. 151. Forgings made by the steam drop hammer. (Courtesy, Chambersburg Engineering Company.)

Fig. 152. Two gravity drop forging hammers in use. These use a piston lift rather than the older "board" type. (Courtesy, Chambersburg Engineering Company.)

Fig. 153. An etched cross section of a drop forging, showing the grain flow for maximum strength that is characteristic of forgings. (Courtesy, Drop Forging Association.)

Fig. 154. A 20,000-lb closed-die forging hammer in operation. (Courtesy, Wyman-Gordon Company.)

Fig. 155. A group of typical small- and medium-size drop forgings. (Courtesy, Drop Forging Association.)

Fig. 156. A large aircraft landing gear forging weighing 2200 lb. Forgings weighing several tons are made regularly. (Courtesy, Drop Forging Association.)

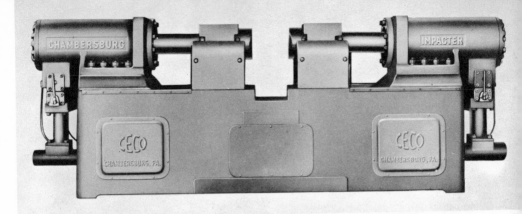

Fig. 157. A new type of forging hammer, known as the "Impacter," uses two opposing rams operated by air cylinders. The work is located in the center where the two rams, carrying the halves of the die, collide. There is an almost complete absence of the shock and vibration usually associated with forging operations since the energy is all absorbed in the forging. (Courtesy, Chambersburg Engineering Company.)

Fig. 158. Electronic controls regulate the rate and the strength of the blows and make the machine (Fig. 157) easily adaptable to completely automatic operation. Here aluminum fin blades are produced automatically from cut lengths of aluminum bar which are heated, conveyed to the forging point, formed in a single blow, and discharged onto a conveyor belt. (Courtesy, Chambersburg Engineering Company.)

Fig. 159. A heavy press used to produce brass, bronze, and aluminum forgings. (Courtesy, Mueller Brass Company.)

Fig. 160. Typical forgings produced in brass. (Courtesy, Mueller Brass Company.)

Fig. 161. Typical aluminum forgings. These parts have excellent physical characteristics, high density, and fine surface finish. (Courtesy, Mueller Brass Company.)

Fig. 162. This giant forging press, said to be the biggest industrial machine man has ever made, has recently been placed in operation. It weighs 10,605 tons, is 10 stories high, and exerts a 50,000-ton pressing power. It will be used primarily for making large aluminum aircraft forgings, beyond the capacity of other presses. (Courtesy, Wyman-Gordon Company.)

Fig. 163. Aluminum wing spar for a jet fighter plane, 165 in. long, weighing 204 lb, made as a closed-die forging on the 50,-000-ton press. (Courtesy, Wyman-Gordon Company.)

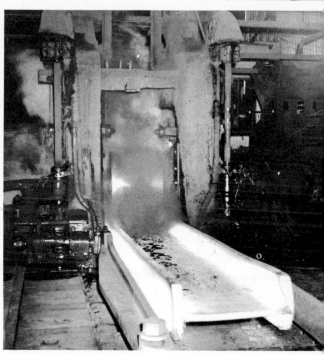

Fig. 164. A large I beam emerges red hot from the rolling mill. (Courtesy, Bethlehem Steel Company, Inc.)

Fig. 165. A roll forging machine in operation forming the axle shaft in the foreground. (Courtesy, The Ajax Manufacturing Co.)

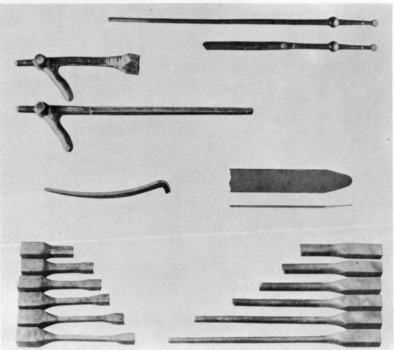

Fig. 166. Showing a group of typical parts formed by roll forging. (*Upper right*) A gear-shift lever. (*Upper left*) A brake pedal. (*Center right*) A leaf spring. (*Center left*) A brake shoe key. (*Lower right*) An eye bolt blank. (*Lower left*) A connecting rod blank to be formed by drop forging. (Courtesy, The Ajax Manufacturing Co.)

Fig. 167

Figs. 167–168. A 1000-ton extrusion press for forming low carbon steel extrusions and a die for use on it (Fig. 168). Powdered glass is used as a lubricant and after each extrusion the die has to be taken out and shot blasted to remove the adhering glass. (Courtesy, Jones & Laughlin Steel Corporation.)

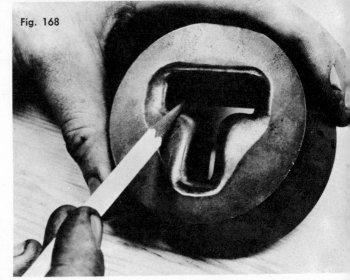

Fig. 168

Fig. 169. A group of typical shapes extruded in low carbon steel on the press shown in Fig. 167. (Courtesy, Jones & Laughlin Steel Corporation.)

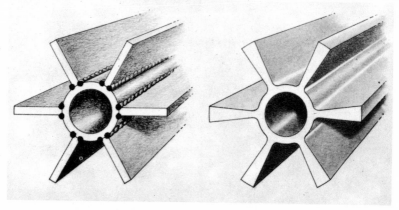

Fig. 170. Welded assemblies can often be redesigned to extrusions. Cost is reduced and strength and accuracy improved. (Courtesy, Reynolds Metals Co.)

Fig. 171. Crimped tubular sections often permit redesign to extrusions with gain in stiffness and strength. Too, cost can be reduced. (Courtesy, Reynolds Metals Co.)

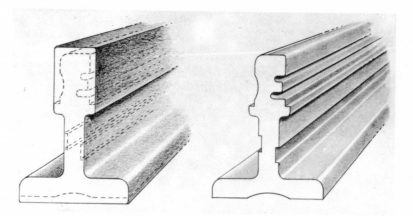

Fig. 172. Machining cost of long cast iron frame members is minimized by redesigning the section to an aluminum extrusion. (Courtesy, Reynolds Metals Co.)

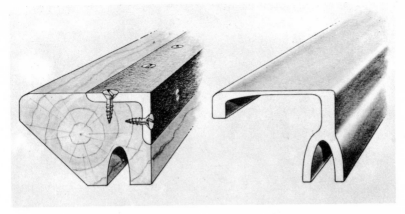

Fig. 173. Aluminum extrusions are free from the warping and the splintering often associated with wood sections. Frequently the aluminum shapes can be made lighter, stiffer, and stronger. Necessity for metal reinforcement is eliminated. (Courtesy, Reynolds Metals Co.)

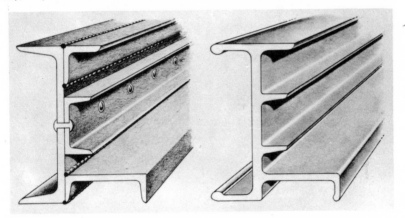

Fig. 174. Several rolled structural steel shapes can be combined into a single aluminum extrusion, thus eliminating joining costs. (Courtesy, Reynolds Metals Co.)

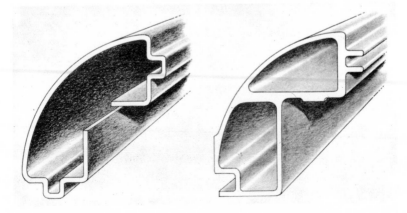

Fig. 175. Because extrusions permit changes of cross section, they can be "tailored" more readily than roll-formed sheet sections to meet specific design requirements. (Courtesy, Reynolds Metals Co.)

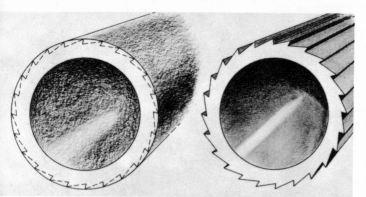

Fig. 176. Sections machin̊
from bar stock or pipe can oᵗ
be replaced by aluminum
tions extruded to exact shᵉ
and size. (Courtesy, Reyn̊
Metals Co.)

Fig. 177. Small castings, forgings, or parts machined from
bar stock may permit redesign
to an extruded shape, if their
cross sections are symmetrical in
one plane. (Courtesy, Reynolds
Metals Co.)

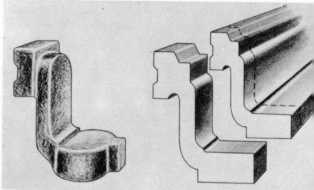

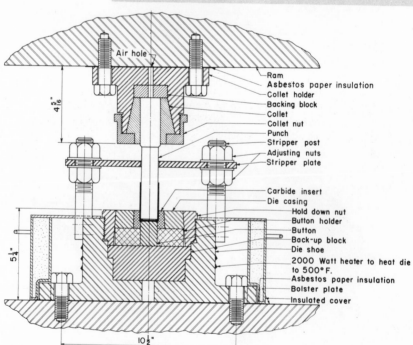

Fig. 178. A cross section of a die for magnesium impact extrusions. (Courtesy, The Dow Chemical Company.)

95 Ton - 75 S.P.M
Tube Extruding Press

Slug Hopper

Temperature
Recorder &
Controller
for Slug Heater

Safety glass
guard

Press
Switch
Panel

Slug Track
inside 1750 W
heater

Chute for
air ejected
parts

Temperature
Controller
for Die

Tote
Box

Fig. 179. An automatic impact extrusion press with the parts identified. (Courtesy, The Dow Chemical Company.)

Fig. 180. A tooling setup for this press to produce magnesium cups. (Courtesy, The Dow Chemical Company.)

Fig. 181. A group of magnesium impact extruded cans and the slugs (*foreground*) from which they are produced. (Courtesy, The Dow Chemical Company.)

Fig. 182

Figs. 182–185. Four groups of aluminum impact extrusions showing the wide variety of forms that can be made economically in large quantity by this process. (Courtesy, Hunter Douglas Corporation.)

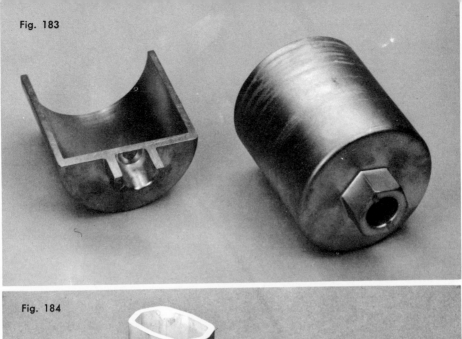

Fig. 183

Fig. 184

Fig. 185

Fig. 186. An etched cross section of an aluminum impact extrusion showing the grain flow that is characteristic of forgings and that gives them their high strength and fatigue resistance. (Courtesy, Hunter Douglas Corporation.)

Fig. 187. A group of the large presses used for cold extrusion work in steel. (Courtesy, Heintz Manufacturing Company.)

Fig. 188. The working parts of the press showing the backward extrusion of a sized billet with a 52 percent reduction in cross-sectional area. Approximately 700 tons is used on this piece. (Courtesy, Heintz Manufacturing Company.)

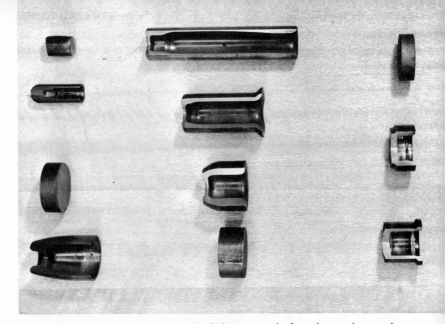

Fig. 189. A group of typical cold extruded parts made from low carbon or low alloy steels. The finished parts are made from the slugs shown in from one to three operations as indicated in the cross-sectional views. (Courtesy, Heintz Manufacturing Company.)

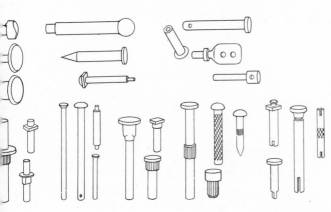

Fig. 190. A group of typical small cold headed parts. (Courtesy, Hercules Fastener Company.)

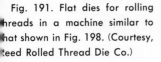

Fig. 191. Flat dies for rolling threads in a machine similar to that shown in Fig. 198. (Courtesy, Reed Rolled Thread Die Co.)

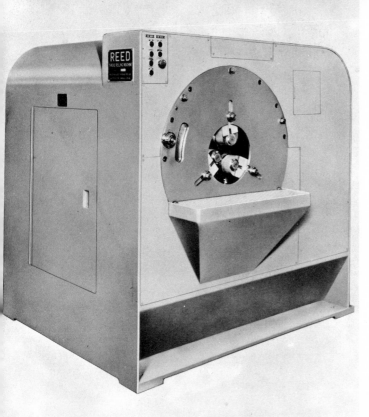

Fig. 192. A machine for rolling threading with round dies. (Courtesy, Reed Rolled Thread Die Co.)

Fig. 193. The action of the round dies in rolling a thread. The cold working of the metal provides excellent strength and smooth finish. (Courtesy, Reed Rolled Thread Die Co.)

Fig. 194

Figs. 194–196. Three groups of standard and special threaded parts made with rolled threads. (Courtesy, Reed Rolled Thread Die Co.)

Fig. 195

Fig. 196

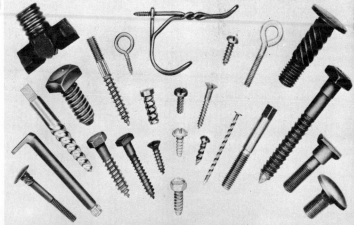

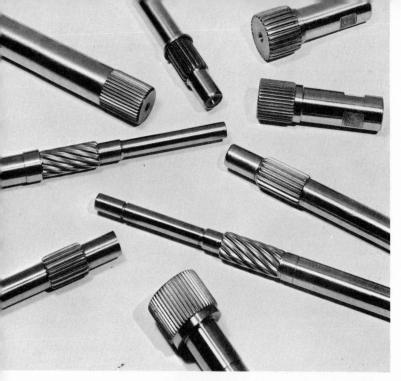

Fig. 197. A group of splined and serrated parts produced by the "Roto-Flo" process. The splines are cold-rolled into the surface of the shafts by rolling them, under heavy pressure, between flat racks or dies of the proper form, as shown in Fig. 198. (Courtesy, Michigan Tool Company.)

Fig. 198. "Roto-Flo" dies are designed to press deeper into the blanks as the work progresses and the entire shape is formed at a single pass through the dies in a few seconds' time. The process is very economical for quantity production; the flow of the metal gives good grain structure and high strength with fine surface finish. Parts from ½-in. to 2-in. diameter can be handled with splines up to 4 in. long. Note the similarity of this process to the thread rolling shown in Fig. 191. (Courtesy, Michigan Tool Company.)

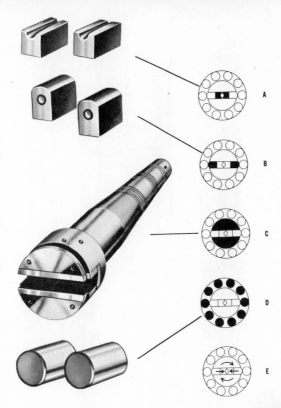

Fig. 199. The working parts of the rotary swaging machine and their action. (A) The dies which are made to produce the shape and the size required. (B) The backers with rounded ends which impart the blows to the dies. (C) The spindle with slots to hold the dies and backers and a hollow center through which the work is fed. (D) Hardened steel rolls loosely retained by a rack surround the spindle. (E) As the spindle revolves, the backers pass over successive pairs of rolls and force the dies together. (Courtesy, The Torrington Company.)

Fig. 200. A small- and a large-size rotary swaging machine. (Courtesy, The Torrington Company.)

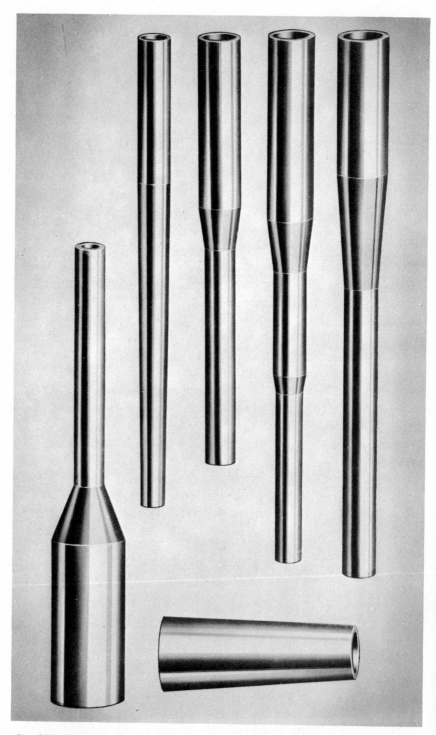

Fig. 201. Some typical work done on the rotary swaging machine. (Courtesy, The Torrington Company.)

Powder Metallurgy (Sintering)

Powder metallurgy is one of the most rapidly developing of the new production processes. In its present form, it was introduced by the Germans during World War II, and improved on and commercialized in this country in the last few years. Its original application was for the forming of tungsten carbide, the Alnico alloys, and other materials that are extremely difficult to machine or to form by other methods. Another early application was for forming the porous bronze type of "oilless" bearing that is widely used for light-duty, high-speed applications, or for bearings that have to operate for long periods without lubrication. A wide range of metals is now available in powder form for use in powder metal parts, generally known as sinterings, and the physical characteristics obtainable are being improved constantly.

Materials in common use for sinterings are brass, bronze, iron, steel, stainless steel, nickel, chromium, and various combinations of these metals. Aluminum and magnesium are not practical for standard sintering techniques, although promising results have been obtained by special hot pressing methods.

The process is best adapted to high-production parts such as gears, cams, lock cylinders and bodies, and similar parts where considerable machining can be saved. Both surface finish and accuracy are better than that obtained by any of the casting processes.

The first step in the forming of powder metal parts is the mixing of the powders, and at this point one of the major advantages of the method becomes apparent. Many combinations of metals and of metals with ceramics (ceramets; see Chap. 20) or other materials are possible that cannot be used as melted alloys. These often give characteristics of heat resistance, frictional properties, heavy weight, and hardness that are not obtainable by other methods.

The dies are quite expensive, so usually the process is not practical unless quantities of at least a few thousand pieces are required. The die consists of a cavity, the shape of the desired part, but from two to ten times deeper, according to the material to be handled. Metal powder is poured in this and leveled off flush with the top of the die. The punches, usually working from both the top and the bottom of the die, must be a close fit in the cavity. They are forced together under pressure into the die cavity, compressing the metal powder. The pressure used is from 20 to 50 tons per sq in., and presses of both the mechanical and the hydraulic type are used. The pressed piece is then ejected from the die by the upward movement of the lower punch, all of these operations being done automatically at high speeds in the press. The speed on small pieces may run from 30 to 75 per min, on large pieces as low as 3 or 4 per min. Usually single-cavity dies are used, although multiple cavities can be used for small pieces that are required in very large quantities. The porosity can be controlled, from porous parts like oilless bearings and metallic filters, to extremely dense parts like carbide tools and Alnico magnets. Dies are made usually of high-grade steel, finely finished and hardened, but carbide dies are used for long production runs.

The part comes from the press looking like solid metal, but it is still very fragile and will shatter if dropped on the floor, or it can even be crushed between one's fingers.

These "green compacts," as they are called, are placed on racks and enter the "sintering" furnace, where they are baked at a temperature slightly below their melting point in a controlled atmosphere of inert gas. This sintering is what develops the strength of the material; a close control of temperature, time, and atmosphere is needed for best results.

Many powder metal parts are used just as they come from the sintering furnace, and, for many applications, these are perfectly satisfactory. However, there is a certain amount of shrinkage and distortion caused by the sintering and a certain amount of porosity that is inherent in the powder metal structure. Where the greatest accuracy and the best possible physical characteristics are required, additional processing is necessary. The most common treatment after sintering is a coining or sizing operation, which consists of placing the part in a die similar to or identical with the original pressing die and subjecting it again to pressure of some 40 or 50 tons per sq in. This not only removes the distortion, making closer tolerances possible, but also improves the density and the physical characteristics of the metal and gives a very fine burnished surface finish. Most high-quality sinterings are coined after sintering.

Occasionally, an additional sintering and coining cycle follows the first coining, but this is seldom required. A more common treatment that often follows the first sintering is the infiltration or the impregnation of the part with a metal of lower melting point. Iron parts are often infiltrated with copper to increase their density and toughness. This is done by placing on each piece a copper slug with a volume equal to the porosity of the original part and heating them in a controlled atmosphere furnace until the copper melts and is drawn by capillary action through all the pores of the iron structure. This infiltration may be followed by a coining operation, if required for dimensional tolerances or surface finish. The density of powder metal parts may be controlled from about 50 percent on parts like bearings and filters, where porosity is desired, to 95 percent or more on high-strength parts. Where porosity is required, an organic material may be mixed with the metal, which burns out in the sintering.

Heat-treatable steel powders are available that give tensile strengths up to 115,000 psi. Although sinterings are inherently more brittle than wrought metals, good ductility may be obtained in coined and annealed parts, as shown in Fig. 210.

Iron parts can be carburized for maximum surface hardness where this is required. Hardness readings are not too reliable because of the more or less granular nature of the surface, but the wearing qualities are excellent.

The physical characteristics of sinterings depend as much on the processing as on the material. Improvements constantly are being made in sintered materials, though at the present time these materials and their characteristics are not well standardized. Sintered iron with 1 percent carbon, which is a good material for general use, shows a tensile strength of from 35,000 psi to 55,000 psi. The same material, infiltrated with copper, usually runs 70,000 psi to 80,000 psi, with strengths over 100,000 psi not uncommon. Sintered bronzes develop from 15,000 psi to 35,000 psi, with elongation up to 15 percent in the more ductile materials. New high-strength steel powders, coined and properly heat-treated, average around 100,000 psi to 120,000 psi tensile strength, with figures of over 190,000 psi reported under closely controlled conditions.

Tolerances as close as ±0.0005 in. often can be held in lateral dimensions, but somewhat more tolerance (±0.003 in. to 0.005 in.) is required in the direction of the pressure. On parts that are not to be coined, tolerances should be several times as great. A limitation in the design of parts that can be made by powder metallurgy is the fact that the piece must be a straight draw from the die, since undercuts or lateral holes are not practical at the present time. Other design factors must be considered since the powder does not flow as freely into small recesses or thin wall sections as the melted metal in castings.

The shape of the die cavity and the resulting contour of the piece can be very complex, although narrow slots and projections and holes of small diameter should be avoided since they result in weak sections on the punches which can cause trouble with breakage or short die life. The length of the piece preferably should be no more than three times the diameter, although sometimes this may be exceeded by careful design. Projections and recesses in the upper and the lower surfaces should have large radii and smooth contours, wherever possible, to promote the flow of the powder, and should be no more than one fourth of the piece length, if the die cost is important. Various thicknesses and more complex contours on the top and the bottom surfaces can be obtained by means of sectional punches, but this increases the die cost considerably. A rounded edge, having a complete radius, must be avoided at the outer edges of the piece, since this would leave a fragile "feather edge" on the punch which would not stand up. A shoulder of at least 0.010 in. to 0.015 in. at the lower edge of the radius will prevent this condition, as shown in Fig. 211.

Sinterings that have been infiltrated usually can be electroplated without difficulty. More porous parts cause some trouble in plating due to the chemicals becoming trapped in the pores and resulting in surface failure. Such parts are often vacuum-impregnated with plastic resins prior to plating, and this procedure has given satisfactory results.

The size of powder metal parts is limited chiefly by the presses available. Since pressures of 50 tons per sq in. of surface area may be required, it is easy to see that parts of more than 6 sq in. of area are not often economical. The powdered metal material is also much more expensive than metals for casting, and this is another reason why relatively small, intricate parts, where material cost is minor and where expensive machining operations can be saved, are the ones where powder metallurgy shows up to the best advantage costwise. On small gears, cams, and other parts that are adapted to the process, parts are often produced for one half to one tenth the cost of machined pieces.

In addition to the typical parts discussed above, there are certain special materials that can be worked by no other method than sintering. Among these are parts of tungsten carbide used for facing cutting tools, and permanent magnets of aluminum-nickel alloys. Certain other tungsten alloys, of very high density, are used for counterweights and instrument parts where maximum weight is required in small space.

Mixtures of ceramics and metals combine the heat resistance of ceramic and the heat conductivity of metal. They are formed by powder metal techniques and are finding application in certain jet engine parts.

Iron and graphite mixtures are being used for piston rings and are showing greater strength and better lubricating qualities than the cast iron generally used for this purpose.

Iron powder, combined with insulating materials in carefully controlled proportions, is used widely in the electronics industry for a magnetic core material in coils for use at high frequencies. It has proved superior to any other material for this purpose, and is formed into many standard and special shapes by specialized powder metallurgy techniques.

Sheet metals are being produced experimentally from metal powders and show considerable promise for use in their more porous form as filters and in their denser forms for bimetallic applications where special frictional or electrical properties can be obtained.

Metals in the form of very fine fibers are being produced in experimental quantities and show considerable promise for certain applications. The material can be "felted" like other fibrous materials and is then pressed and sintered like powdered metal. Extremely porous parts having as little as 2 percent density can be formed and have a higher strength to porosity ratio than powder parts. They also form a stronger skeleton to support such other materials as plastics, ceramics, and friction materials for specialized applications. In parts of greater density, the fibrous material shows promise of giving greater impact strength than the usual sinterings made of powders.

Fig. 202. A hydraulic compacting press for forming powdered metal parts. This operates automatically and the finished compacts drop out the chute in the foreground ready for transfer to the sintering furnace. (Courtesy, Baldwin-Lima-Hamilton Corp.)

Fig. 203. A briquetting press forming powder metal gears ready for sintering. (Courtesy, Moraine Products Div., General Motors Corporation.)

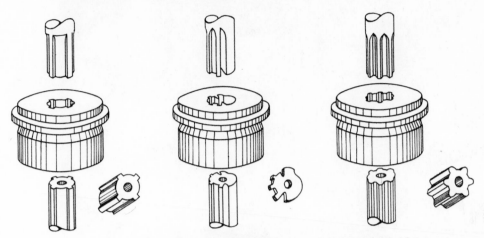

Fig. 204. Typical powder metal dies and the parts produced by them. (Courtesy, Moraine Products Div., General Motors Corporation.)

Fig. 205. A group of small parts made by powder metallurgy. (Courtesy, American Sintterings, Div. of Engineered Plastics, Inc.)

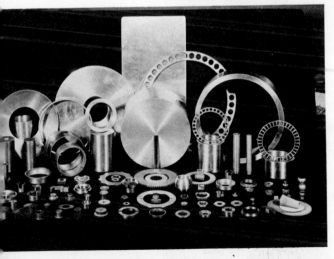

Fig. 206. A group of large and small bearings, filters, and mechanical parts made from powdered metal. The large cylinder in the center is 18 in. in diameter. (Courtesy, Amplex Division, Chrysler Corporation.)

Fig. 207. A group of Oilite porous bearings made by powder metallurgy. These are oil impregnated and operate for long periods without lubrication. (Courtesy, Amplex Division, Chrysler Corporation.)

Fig. 208. A group of porous filters made from powdered metal. The porosity can be controlled closely for various requirements. (Courtesy, Amplex Division, Chrysler Corporation.)

Fig. 209. Some of the larger pieces made economically as sinterings. (Courtesy, American Sinterings, Div. of Engineered Plastics, Inc.)

Fig. 210. These powder metal test bars have been coined and annealed for maximum ductility, then twisted cold without any sign of fracture. The brass bar on the left is twisted through 360 deg, the iron bar on the right, through 180 deg. (Courtesy, American Sinterings, Div. of Engineered Plastics, Inc.)

Fig. 211. Showing why a complete radius is not good practice on powder metal parts. (Courtesy, Moraine Products Div., General Motors Corporation.)

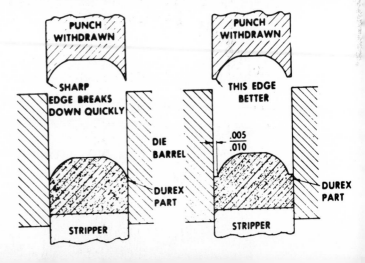

5

Machining Processes

Basically, all machining processes are methods of cutting away portions of metal parts that have already been formed more or less closely to their final shape by casting, rolling, forging, or stamping. The machining may involve the removal of only a small amount of stock to improve the accuracy or the finish of certain surfaces or it may involve a whole series of operations necessary to shape a complex piece from a block or bar of material. Machining operations of some kind are needed on most pieces of mechanical equipment, and the machine tools that perform these operations are among the most fundamental and important equipment of modern industry.

Volumes have been written about each class of machine tools and its uses; herein we shall describe briefly the type of work that is done by each.

LATHE AND SCREW MACHINE WORK

Next to the simple drill press, the lathe is probably the most widely used and the most versatile of all machine tools. In its simplest form, a metal bar or blank is held in a chuck or between centers and rotated while a cutting tool is moved along parallel with it, cutting away a portion of the material to reduce its diameter or improve its accuracy. A simple variation of this is to use a shaped cutting tool and to move it along at a controlled rate so that it cuts a thread on the workpiece. Other shaped tools may be used to form more complicated profiles, and these tools may approach either from the sides or from the end of the work.

Castings or forgings are often machined on a lathe, by means of such operations as facing of flat surfaces, boring of internal diameters, and turning of external diameters. The machined surfaces are much better in finish and accuracy than can be obtained by any casting process. Machining adds considerably to the cost of such pieces and should be used only where it is necessary.

The modern engine lathe is the most versatile of all machine tools, and, in the hands of a skilled operator, can do an extremely wide variety of precision work. Adjustments provide a wide range of speeds for the spindle to adapt it to various sizes of work and various metallic and nonmetallic materials. The carriage which supports the cutting tool can be fed automatically, crosswise, or at any angle, at any required rate of feed. Positive lateral feed at fixed rates is provided for cutting all standard and many special screw threads.

The tailstock, in addition to carrying the "dead" center to support the work, can be moved crosswise to provide for cutting tapered work, or can be equipped with a chuck for holding drills, reamers, or taps or a boring head for accurate boring of large or small diameters. Attachments provide for using the lathe for milling operations, for external and internal grinding, for the production cutting of tapers, and many other applications.' A shape-turning attachment follows a template to enable the lathe to turn out an infinite variety of extremely complex irregular shapes.

More complex work may require a series of operations, such as turning, facing, drilling, and tapping. When a quantity of like pieces are required, this series of operations usually is done on a turret lathe, where a number of tools are set up and adjusted so that they can be brought quickly into position to perform their various operations rapidly and without stopping the machine. It requires time to set up such a machine, but the saving in piece cost is tremendous if the quantity of pieces required is large enough.

Large turret lathes are made for both manual and automatic operation, and are capable of high precision work. Tolerances of ± 0.001 in. are common and much work is being done on such machines with tolerances of ± 0.0001 in. on critical dimensions. However, close tolerances always increase the cost of the work.

Small manually operated turret lathes are called hand screw machines. For moderate quantities (approximately 100 to 5000 pieces) of small turned parts, these machines do a very fine and economical job. For larger quantities, where a higher setup cost can be justified, automatic screw machines can turn out even complex small parts at an amazing rate of speed and at very low cost. The setup on these automatic screw machines for complex jobs requires a considerable amount of time of highly skilled mechanics and it is correspondingly expensive. If the quantity of parts required is large enough, this setup charge will soon be amortized.

For quantity production of very small turned parts of high accuracy, the Swiss type of automatic screw machine is often used. Instrument parts, such as small spindles and shafts for watches, clocks, and meters, can be made to a tolerance of a few ten thousandths of an inch on these machines.

SHAPING AND PLANING

These processes both use a tool with a single cutting edge which makes a straight cut across the workpiece, the work or the tool being advanced slightly toward the cutting edge after each stroke to provide the desired cut. The shaper is used for facing the smaller pieces, up to 24 in. or so in maximum dimension, and also for cutting splines, keyways, or angular openings on internal or external surfaces. Much of this internal work can be done practically in no other way. Special gears can also be cut on the shaper, although there are more economical ways of cutting gears in production quantities. Shapers are made with the ram which holds the cutting tool, either vertical or horizontal, and with the length of stroke varying from 7 in. in small bench models to 36 in. in large, heavy-duty units. The vertical shapers or slotters usually have rotating tables on which the work is clamped. These increase the variety of work to which the machine is adapted. Some shapers can be arranged with a duplicating device in which a template, cut to the desired shape, guides the cutting tool in reproducing the shape of the template on the workpiece. Forming tools, ground to the shape of the cut desired, are often used, and, because only a single cutting edge is needed, they are often the cheapest way of forming straight cuts with an irregular contour.

The planer is not so versatile as the shaper, but is adapted to forming plane surfaces or straight slots or grooves on pieces that are much too large for the shaper. The workpiece is clamped to the table of the planer and the tool or tools mounted on heads above it. The table moves back and forth to provide the cut and the tool is advanced slightly across the width of the table after each cut, to provide the desired feed.

Planers are made in various sizes, with large standard ones handling work up to 12 ft wide, 10 ft high, and 30 ft long. Special planers much larger than this have been made and are in use.

Shaping and planing are used mostly for tool and die work and the production of special machine parts in individual units or small quantities. The process is relatively slow and requires skilled operators, so it is not generally used in mass production. Much of the work that is done on the shaper and the planer can be done faster and more economically on milling machines, broaching machines, and, where the quantities justify, on specially designed machine tools.

ANSley (1968)   **MILLING**

" Next to the lathe, the milling machine, in its various forms and sizes, is probably the most useful and the most versatile of all machine tools." Basically, it is a method of cutting metals or removing surplus metals by means of rotating multiple-tooth cutters. The spindle carrying the cutter may be either vertical or horizontal. The cutters are available in a wide variety of shapes and sizes, from small-end milling cutters, ⅛ in. in diameter or less, to large-face milling cutters 14 in. in diameter or more for heavy facing operations, similar to those performed on the planer.

The various types of milling machines are capable of doing a wide variety of work. The horizontal milling machine in its simplest form can do facing, cutting, grooving, and similar work. The table can be moved laterally, crosswise, and vertically by means of manual or automatic controls.

Various attachments or refinements in the design of the machine make it possible to handle more complex jobs. An indexing or dividing head makes the milling machine suitable for cutting spur gears, straight reamers, splines, and flutes in many sizes and materials. In some machines, known as universal milling machines, the table may be rotated so that it moves at an angle with relation to the cutter. This makes it possible to cut such parts as helical gears, spiral reamers, and drills.

Swivel heads make it possible to change the axis of the cutter spindle from horizontal to vertical, or any angle between. This also permits the cutter to run horizontally, but at 90 deg from the main spindle, to permit cutting teeth in a long rack which may project out over the ends of the table. Special rack milling attachments are also made for this specific purpose.

A slotting attachment provides a ram moving up and down with a short stroke to cut keyways and internal splines and grooves in much the same manner as the shaper or the slotter. A rotary work table with an indexing device is often used in connection with this to provide an easy way to locate the grooves or the teeth that are being cut at accurately spaced intervals around a circular hole or workpiece.

Vertical milling machines have the cutter spindle vertical with the table movable in three directions below the cutter. Attachments are available to convert the vertical spindle to a horizontal one, which makes an extremely versatile unit. This attachment is also capable of milling the teeth in long racks, as described above.

With a rotary table on a vertical milling machine, it is possible to mill circular slots and other round work. By combining a rotary feed with a transverse feed, spirals can be cut.

The cutter is really the working tool of the milling machine. The most commonly used cutters in the horizontal machine are plain milling cutters and helical mills, both of which are used for flat surfaces; metal slitting saws; for narrow grooves and cutting off work; and profile millers for special shapes. Profile cutters are available in standard types such as gear-tooth cutters and corner-rounding shapes. They can also be made up in special shapes for more unusual jobs.

For vertical milling machines, the commonest cutters are the shank type, side- and end-cutting mills, and shell-type end mills for heavier facing work. Profile cutters can be used also with the vertical spindle for cutting grooves or other shapes in the sides or the edges of the workpiece.

Milling machines can be set up for production work and are often the most economical method of production on parts requiring machining on flat or large circular pieces. However, like all machining processes, it requires skilled operators and expensive machines, and the rate of production is not high. As on the lathe, very close tolerances and smooth surfaces can be obtained.

The jig borer is a specialized type of vertical milling machine which is used primarily for die making rather than production. In the jig borer, lateral and crosswise motion of the work table is controlled very accurately by means of micrometer adjustments. This makes it possible to bore holes in a workpiece, clamped to the table, which can be located at specified points on the surface. It is a machine of great precision and not only saves time on the layout of dies and fixtures but also makes possible tolerances of 0.0001 in. (one ten thousandth) or better on the location of holes and milled surfaces.

Grinding attachments are available for the jig borer which can grind the internal diameter of holes in the workpiece to tolerances of better than 0.00005 in. (one half of one ten thousandth).

DRILLING, BORING, AND TAPPING

The drill press is one of the simplest of machine tools and is found in some form in almost every factory and shop. Its primary application is the drilling of various-size holes, the size being determined by the diameter of the drill used, the drill being rotated while the work is held stationary. The spindle holding the drill is usually vertical, with the work below it. The size of the drill press is usually given as the largest circle whose center can be reached by the drill. Sizes run from 6 in. to 50 in. Radial drill presses with movable heads which may be moved horizontally on an overhead arm run into much larger sizes, usually rated by the length of the arm in feet.

Twist drills, which are the most commonly used type, are made in numbered sizes from the smallest, No. 80 (0.0135 in.) to No. 1 (0.228 in.) and in fractional sizes from $\frac{1}{64}$ in. to 2 in. by 64ths. Letter drill sizes from "A" (0.234 in.) to "Z" (0.413 in.) fill in some of the gaps in this series. Larger size twist drills up to $3\frac{1}{2}$ in. are also available, usually varying by $\frac{1}{32}$-in., or in the largest sizes by $\frac{1}{16}$-in. steps.

Twist drills are made of carbon steel or high-speed steel, and, in the medium and the larger sizes, they are also available with carbide tips. Usually the high-speed drills are preferred for production drilling and the carbide-tipped drills for heavy cuts or for hard or abrasive materials.

The speed of rotation and the rate of feed depend on the size of drill, the material being worked, and the rigidity and the power of the drill press. The smaller drills are run at higher speeds with a lower rate of feed per revolution. Softer materials, such as brass, aluminum, and plastics, can be drilled at higher speeds than steel or iron.

The accuracy of hole size and location which it is possible to hold depends to a large extent on the care with which the drills are ground and the method of locating the holes. Drill jigs with hardened steel bushings to guide the drill are usually used in production work. For small quantities, the holes may be located by center punch marks to start the drill properly. Standard tolerance for the diameter of drilled holes varies from plus 0.001 in. in very small holes to plus 0.010 in. or 0.012 in. in the large sizes. When closer tolerances are required, the drilling may be followed by a reaming operation to size the drilled hole accurately.

Drilling is a very common production operation and is quite inexpensive. The machines used are simple and inexpensive and usually are operated by semiskilled operators. Production rates can be quite high.

Where several holes are to be drilled on a production basis, in fixed relation to each other and in the same plane, multiple-spindle drill heads can be used which greatly increase production and reduce cost. From 2 to 20 or more holes can be drilled at one time with these attachments.

Tapping attachments for the drill press are also available for cutting screw threads in drilled holes. These are also inexpensive and have quite high production rates without skilled operators.

Where a series of operations is required in one workpiece (such as drilling of various-size holes, reaming, and tapping), a group of drill presses, either separately or in a single unit, is often used. Then the work is passed from one operator to another, or one operator may pass from one machine to another without stopping the machines to change setups.

Other operations commonly performed on the drill press are countersinking (cutting a taper on the end of a hole for a screw head), counterboring (forming an enlarged diameter on the end of the hole to recess a screw head or other part below the surface), and cutting large holes or disks by means of a fly cutter. This is a tool having a single cutter similar to that used in a lathe or shaper which is located adjustably with relation to a center spindle which guides the tool through the work.

Drill presses are also made with horizontal spindles for certain types of work, and many special drilling machines are made for special purposes. These often use standard drill heads, which are quite inexpensive, mounted at various angles and positions around a workpiece to perform a whole group of drilling, reaming, counterboring, and tapping operations simultaneously. Of course the construction and the setup of such a machine take so much time that they are practical only for long production runs. However, when the quantities of a given piece justify such a setup, it can be a great labor- and cost-saver.

Drilling is also often done on a lathe, as mentioned in the section on lathe and screw machine work. In this case, the work may be rotated and the drill held stationary.

For heavy drilling and boring work, vertical or horizontal boring machines are available which may resemble both the drill press and the lathe. They are usually made for work that is too heavy to be handled conveniently in a drill press. Either the work or the tool may be rotated and adjustments are provided for a wide range of jobs. The tools may be standard types of drills or reamers, or, more commonly, they are single-point tools similar to those used in lathes or shapers. Some types of boring machines are equipped with turret type tool holders, which enable several tools to be mounted and adjusted so that they may be rapidly brought into position for a series of operations on the same workpiece. These are suitable for production work where accurate machining is required on large pieces.

GRINDING

Grinding is the process of removing material by means of abrasives. Usually it is used as a finishing operation on machine parts where the finest finish and the greatest accuracy are required or where the material is too hard to work by other methods. It is not usually an economical method of removing large amounts of material.

Most grinding is done with abrasive wheels which come in a wide variety of shapes and sizes. They also vary in the type and the coarseness of the abrasive used as well as in the material and the structure of the bonding material which binds the abrasive material together. The most commonly used abrasive materials are silicon carbide, which is a very hard material but with a tendency to be brittle, and aluminum oxide, which is much tougher but not so hard. The silicon carbide is used for grinding hard materials such as cast iron, carbides, and ceramics. The aluminum oxide is better for tough materials such as tool steels and malleable iron. The grain size varies from the coarsest, No. 6, to the finest, No. 600. Most production grinding is done wet, with a coolant flowed over the point where the abrasive contacts the work.

The abrasive material is also bonded to cloth belts which are being used more and more in certain grinding and finishing operations, described more fully in the following section.

The simplest type of grinding machine is the common floor stand or bench grinder where the work is held manually against the wheel. This is used for sharpening tools where no great accuracy is required and also for rough grinding of castings and forgings and welds.

The surface grinder is a machine for finishing flat or plane surfaces. The spindle holding the grinding wheel may be either vertical or horizontal. The wheel revolves at high speed while the work is moved slowly under it. The work is moved back and forth in the horizontal spindle machine while the wheel or the table is fed slowly across the work area. This is used primarily for tool and die work requiring very fine finish and the closest tolerances.

The vertical-spindle surface grinder uses a cup-type wheel and the work is fed under the wheel on a rotary table. This type of surface grinder can do close-tolerance work on a production basis. The operator simply removes the finished pieces and replaces them with unfinished blanks as the work table rotates slowly. Magnetic chucks are usually used to hold the workpieces or the work-holding fixtures to the table.

External grinding of cylindrical work may be done on a lathe, with the work supported between centers and rotated while the grinding wheel, turning at high speed, is moved along on the lathe carriage, just as a cutting tool would be. There are also special grinding machines which operate in the same way but are more efficient for this particular operation. Extremely fine finish and close tolerances can be maintained.

A more economical method of grinding external cylindrical work is known as centerless grinding. Instead of being mounted on centers and rotated against the grinding wheel, the workpiece is fed automatically between a back-up roller, which causes the work to rotate, and the grinding wheel, which does the work. The longitudinal feed is obtained by setting the back-up roller at a slight angle from the grinding-wheel spindle. Centerless grinding is used for production grinding of such things as shafting and also for small cylindrical parts such as pins, bushings, and arbors requiring a ground finish and a close tolerance. The production rate is high and the cost low, considering the finish and the accuracy of the work. In parts having several diameters or both an internal and an external diameter, centerless grinding will not correct any lack of concentricity between the various diameters in the original rough piece. Grinding on centers is required to obtain accurate concentricity.

The grinding of internal diameters or bores can be done on a lathe or on special internal-grinding machines. On a lathe, the piece is usually held in a chuck or collet and rotated while the grinding wheel, rotating at high speed, is fed back and forth through the bore and advanced slightly as the grinding proceeds. Good results can be obtained this way, but it is hardly a production process.

Internal-grinding machines accomplish the same thing on a production basis; many types are made for various kinds of work. In some of these, the work is stationary and the grinding-wheel spindle, turning at a high rate of speed, is also moved around in a circle at a much lower rate. The diameter of this circle determines the bore of the hole being ground, and this diameter is increased slowly until the desired bore is obtained. The entire wheel and arbor mechanism is also moved back and forth throughout the length of the bore.

The diameter of the wheel used for internal grinding must, of course, be substantially less than the diameter of the hole in which it is working. Since holes as small as $\frac{1}{16}$ in. or less can be ground, many of these wheels are extremely small and operate at very high speeds, 40,000 rpm being common. Larger wheels and lower speeds would be used for larger holes, such as automobile cylinders and hydraulic cylinders.

Internal grinding is used to obtain fine finish and great accuracy on internal diameters, or where the material is too hard to work by other methods. However, it is fairly expensive, and should be avoided on jobs where a reamed or broached finish would be adequate.

The surface finish or smoothness of metal parts is measured in microinches, this being the average height of the minute roughnesses that are present on even the smoothest surfaces. More and more commonly the degree of surface finish required is being specified on drawings, so that this very important quality is not left to the judgment of the individual machine operator in the shop. The cost of a piece is increased greatly if a very fine finish is specified. Finishes obtained by machine processes, such as milling, shaping, and turning, are of the order of 125 to 8 μin. Those obtained by grinding vary, according to the coarseness of the wheel and the rate of feed, from 64 to 4 μin.

If still finer surface finishes are required, they can be obtained (at considerable expense) by honing or lapping. These processes are commonly used after the grinding operations on such surfaces as automobile cylinder bores, pistons, wrist pins, and crankshafts. The extremely fine finish obtained by this means permits a closer fit on these critical parts and reduces the "breaking-in" period that is otherwise required on a new car.

In the honing process, blocks of very fine abrasive material are pressed under light spring pressure against the work surface, such as the inside of a cylinder, and are rotated at a relatively low rate of speed, at the same time being moved back and forth laterally. The rates of rotation and of lateral movement preferably are adjusted in some odd ratio so that an individual spot on the hone does not cover the same path on the work more than once.

Lapping is quite similar to honing except that the lapping plate or block is of metal with the fine abrasive material, in paste or liquid form, used between the metal lap and the work surface.

The amount of metal removed by honing or lapping is usually kept very small, since the object of these processes is primarily the removal of microscopic surface irregularities. Surface finishes as fine as 2 μin. can be obtained in production by these methods, but these should be specified only where they serve a necessary purpose since the cost will be high.

Another process closely allied to grinding is the use of thin abrasive wheels, usually with a rubber or resin bond, for cutting metal, plastic, ceramic, or masonry. This is done quite commonly and is a rapid and economical process. The work is usually stationary and the rotating wheel is pressed against it, either manually or automatically. The wheels may be used either wet or dry, and the cutting rate is amazingly fast. Large alloy steel bars can be cut quickly and with a smooth surface. Tubing is cut without crushing and with only a small burr. The cut is wider than that made by a metal-cutting band saw or a narrow milling cutter, so there is somewhat more waste of material. The abrasive wheels, which are usually $\frac{3}{32}$ in. to $\frac{1}{8}$ in. thick, wear away fairly rapidly, so their cost should be considered as part of the cutting cost. Even with these factors considered, abrasive wheel cutting is often economical, especially with hard or abrasive materials such as alloy steels or ceramics.

ABRASIVE BELT GRINDING

This is a form of grinding that is a very useful production process for many applications. Cloth belts coated with abrasive particles operate over two or more pulleys at a speed of about 2,000 to 10,000 fpm. At the point of contact with the work, the belt usually is backed up with a flat metal plate to provide a true surface. Usually the work is supported on a table at right angles to this belt surface and is pressed either manually or automatically against the moving belt. Smooth and quite accurate surfaces can be obtained very rapidly by this method. The belts are usually operated wet to reduce heating and clogging of the abrasive.

The working surface may be either vertical or horizontal, and belt widths from 6 in. to 10 in. generally are used. Not only metals but also plastics, glass, and ceramics are often worked by belt surfacing. Flatness to ± 0.001 or better can be obtained, as well as good surface finish, depending on the grade of abrasive used. It is often a very economical method of finishing smooth flat surfaces since the production rate is quite high and the machines are very inexpensive, compared with other precision grinding equipment.

More recently, abrasive belt machines have been designed for centerless grinding of cylindrical work. Contact with the abrasive belt is made at the point where it runs around one of the pulleys and the work is backed up by a regulating wheel. This wheel controls the rotation and forward movement of the work just as in other centerless grinding machines. On many types of straight work, a finish and accuracy comparable with that of the abrasive wheel type of centerless grinder are reported, and the belt machines themselves are much less expensive.

Abrasive belt grinders are also often used for many hand-grinding and -polishing operations with various types of shaped and flexible wheels and backing plates used to support the belt where it makes contact with the work.

BROACHING AND REAMING

Broaching is similar in its action to shaping, but, instead of the cutting tool being advanced slightly after each stroke across the work, the feed is built into the broaching tool. This broaching tool (or broach, as it is commonly called) consists of a series of teeth of the desired shape with each tooth projecting slightly farther than the one before it. Thus, as the tool (which is held firmly in position) is passed over the work, it takes a whole series of cuts, depending on the number of teeth, and a single stroke completes the entire cut desired.

A simple form of broach is the type used to cut a keyway on the inside of a pulley or a gear hub. This consists of a round bar which is a sliding fit in the shaft hole, with a series of teeth along one side the width of the desired keyway. The front end of the broach is left round to act as a pilot. The first of these teeth projects only a few thousandths of an inch beyond the round shaft and they get progressively higher until the last one is the full depth of the keyway. In use, the pilot is inserted through the hole in the hub; pressure, usually from a hydraulic press, is applied to the broach; and it is pushed or pulled completely through the hole, completing the cutting of the keyway.

The broach can be designed also to form a square or a splined hole, or to true up a round hole and cut it accurately to size. Broaches also can be made to be pressed over the outside of a piece, shaping the external rather than the internal surfaces. They can be made also to cut on one side only, in which case they are backed up by the rigid frame of the broaching machine and moved across the surface of the work to make the required cut.

Broaching is obviously a simple and economical way of performing certain types of cutting operations. The broaching machines are not expensive, as machine tools go, and production rates, even with semiskilled operators, are quite high. The design of the broaches requires a high degree of specialized skill. Certain shapes of broaches are standard, such as those for standard keyways and round and square holes. Special shapes can be made to order and will cost considerably more than standard ones. The cost of the tooling is not high, and, if even a moderate quantity of pieces is required, it will soon pay for itself, when the saving in labor over shaping or milling, which usually would be the alternative processes, is considered.

Reaming is a very simple process used to improve the accuracy and the finish of drilled or cast holes. Reamed holes are always round, but they may be either straight or tapered. The reamer is similar to a drill but has a larger number of cutting flutes (usually 4 to 16) which are designed to cut on the sides of a hole rather than the end. The straight reamer, which may be solid or adjustable, has a short, tapered section on the front to enlarge the hole and a longer straight section to do the final truing to size and to give a fine, smooth finish. The usual allowance for reaming on drilled holes is from 0.005 in. on ⅛-in. diameter holes to 0.015 in. on holes over ⅜ in. The reamer may be turned by hand or by a machine, such as a drill press or a lathe, or the reamer may be stationary and the work turned.

A wide variety of straight reamers (see Fig. 271) is available in stock sizes, and also certain standard tapers, such as those used for taper pins, and the Morse or Brown and Sharpe tapers used for the shanks of various types of cutting tools. Special reamers are often made up for reaming a series of several holes in true alignment.

Reaming is a very commonly used and economical means of machining accurate holes. Tolerances of ±0.001 in. or better are held generally on smaller size holes and about 0.001 in. per inch of diameter or better on the larger ones.

CONTOUR OR BAND SAWING

Special band saws, similar to those used for woodworking but built more heavily and with a greater range of speeds, are most useful tools in the machine shop. Steel up to several inches in thickness can be sawed quite easily and rapidly by these machines and a considerable amount of labor on other machines is saved by cutting irregularly shaped parts roughly to shape before the final machining is started. By this method, unwanted stock can be cut out in a single piece instead of being removed in small shavings, as in other processes.

Its use is largely in the production of dies and individual or small-quantity parts, although some applications have been found where it is economical for larger-quantity work. Thin sheet material may be sawed in stacks so that a number of pieces are formed at one time. Substitutes for forgings or castings can be made without dies or patterns by sawing the required shape from solid stock. If internal contours are needed, the saw blade may be broken, inserted through a starting hole and the ends welded together by means of a small butt welder attached to the saw.

The utility of these special band saws is extended considerably by a recent development known as friction sawing. A relatively soft blade, in some cases without teeth of any kind, is run at very high speeds, around 10,000 fpm to 15,000 fpm. The metal to be cut, which may be hardened steel, is pressed firmly against the rapidly moving blade. Heat, sufficient to soften or even melt the metal, is generated at the point of contact. The heat in the work is concentrated at one point while that in the saw is dissipated along the whole length of the blade so that the blade cuts its way quite rapidly through the work without being seriously affected itself. Friction sawing usually is limited to cutting stock 1 in. thick or less.

Flexible filing bands are available for use in these band saws for smoothing and truing the edges of cut parts. Diamond-edged blades are also made for cutting very hard materials such as carbides and ceramics.

GEAR FORMING

Many processes are available for making gears and the choice of which is best in a particular case will depend on a combination of factors, such as size, quantity, material, and the accuracy and the finish required.

The usual form of gear tooth is known as the involute shape, and, when this is designed properly, it gives a rolling contact between the teeth without any sliding friction. The point of contact between two gears is known as the "pitch circle," and the diameter of a gear at this point is known as the "pitch diameter." The number of teeth per inch of pitch diameter is called the "diametral pitch" of the gear, often simply referred to as the pitch. This determines the size and the spacing of the teeth, and any gear of the same pitch will have the same size and the same spacing of teeth, although the number of teeth will vary according to the pitch diameter. For example, a 12-pitch gear of 4 in. pitch diameter would have 48 teeth and a 12-pitch gear of 6 in. pitch diameter would have 72 teeth. The teeth on both would be the same size and the same distance apart, and these two gears would mesh with each other and operate together properly.

The speed ratio between them would be the same as the pitch diameters, or 4 to 6. The shape of the teeth varies slightly according to the size of the gear to give a true rolling action.

The "pressure angle" is determined by the shape of the tooth, and two standard pressure angles are commonly used, 14½° and 20°. Gears must have the same pressure angle to work together properly.

Plain sand-cast gears of iron or steel may be adequate for certain applications and, of course, they are low in cost. They would be suitable only for very rough, crude machines operating at low speeds where noise or efficient transmission of power is not important. For most purposes, more accurate gearing is required.

Several methods are available for cutting gear teeth to the proper shape. The simplest method is to form the teeth one at a time in a shaper or milling machine, using a cutter of the proper shape for the pitch and the diameter of the gear and an indexing fixture to advance the gear blank exactly the right distance after each tooth is cut. Each tooth will be formed by a single cut with a milling cutter or by a series of cuts with the shaper to give the proper depth.

Gear cutting with the shaper is quite a slow process, and is limited to the manufacture of very large gears or to very small quantities of gears. Since the cutting tool has only a single cutting edge, it is fairly easy to grind to the correct shape of the tooth in the gear being cut. The "generating" of gears in a special gear shaper is a production process, and will be discussed later.

The milling of gear teeth is much faster than shaping although not so fast as the generating or hobbing method discussed later. Theoretically, a different shape of cutter should be used for each diametral pitch and for each number of teeth in the gear. Actually, a set of eight cutters numbered from 1 to 8 for each pitch of gear is usually adequate, although seven half sizes are provided if a more accurate shape is required.

The above discussion of gears has been confined, for the sake of simplicity, to the straight or spur type of gear. Books have been written on the subject of gearing and a complete discussion of the more complex forms of gears (such as bevel, spiral bevel, helical, worm gears and worms and hypoid gears) is beyond the scope of this book. Most of these special gears can be cut on the milling machine by means of proper cutters and setups, but all of them can be cut more accurately and more economically in production quantities by the generating or hobbing process.

The hobbing of spur gears will be described and the same basic principles apply to the other types of gears. The hob, or cutter, is similar to a milling cutter with the teeth cut in the form of a spiral or worm. These teeth are the proper shape to cut a rack, which is really a gear of infinitely large pitch diameter. Only one hob is required for each pitch of gear, and this will cut teeth of the correct shape on any size of gear. In cutting a spur gear, the hob is rotated at an angle to the gear blank so that the teeth in the hob are parallel with the arbor holding the gear blank. The gear blank is rotated the distance of one tooth while the hob is moved slowly across it, cutting the full depth of the tooth. This combination of the rotation of the gear blank and the hob generates a tooth of the correct involute shape. Helical gears are also cut by hobbing and also worm wheels, spiral bevel and hypoid gears on special gear-cutting machines designed for this purpose. Hobbing is a very economical method of producing precision gears in quantity. It is also used to produce a wide variety of shapes having uniformly spaced projections such as various shapes of sprockets, ratchets, splines, and similar cylindrical work.

Another efficient method of gear production is the generating of gears on a special gear shaper. This operates basically on the reciprocating principle of the shaper, but the cutter is made in the form of a small gear of the desired pitch and both this cutter and the gear blank are rotated slowly as the cutting action progresses. Only one cutter is required for each pitch of gear, and the combined rotation of the cutter and the gear blank gives teeth of true involute shape on any diameter of gear. Gear shapers are made as high-production machines, and the quality and the cost of gears produced by this method are comparable with those of hobbed gears.

Another method of gear shaping uses a group of cutters, each having the correct shape for one tooth of the gear. These are mounted around the periphery of a heavy cutting head (see Fig. 312) which, in the case of an external gear, surrounds the gear blank. The blank reciprocates repeatedly through the cutting head with the cutters being advanced slightly after each stroke to take the proper depth of cut. The action is quite similar to broaching except that a series of strokes is used instead of a series of cutting teeth on the tool. Gears up to 20 in. in diameter and 6 in. face width can be handled on large machines of this type (see Fig. 311). They are extremely rapid in action and economical for large-scale production. Both external and internal gears and splines and other toothed parts can be produced by this method.

Gears often require heat treatment after cutting, to develop the maximum strength and hardness of the steel. Since the heat treatment sometimes causes a certain amount of distortion and surface scale, it is often desirable to finish the teeth after the heat treatment. This usually is done by grinding, although shaving, lapping, and burnishing are also used. All of these processes leave a fine finish on the tooth surface.

In gears, as with other parts, one should remember that the holding of close tolerances, high physical characteristics, and fine finish, all add to the cost of the finished gear, and the application should be examined closely to be sure that the specifications are as broad as possible for the required use.

Small- and medium-sized spur gears and bevel gears that are required in quite large quantities can often be produced most economically by powder metallurgy. Gears produced in this way, known as "sinterings," have excellent finish and accuracy and a low piece cost, but the high die cost usually limits the process to runs of a few thousand or more of a particular size (Fig. 313). Chapter 4 gives more details on the physical characteristics that can be obtained from sinterings.

Small gears for light loads are often produced as stampings from sheet metal. If more width of face is required, several stampings can be assembled together. A shaving or grinding operation, after stamping, can be used for improving finish or accuracy. Where the load is light and no backlash is required, as in a radio dial drive, a spring-loaded gear may be used. Two stamped gears are assembled, side by side, with one gear fastened to the shaft and the other floating. A spring mounted between them is compressed when the gear is assembled with its mating pinion, and the constant pressure takes up any play between the teeth. Stamped gears are inexpensive in quantities and should be considered for lighter and less critical applications.

Small brass and aluminum pinions are often made from extruded rods (see Chap. 3). These are formed to the desired shape in the extruding process and then simply cut to length. Such pinions are often suitable for use with stamped gears for light applications.

Plastic gears of various types have wide application for certain purposes. The strength, of course, does not compare with that of steel gears, but they operate more quietly and often with less friction. Usually one of a pair of gears will be plastic, the other of metal. Plastic gears may be cut by any of the methods described earlier for metal gears, or they may be extruded or molded in the desired shape. The most commonly used plastics for gears are (1) the phenolics, usually with a fabric or a fibrous filler to increase the impact strength, and (2) nylon. Fabric-base phenolic is often machined into quite large gears. While it might seem that these would be less expensive than a steel gear of the same size, this is not usually the case. The material is expensive and the cutting tools wear much faster than they would in cutting metal. The use of machined phenolic gears would be justified, therefore, only where quietness or lack of friction is a factor.

Molded plastic gears, on the other hand, are quite inexpensive in quantities large enough to amortize the rather high mold cost, and are coming into more general use. Nylon is much favored for small gears, and this material may be extruded or molded or it may be sintered in much the same manner as powdered metal. Nylon is also relatively easy to machine if gears are required in smaller quantities.

ENGRAVING AND TRACER MILLING

These processes are quite similar to vertical milling although the cutters are usually small and operate at high speeds. The spindle which carries the cutter is mounted on a pantograph mechanism and is guided by a master pattern, which is made to scale, although it may be larger or smaller than the desired piece. The pattern may be of metal, plastic, or even plaster or wood. Some of the machines operate in only two dimensions, for work on a flat surface. These are used for the engraving of lettering on panels or dials and for the forming of intricate shapes, such as cams where movement in two dimensions is sufficient. Other machines work in three dimensions and can be used for very intricate carving and the forming of dies and similar parts. The lighter machines are guided by hand and are adapted primarily to toolroom or laboratory use. Larger machines, operating on similar principles, with automatic tracing controls, have been developed and show great promise in the high-speed, automatic production of intricate machined parts. The control can be obtained either by tracing a master pattern or from a perforated or magnetic tape which guides the movement of the cutting tool in two or three dimensions. A further discussion of these principles will be found in Chap. 23

LATE TRENDS IN MACHINE DESIGN

In all machine tools, the latest developments are in the direction of increased production. This usually takes the form of higher cutting speeds and increased rigidity for heavier cuts. More powerful motors are required to drive these new high-production units. For example, 50- to 100-hp motors are now common on large vertical millers, and lathes are using motors four times as large as those used a few years ago on the same size machine. Modern planers are operating at cutting speeds of more than twice that formerly considered maximum.

To supplement these large, heavy machines, many small machine tools, manufactured in quantities on a mass-production basis and selling at lower prices, are taking over light operations that were done formerly on heavier, slower machines.

"Human engineering" is being applied to reduce operator fatigue and to improve efficiency. The result of these improved methods and machines is often more investment in equipment per man but greatly increased output per man-hour.

Automatic controls in varying degree are coming into use, not only for specialized high-production machines but also for those doing a series of complex operations where electronic control units, working from perforated or magnetic tapes or cards, remove the need for continuous attention of a skilled operator. These are discussed more fully in Chap. 23.

CERAMIC CUTTING TOOLS

One limiting factor in the cutting speed of machine tools is the material of the cutting tool itself. The first major improvement in tool materials was the introduction of the tungsten carbides about 1929. It was almost ten years, however, before new and more rigid machines were developed to take full advantage of the possibilities of carbide tooling. When this was accomplished, the cutting speeds commonly used on iron and steel were increased from the 75 to 150 surface feet per minute of high-speed steel tools to 300 to 600 ft or more for carbide tools.

The introduction of ceramic and other cemented oxide cutting tools promises a comparable further development in potential machining speeds. Experimental work in the use of ceramics for cutting tools has been going on for several years, partly because of possible wartime shortages of tungsten and cobalt and partly because the extreme hardness and heat resistance of ceramics looked attractive. Although some of these ceramic tools were used successfully for machining relatively soft but abrasive materials, it was not until 1955 that promising results were obtained in machining steel. Under favorable conditions, these results have been most impressive. The hardness and the temperature resistance are much superior to carbides, and higher cutting speeds are possible. Most favorable results have been obtained around 1000 surface feet per minute although 2000 to 3000 ft have been used in some cases for finishing cuts and 200 ft for heavy cuts and feeds. The surface finish is exceptionally fine. The characteristic brittleness of ceramics has been the chief difficulty, and this requires that small inserts of the ceramic be supported very rigidly in metal shanks. These inserts and holders are now available commercially in many shapes and a variety of sizes. With some types, the inserts are cheap enough so that it is more economical to replace them than to regrind. Where they are ground, usually diamond wheels are used.

Metal oxides are the ceramic materials most commonly used with aluminum oxide, the principal ingredient. This is formed by techniques very similar to those used in powder metallurgy but with higher sintering temperatures. The use of other ceramics, especially nitrides and borides, is also promising. A new type, shown in Figs. 324 and 325, is fused until it resembles synthetic sapphire, and will actually cut the natural gem stone.

Much development is still to be done in ceramic materials and their application as cutting tools, but this seems certain to have an important bearing on machining practice in the very near future.

Fig. 212. A modern 13-in. lathe for toolroom and production use. This one takes work 34 in. long between centers and has a 1⅜-in. hole through the spindle. (Courtesy, Sheldon Machine Co., Inc.)

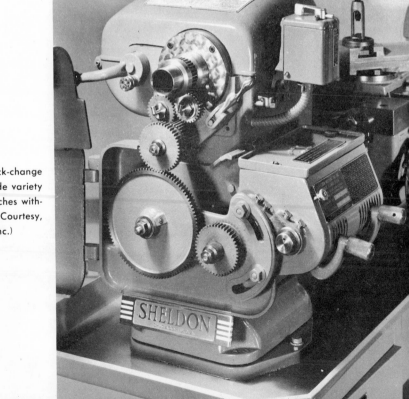

Fig. 213. The quick-change gear box provides a wide variety of feeds and thread pitches without stopping the lathe. (Courtesy, Sheldon Machine Co., Inc.)

Fig. 214. Back gearing on the lathe spindle provides reduced speeds and increased power for heavy turning. (Courtesy, Sheldon Machine Co., Inc.)

Fig. 215. The lathe carriage supports the cutting tool and provides cross feed, either straight or at various angles. (Courtesy, Sheldon Machine Co., Inc.)

Fig. 216. The lathe tailstock carries a "dead" center that supports the outer end of the work. It can be offset for cutting tapers and can also carry a chuck for drilling, reaming, tapping, or boring. (Courtesy, Sheldon Machine Co., Inc.)

Figs. 217–222. A group of pictures showing typical operations on the lathe and giving an idea of its versatility. Fig. 217, rough turning; Fig. 218, finish turning; Fig. 219, parting or cutting off; Fig. 220, cutting screw threads; Fig. 221, knurling; Fig. 222, boring. (Courtesy, Sheldon Machine Co., Inc.)

Fig. 217

Fig. 218

Fig. 219

Fig. 220

Fig. 221

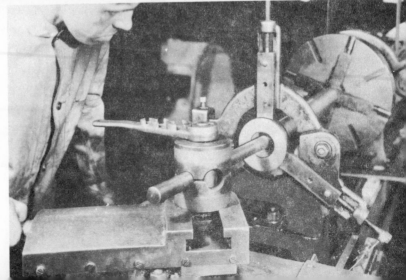

Fig. 222

Fig. 223. A ram type universal turret lathe. Machines of this type can do a large variety of high precision work and are found in almost every machine shop. (Courtesy, Jones & Lamson Machine Company.)

Fig. 224. Showing a turret lathe setup for performing a series of operations on a stainless steel valve body. (Courtesy, Jones & Lamson Machine Company.)

Fig. 225. A hand screw machine. (Courtesy, Brown & Sharpe Mfg. Co.)

Fig. 226. A closeup of the hand screw machine at work. (Courtesy, Brown & Sharpe Mfg. Co.)

Fig. 227. A group of typical work done by the hand screw machine. (Courtesy, Brown & Sharpe Mfg. Co.)

Fig. 228. A 6-spindle automatic screw machine with capacity up to 1⅝ in. (Courtesy, The National Acme Company.)

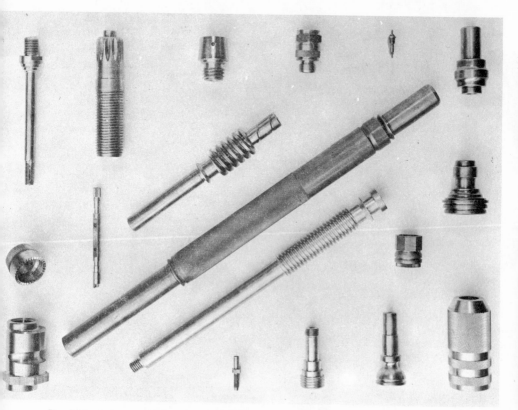

Fig. 229. A group of typical parts produced from bar stock on a machine such as is illustrated in Fig. 228. (Courtesy, The National Acme Company.)

Fig. 230. A small automatic screw machine. (Courtesy, Brown & Sharpe Mfg. Co.)

Fig. 231. The machine illustrated in Fig. 230 pened for setup. (Courtesy, Brown & Sharpe Mfg. Co.)

Fig. 232. A group of typical small screw machine parts. (Courtesy, Brown & Sharpe Mfg. Co.)

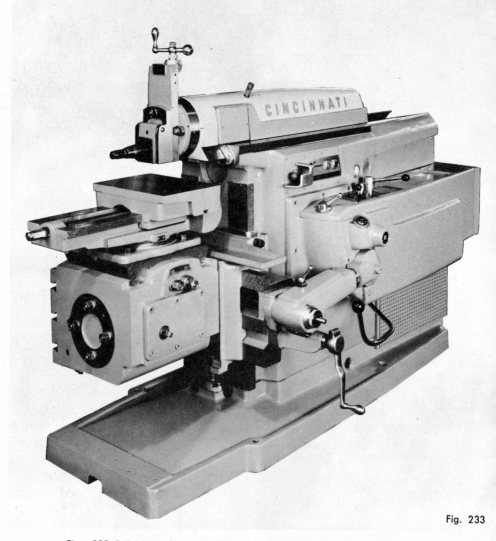

Fig. 233

Figs. 233–241. A modern, heavy-duty shaper with a 20-in. stroke and examples
of the wide variety of work done on such a machine. Fig. 234, taking a 2-in. cut
in a heavy metal removing operation. Fig. 235, cutting an internal keyway in a
gear. Fig. 236, cutting splines on a shaft on index centers. Fig. 237, internal shaping
of Kennedy keyways to close tolerances. Fig. 238, cutting of internal splines by
the use of an index head. Fig. 239, forming the teeth in a long rack, using a
formed cutter of the correct tooth shape. Fig. 240, a cylindrical pitman is contoured
by means of a simple fixture. Fig. 241, the shaper, equipped with tracer or follower
controls, automatically produces form tools, dies, cams, and other intricate shapes
from simple sheet-metal templates. (Courtesy, The Cincinnati Shaper Co.)

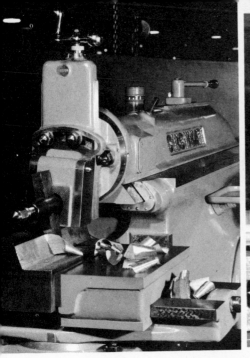

Fig. 234

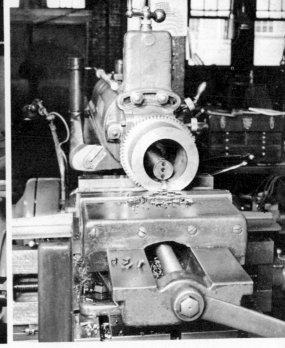

Fig. 235

Fig. 236

Fig. 237

Fig. 238

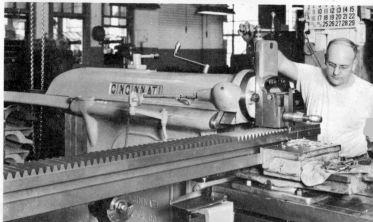

Fig. 239

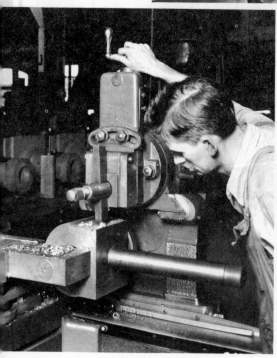

Fig. 240

Fig. 241

Fig. 242. A vertical shaper or slotter with a rotary work table. (Courtesy, Rockford Machine Tool Co.)

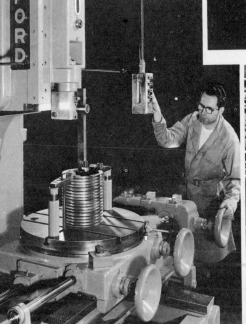

Fig. 243. A view of the machine illustrated in Fig. 242 in use. (Courtesy, Rockford Machine Tool Co.)

Fig. 244. A planer with double cutting heads machining two surfaces on a large casting at the same time. (Courtesy, The G. A. Gray Company.)

Fig. 245. A horizontal milling machine of the universal type. (Courtesy, Kearney & Trecker Corporation.)

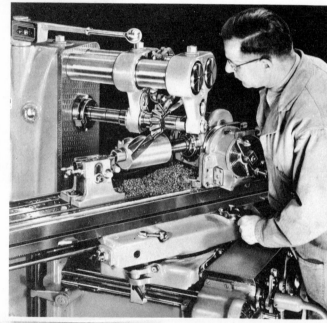

Fig. 246. A closeup of the machine illustrated in Fig. 245 in operation, with the table set at an angle for the milling of spiral flutes. (Courtesy, Kearney & Trecker Corporation.)

Fig. 247. Machining the ways for a grinding machine, using multiple cutters in a horizontal milling machine. (Courtesy, Norton Company.)

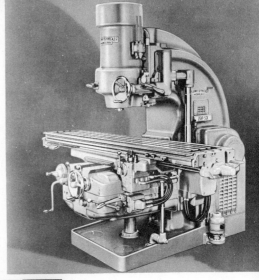

Fig. 248. A heavily constructed vertical milling machine. (Courtesy, Kearney & Trecker Corporation.)

Fig. 249. A closeup of a facing operation in a machine such as is depicted in Fig. 248, using a large inserted tooth cutter. (Courtesy, Kearney & Trecker Corporation.)

Fig. 250. A vertical milling machine using a small end mill for a facing operation. (Courtesy, Barber-Colman Company.)

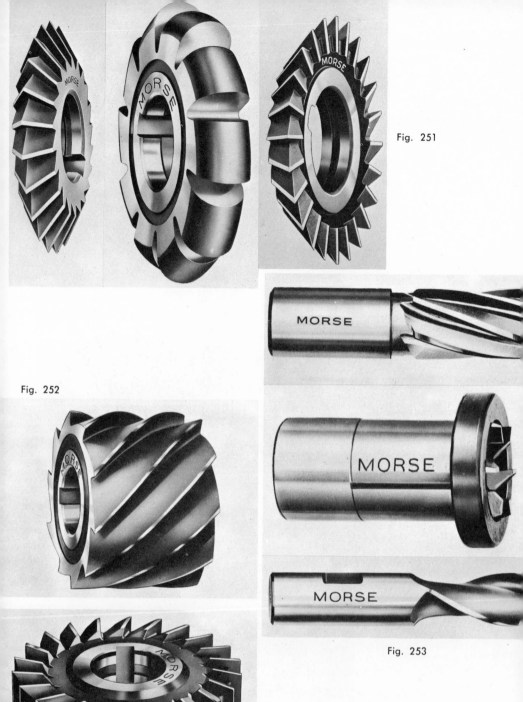

Fig. 251

Fig. 252

Fig. 253

Figs. 251–253. Some of the many standard types of milling machine cutters.
(Courtesy, Morse Twist Drill & Machine Co.)

Fig. 254. A precision internal grinding attachment for use in the jig borer or the vertical milling machine. The small grinding wheel at the bottom is driven by an air motor at 20,000 to 40,000 r.p.m. while it is being moved around a circular path by the machine spindle. The graduations on the collar are in 0.0001 in., and adjustments can be made while the machine is running. (Courtesy, L. G. Rose Associates.)

Fig. 255. Showing the grinder illustrated in Fig. 254 in use. (Courtesy, L. G. Rose Associates.)

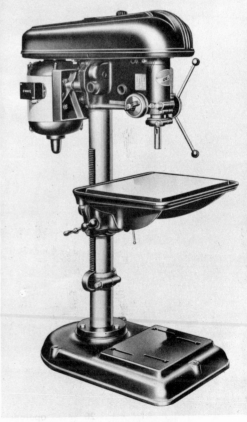

Fig. 256. A medium-size drill press such as this 17-in. one is the most versatile machine in the average machine shop. (Courtesy, Rockwell Manufacturing Co., Delta Power Tool Div.)

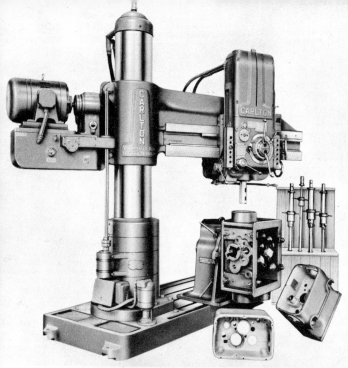

Fig. 257. The radial drill is made in many sizes and does a wide variety of drilling and boring operations. The work is usually clamped to the table and the drill is moved into the proper position above it. (Courtesy, The Carlton Machine Tool Co.)

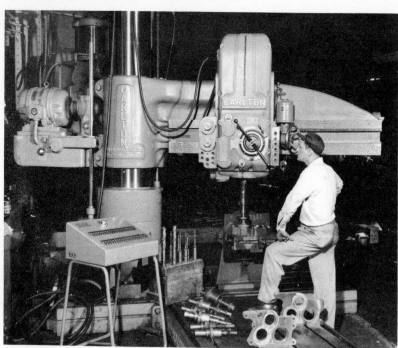

Fig. 258. A radial drill equipped with a pre-select and programming attachment. A series of 20 or 30 operations can be set up on the console in the foreground. The operator inserts the proper tool for each operation and the control selects the proper speed and feed. The unit is very flexible and reduces down time between operations to a minimum. (Courtesy, The Carlton Machine Tool Co.)

Fig. 259. A large radial drill with the base arranged to slide back and forth on a long bed plate to handle very large work such as the planer housing shown here. (Courtesy, The Carlton Machine Tool Co.)

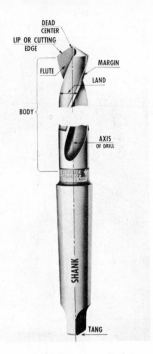

Fig. 260. Terms applied to a standard twist drill, one of the most widely used of cutting tools. (Courtesy, The Cleveland Twist Drill Co.)

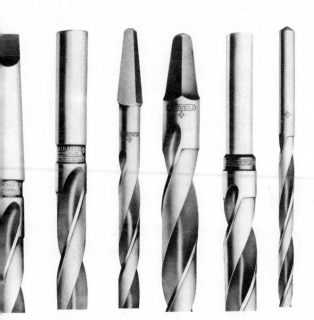

Fig. 261. Various styles of shanks used on standard twist drills. (Courtesy, The Cleveland Twist Drill Co.)

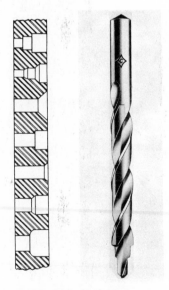

Fig. 262. A three-diameter step drill and various types of holes that can be made in one operation with tools of this type. (Courtesy, The Cleveland Twist Drill Co.)

Figs. 263–265. Three types of multiple spindle attachments for use in a standard drill press. Fig. 263 is a fixed spindle unit built for a specific job. Fig. 264 is a universal joint drive with infinite adjustment of the spindle within its range. Fig. 265 shows a four-spindle head with double eccentric adjustments on each spindle. These can be used not only for drilling but also for reaming, countersinking, spot facing, and many other operations. (Courtesy, Thriftmaster Products Corporation.)

Fig. 263

Fig. 264

Fig. 265

Fig. 266. A four-spindle multiple drill head mounted in a standard drill press with a fixture for production drilling. (Courtesy, Ettco Tool Co., Inc.)

Fig. 267. A tapping attachment mounted in a standard drill press. The tap is driven forward when the pressure is down, reversing when the pressure is up. (Courtesy, Ettco Tool Co., Inc.)

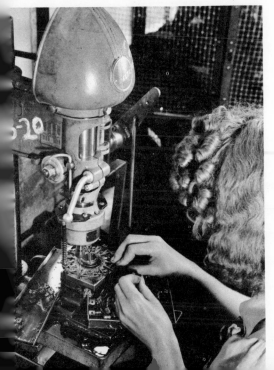

Fig. 268. A 14-in. drill press equipped with a tapping attachment and a rotary work-holding fixture makes a simple and efficient method of tapping small parts. (Courtesy, Rockwell Manufacturing Co., Delta Power Tool Div.)

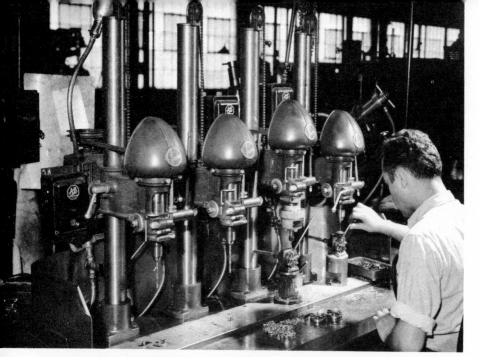

Fig. 269. A group of 14-in. drill presses mounted on a common base forms a convenient tool for a series of drilling and tapping operations, either with one operator or with several. (Courtesy, Rockwell Manufacturing Co., Delta Power Tool Div.)

Fig. 271

Fig. 270

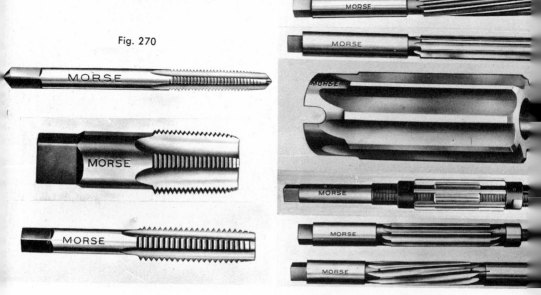

Figs. 270–271. Several groups of cutting tools typical of the wide variety of standard types available. Fig. 270 shows three taps for thread cutting. Fig. 271 shows several reamers, both solid and adjustable. (Courtesy, Morse Twist Drill & Machine Co.)

Fig. 272. A group of seven 17-in. drill heads mounted on a special fixture for a multiple drilling operation at Jacobs Aircraft Engine Company. Many special tools of this kind can be made from these standard units. (Courtesy, Rockwell Manufacturing Co., Delta Power Tool Div.)

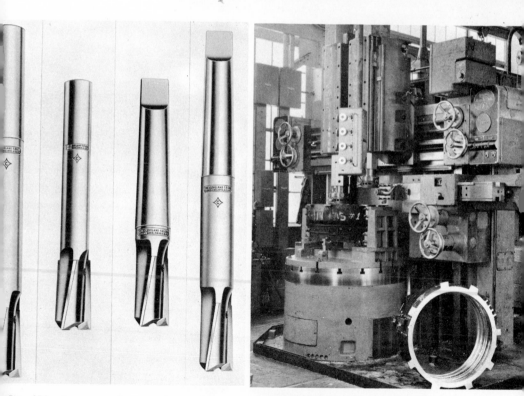

Fig. 273. A group of counterbores. Interchangeable pilots fit in the center of these to locate the counterbore around an already drilled hole. (Courtesy, The Cleveland Twist Drill Co.)

Fig. 274. A vertical boring machine with two tool-holding slides and a typical workpiece in the foreground. (Courtesy, The Bullard Company.)

Fig. 275. The horizontal boring machine is well adapted to many large and heavy boring jobs. (Courtesy, The Bullard Company.)

Fig. 276. The vertical turret lathe is similar to the vertical boring machine with a turret arrangement for holding several tools. It is usually used for work that is too large or heavy for the horizontal turret lathe, but is not suitable for work on bar stock. (Courtesy, The Bullard Company.)

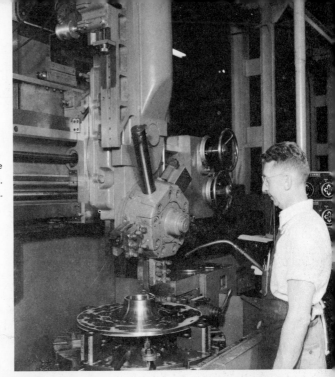

Fig. 277. A closeup of the work illustrated in Fig. 276. (Courtesy, The Bullard Company.)

Fig. 278. Some typical abrasive wheels for use in the many types of manual and automatic grinding equipment. (Courtesy, Norton Company.)

Fig. 279. Two types of small grinders that find use in almost every shop. The bench grinder in the foreground is for general grinding and tool sharpening, either free hand or with special attachments. The one in the background is especially for carbide and high-speed steel cutters for lathe and shaper work. (Courtesy, Rockwell Manufacturing Co., Delta Power Tool Div.)

Figs. 280–281. The horizontal surface grinder does a wide range of high-precision flat grinding both on production, as shown in Fig. 280, and on die work, as shown in Fig. 281. In both of these jobs, the work is held on a magnetic table. (Courtesy, The DoAll Company.)

Figs. 282–285. The vertical spindle surface grinder is an economical production tool for the grinding of flat surfaces. Fig. 282 shows such a machine, Fig. 283 shows a closeup of the work with the pieces held by a magnetic table, Fig. 284 is a group of typical work done on such a machine, and Fig. 285 is a group of the abrasive wheels and segments that are used for the grinding. (Courtesy, The Blanchard Machine Company.)

Fig. 282

Fig. 283

Fig. 284

Fig. 285

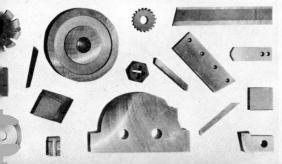

Fig. 286

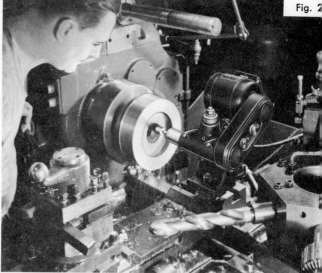

Fig. 2

Figs. 286–288. The grinding attachment is one of the most useful accessories for the lathe and is capable of high precision work. Fig. 286 is a large grinding attachment doing external grinding of nickel steel alloy pins on a heavy lathe. Fig. 287 shows a smaller grinder equipped for internal work on a turret lathe. In Fig. 288, the grinder is facing a gear hub to a finish of 5 μin. to 20 μin. (Courtesy, The Dumore Company.)

Fig. 288

Fig. 289. An internal grinding machine equipped with an automatic loading device grinding the bore of steel bevel gears. (Courtesy, The Heald Machine Company.)

Fig. 290. An automatic cam shaft grinder turns out large quantities of high precision work. (Courtesy, Norton Company.)

Fig. 291. A precision thread grinding machine puts the finishing touches on a machine lead screw. (Courtesy, Norton Company.)

Fig. 292. A two-spindle honing machine finishing the outside and inside diameters of a transmission cover hub. (Courtesy, Micromatic Hone Corporation.)

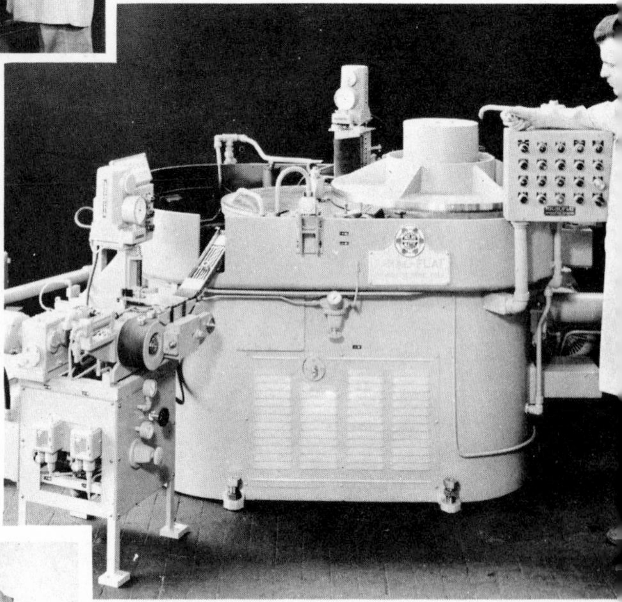

Fig. 293. This completely automatic surface honing machine finished both side faces of gear blanks, flat and parallel at the rate of 1200 to 1800 per hour. (Courtesy, Micromatic Hone Corporation.)

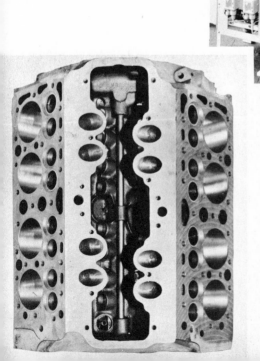

Fig. 294. Automotive cylinder bores finished by honing. (Courtesy, Micromatic Hone Corporation.)

Fig. 295. The type of tools used for the work shown in Fig. 294. (Courtesy, Micromatic Hone Corporation.)

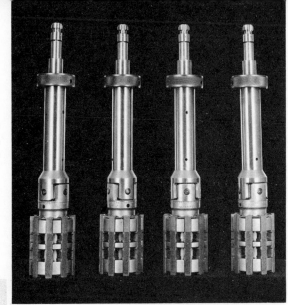

Fig. 296. An abrasive cutoff machine with a capacity up to 6-in. diameter steel bars. This uses a 20-in. diameter abrasive wheel ⅛ in. thick driven by a 15- or 25-hp motor. Even heavy alloy steel bars are cut smoothly in a matter of seconds with such machines. (Courtesy, Campbell Machine Div., American Chain & Cable Company, Inc.)

Fig. 297. A platen type of abrasive belt grinder facing an angle bracket. Stock for machining was reduced from ⅛ in. to ¹⁄₃₂ in. and a saving of 6⅔ hr labor per 100 castings was realized over the milling operations formerly used. (Courtesy, The Engelberg Huller Co., Inc.)

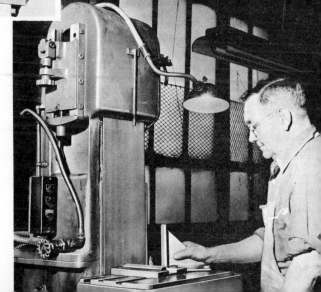

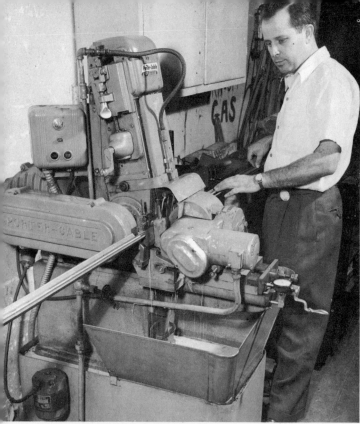

Fig. 298. An abrasive belt centerless grinder sizes and finishes 12-ft lengths of steel and brass for use in automatic screw machines. Tolerances as close as ±.0005 are held. (Courtesy, The Engelberg Huller Co., Inc.)

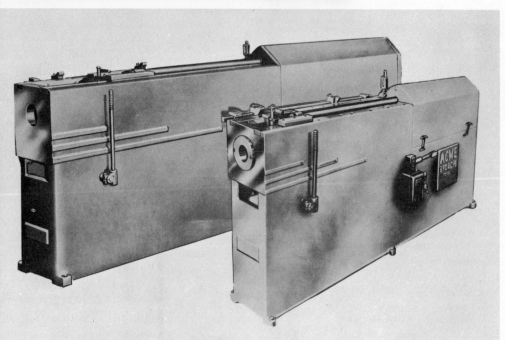

Fig. 299. Two sizes of horizontal hydraulic broaching machines which can be set up for a wide variety of internal and surface broaching jobs. (Courtesy, Acme Broach Corporation.)

Fig. 300. A vertical, single slide surface broaching machine. (Courtesy, Acme Broach Corporation.)

Fig. 301. A multiple tooling setup for broaching the round bore and keyway in four transmission parts at one stroke. Production rate is about 600 pieces per hour. The broaching machine is a vertical pull down internal type. (Courtesy, Acme Broach Corporation.)

Figs. 302–304. The metal-cutting band saw has become a versatile high-production tool for industry. Fig. 302 shows one of these machines with hydraulic feed and controls on a production slotting operation. New band saw blades of high-speed steel have greatly increased the cutting rates. Fig. 303 shows an aluminum aircraft part with complex internal and external contours being cut on a band saw. Fig. 304 shows a block of tool steel 16 in. thick being cut to shape. The unwanted material is removed in a solid chunk that can often be salvaged. (Courtesy, The DoAll Company.)

Fig. 302

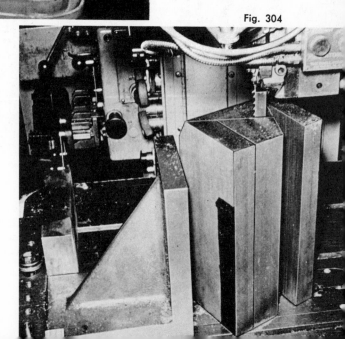

Fig. 303

Fig. 304

Fig. 305. A giant, remotely controlled band saw used for cutting dies for the new, large extrusion presses. The operator observes the work through a system of mirrors and guides it along a layout line by means of the steering wheel. (Courtesy, The DoAll Company.)

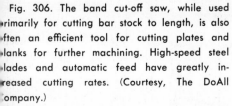

Fig. 306. The band cut-off saw, while used primarily for cutting bar stock to length, is also often an efficient tool for cutting plates and blanks for further machining. High-speed steel blades and automatic feed have greatly increased cutting rates. (Courtesy, The DoAll Company.)

Fig. 307. A gear hobbing machine. The hob is mounted on the lower spindle, the gear blank to be cut on the upper spindle. The angle between the two can be adjusted on the lower spindle. (Courtesy, Barber-Colman Company.)

Fig. 308. The gear hobbing machine in operation. The hob is on the lower spindle, the work above. (Courtesy, Barber-Colman Company.)

Fig. 309. A gear shaper cutting a large coarse pitch spur gear. This machine can cut gears up to 36 in. diameter and 6 in. face width. (Courtesy, The Fellows Gear Shaper Co.)

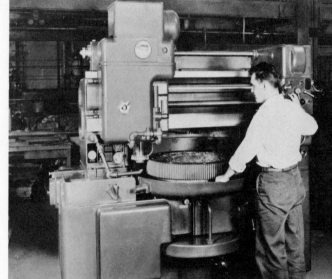

Fig. 310. Showing a closeup of the machine illustrated in Fig. 309 forming an internal gear. (Courtesy, The Fellows Gear Shaper Co.)

Figs. 311–312. A large machine for the "Shear-Speed" method of shaping gears at a single operation. The cutting head used for a large spur gear is shown in Fig. 312. The cutters (one for each tooth of the gear) are advanced at each stroke by means of an outer cone-shaped ring. The cutters are retracted on the up strokes to provide clearance. (Courtesy, Michigan Tool Company.)

Fig. 311

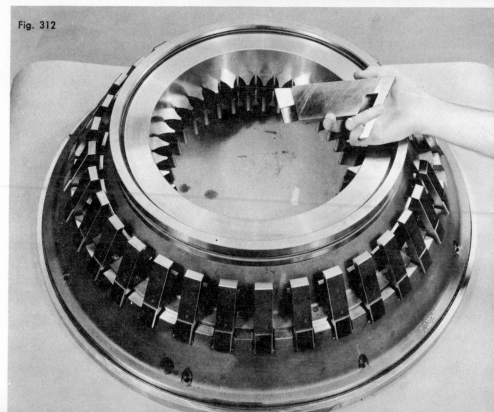

Fig. 312

Fig. 313. A group of gears and pinions made most economically by powder metallurgy (see Chap. 4). (Courtesy, American Sinterings, Div. of Engineered Plastics, Inc.)

Fig. 314

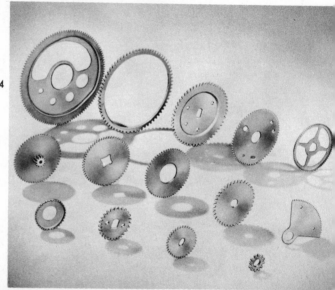

Figs. 314–315. A group of stamped gears. These are the least expensive of all gears for light loads. Fig. 315 shows how several stamped gears can be riveted together where wider faces are necessary. (Courtesy, Winzeler Mfg. & Tool Co.)

Fig. 315

Fig. 316. Gears injection molded of "Zytel" nylon resin are quiet and require little or no lubrication. (Courtesy, E. I. du Pont de Nemours & Company.)

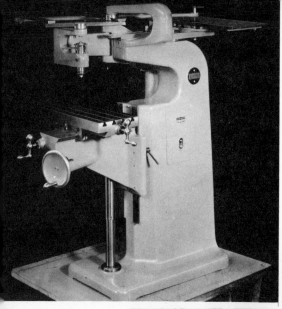

Figs. 317–319. A two-dimensional pantograph engraving and tracer milling machine (Fig. 317) and two views of the machine at work on flat (Fig. 318) and cylindrical (Fig. 319) work. The operator moves the stylus around a template and the cutter follows the same pattern on a dimensional scale determined by the ratio of the pantograph arms. (Courtesy, George Gorton Machine Co.)

Fig. 317

Fig. 318

Fig. 319

Fig. 320. Typical work done on an engraving machine. (Courtesy, George Gorton Machine Co.)

Fig. 321. Front and back views of a drawing die (*right*) formed from the greatly enlarged template in the background. These dies form bronze strips which interlock to produce the cylindrical sheath (*left*) for high-voltage cables used at Boulder Dam. (Courtesy, George Gorton Machine Co.)

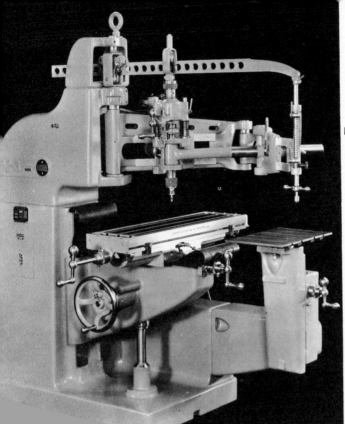

Fig. 322

Figs. 322–323. A three-dimensional pantograph machine and its work in engraving a complex pattern on a mold for a plastic chest. The template can be of plastic or soft metal. This is a very economical method of forming intricate dies and molds. (Courtesy, George Gorton Machine Co.)

Fig. 323

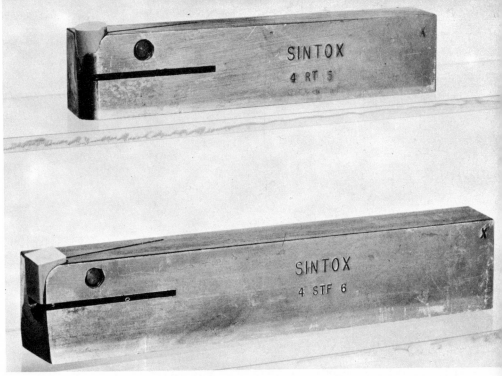

Fig. 324. Two types of Sintox cutting bits and tool holders. The top one is a round insert for turning or facing. The bottom one has a ½-in. square insert for facing. (Courtesy, Sintox, Inc.)

Fig. 325. A square Sintox insert tool with a chip breaker making an interrupted cut on a square bar in a lathe. This type of cut was very difficult or impossible with the earlier ceramic tools. (Courtesy, Sintox, Inc.)

6

Electroforming

This process is closely related to electroplating (see Chap. 16) except that the action is carried much farther. A substantial shell of the electrolytically deposited metal is built up on a mold or form of the desired shape. The side next to the mold duplicates with great accuracy the finish and the detail of the original. This may be either the inside or the outside of the piece, as required. The part away from the mold will be quite rough and subject to wide variations in thickness. The mold may be of metal if the shape permits of easy removal, or of wax or plastic or low melting point alloys which can be melted out after the piece is formed. The wax or plastic molds must have some surface treatment to make the surface electrically conductive to start the plating action. The grain structure of the deposited metal is very fine and dense next to the mold and tends to become more open and porous as the thickness of deposit increases. Close control and special precautions can minimize this effect.

Most metals can be deposited electrolytically, but the only ones used commercially for electroforming are copper, iron, nickel, and silver. Copper is the easiest and fastest to form but is, of course, relatively soft. Nickel is the hardest and the most durable, and is often used for forming molds for plastic molding or for making the wax patterns for investment casting. The electroformed part may be made in layers of different metals. For example, a layer of nickel might be used for surface hardness in a mold, backed up by iron to reduce material cost, or a layer of silver on the inside of a wave guide fitting for highest conductivity, backed up by copper.

Finishes on the mold surface of electroformed parts duplicate very closely that of the original pattern and can be as fine as 8 μin. Tolerances can be very close, and in some cases the mold size can be reproduced to ±0.0005 in. If close tolerances or smooth finish are required on the side away from the mold, machining must be used.

Common examples of electroforming are the making of halftone plates or electrotypes for printing and the forming of molds for pressing phonograph records. These make use of the very fine detail that can be reproduced by this method. Another application is the making of wave-guide fittings for the electronics industry. These require close tolerances and a fine finish on internal surfaces, often of very complex shapes. Some of them are almost impossible to form by any other method. Electroformed spray masks are widely used to protect parts of a surface being sprayed with paint, enamel, or lacquer. These masks can be made to conform closely to irregular surfaces and thereby give clean, accurate outlines to the finished parts.

While electroforming is not usually economical for the mass production of parts that can be made by casting or stamping, some such applications have been found. Fountain-pen caps of unusual fluted shapes have been produced economically on a large scale in a highly mechanized electroforming setup that proved to be less expensive than deep drawing or impact extrusion.

Molds for other forming processes comprise an important field for electroforming. Molds for low-pressure applications, such as plastic casting or slush molding (see Chap. 14), present no problems. Molds for injection molding of plastics, where considerable pressure is involved, require either a very thick shell of the electroformed metal or a thin shell backed up with other metal. This sometimes increases the cost to such an extent that the process is not economical. However, if very fine, irregular texture such as a leather surface or a fabric is required, electroforming is likely to show savings.

Other applications that are really intermediate between electroplating and electroforming are the deposition of a heavy metal coating on nonmetallic parts made of plastic or wood, and the building up of worn or undersize machine parts. The former application involves a coating of 0.010 in. or more and is for purposes of strength and mechanical protection. Laminated wood aircraft masts and propeller blades were made in this manner during World War II. The latter use is usually done with chromium, which not only builds up the worn or undersize surface, but also gives much greater hardness and longer wear than the original steel.

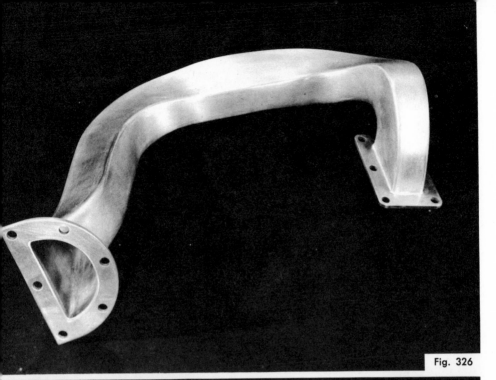

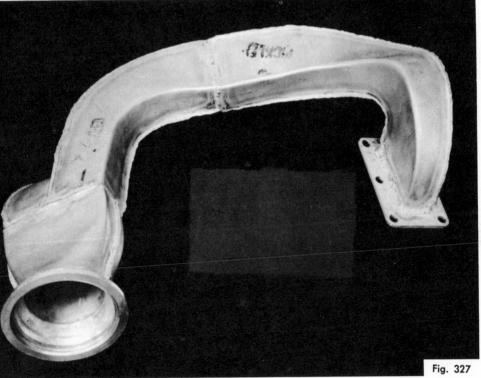

Figs. 326–327. Showing a complex aircraft hot-air duct fitting made by electro-forming (Fig. 326) and the same part (Fig. 327) as formerly made of stainless steel stampings welded together. (Courtesy, Bone Engineering Corporation.)

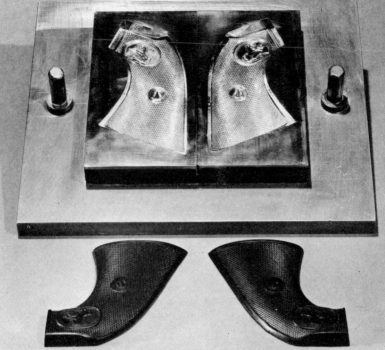

Fig. 328

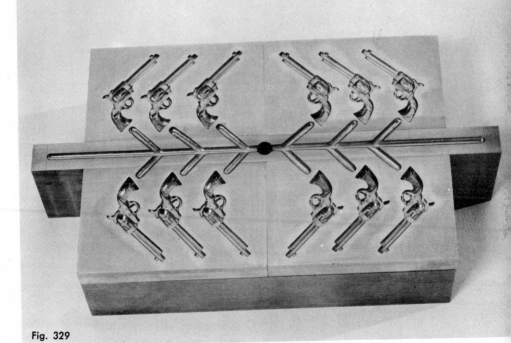

Fig. 329

Figs. 328–329. A 2-cavity and a 12-cavity injection mold for plastics made by electroforming. Note the sharp detail reproduced on the parts in the foreground of Fig. 328. (Courtesy, Electromold Corp.)

Fig. 330

Figs. 330–331. Two mold cavities for plastic gears made by electroforming. These are made about ⁵⁄₃₂ in. thick with a hardness of 45–50 Rockwell C without heat treating and are then backed up by another metal alloy. (Courtesy, Electromold Corp.)

Fig. 331

Fig. 332. The fine surface textures of fabrics, leather, and similar materials can be reproduced in metal molds by electroforming. (Courtesy, Electromold Corp.)

Fig. 333. One of the largest electroformed molds ever made. This is for forming an aircraft radome. The shell is ¼-in. thick nickel reinforced with steel ribs and heated from the back with tubing. (Courtesy, Bone Engineering Corporation.)

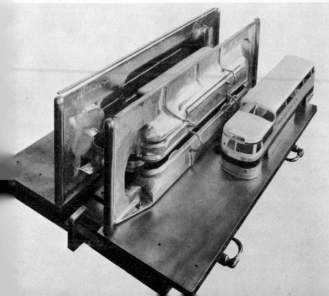

Fig. 334. An electroformed spray mask for selective spraying of the toy bus body shown in the foreground. These masks can be formed around the part itself to insure a close fit and clean color lines. Chapter 22 shows other applications of these masks. (Courtesy, Conforming Matrix Corp.)

7

Metal Spraying or Metallizing

Melted metals can be sprayed by air pressure, almost like paint or lacquer, to build up worn parts, to protect the surface, or to form molds for plastic or soft-metal casting. A gun, similar to a paint spray-gun, is used with the metal in the form of a wire or a powder. The metal is melted by an oxyacetylene or other gas flame at the nozzle of the gun and is sprayed in the form of a fine mist onto the work. Upon striking the work, the minute drops of metal flatten out into thin flakes and, if the surface of the work has been cleaned and roughened properly, a good bond is obtained.

There is no actual fusing or welding of the sprayed metal to the base, but only a mechanical bond. The proper preparation of the base metal, which takes the form of a very rough machining operation or blasting with coarse grit and air pressure, is essential to the forming of a satisfactory bond. For this same reason, a coating at least $\frac{1}{32}$ in. thick should be applied in building up parts that require machining so that a substantial layer is left over the roughened surface after machining. Heavy coatings can be built up by spraying —up to $\frac{3}{4}$ in. or more in some cases. This requires a long time, however, and in most cases is not economical.

The process is often used in maintenance work for building up worn shafts which might otherwise have to be scrapped. It can be used also to apply a protective coating of very hard metal on wearing surfaces. For these purposes, the parts must be machined or ground after being coated to provide a smooth bearing surface. In production, undersize parts can often be reclaimed by this method.

Metals that are commonly sprayed are iron, bronze, low and high carbon steel, stainless steel, nickel, zinc, tin, lead, and aluminum. Wire or rod $\frac{1}{8}$ in. in diameter is the form of metal most commonly used.

Molds can be built up by spraying melted metal over a pattern of metal, plastic, or other material. The pattern is first coated with a release agent so that the sprayed metal will not adhere. The spraying is then continued until the desired thickness of mold has been built up. Molds such as this are often used for slush molding of rubber or plastic or soft metals. These molds are formed more quickly than similar ones made by electroforming, but they do not have the fine detail and the accuracy that can be obtained by the latter process.

Spray metallizing is also used to apply protective coatings of zinc, aluminum, or other metal to iron or steel surfaces for rust or corrosion protection. These coatings can be applied to the inside of tanks and to structural assemblies that would be difficult or impossible to plate by any other method. A fairly thick coating of 0.010 in. or so usually is applied, and the resulting protection seems to be comparable with that of galvanized or plated surfaces. It has the further advantage that it can be applied to complete assemblies after fabrication so that it covers rivets, welds, and other places that are often weak spots in other finishing processes.

Since the temperature of the metal particles is quite low by the time they strike the work surface, very little heating of the work takes place and distortion is not a problem. For the same reason, metal coatings can be sprayed on plastic, wood, or leather surfaces, either for decorative purposes or to form molds which reproduce the surface texture of the base material.

A variation of the metallizing process, which is adapted only to the low melting point alloys, uses a heated container of molten metal on the gun and sprays from this just as a paint spray-gun does from the container of paint or lacquer. The apparatus for this work is, naturally, much simpler and less expensive than the regular metallizing gun since electricity is used to heat the metal pot and no gas flame or wire-feeding mechanism is required. However, its use is limited to low melting point alloys of bismuth, lead, or tin. Its application, therefore, is restricted to applying protective coatings to such items as wood foundry patterns and the forming of soft molds for plastic casting and other applications where heat or pressure are not involved and where the long life of harder metal molds is not required.

The metal temperature as it strikes the surface is so low that it can even be sprayed on the hand without discomfort, and no difficulty is experienced in spraying over wood or plastic patterns.

FLAME PLATING

A new development of the metal-spraying process is known as flame plating. It deposits a very thin coating of tungsten carbide over the wearing parts of machinery, dies, and cutting tools. The thickness is usually only 0.001 in. to 0.005 in. The finish as applied gives a surface of about 125 μin., but it can be ground after application to give any finish required. An increase in life of from 4 to 20 times is reported on shafts, dies, gages, and the teeth of circular saw blades that have been treated by this process.

As with spray metallizing, the bond of the carbide to the base metal is purely mechanical, but this bond is very good because the carbide particles are driven against the work at high speeds. Coatings of 0.001 in. to 0.003 in. after grinding show the best resistance to thermal and mechanical shock. The coating can be applied to almost any metal, such as steel, iron, aluminum, magnesium, and the copper-base alloys. The flame plating gun is shown in Fig. 345.

Fig. 335. Building up a worn shaft by metal spraying. (Courtesy, Metallizing Engineering Company, Inc.)

Fig. 336. The bore of a compressor cylinder being metallized while it turns in an improvised fixture. (Courtesy, Metallizing Engineering Company, Inc.)

Fig. 337. These pump pistons are spray metallized with bronze to prevent scoring of cylinder walls and the rods with stainless steel to increase wear resistance. (Courtesy, Metallizing Engineering Company, Inc.)

Fig. 338. The interior of this 15,000-gal sprinkler tank was metallized with 0.006 in. of pure zinc, and shows no trace of corrosion 16 yr later. (Courtesy, Metallizing Engineering Company, Inc.)

Fig. 339. Paint jobs on this underground conduit looked like this after 6 mos. to 1 yr. (Courtesy, Metallizing Engineering Company, Inc.)

Fig. 340. Showing the same conduit as illustrated in Fig. 339, after metallizing with zinc and coating with vinyl. The vinyl is renewed about every 5 yr but the zinc still gives complete protection. (Courtesy, Metallizing Engineering Company, Inc.)

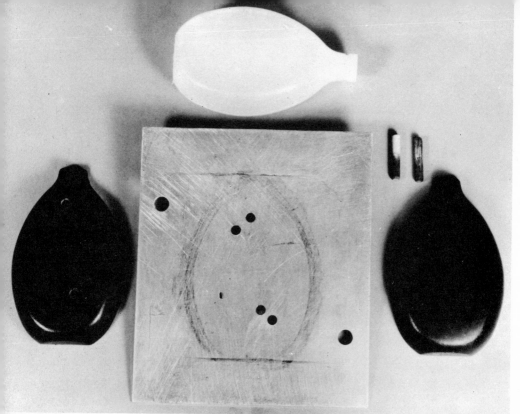

Fig. 341

Figs. 341–344. These photographs show the steps in making a mold for polyethylene bottles by spray metallizing with a low melting point alloy, Cerrocast ®. Fig. 341 shows polished wood half patterns coated with graphite for easy release and a metal plate for holding the patterns in position. The finished bottle desired is shown above. Fig. 342 shows the patterns on the plate. Fig. 343 shows the pattern being sprayed with the Cerrocast ® until a shell about ⅛ in. thick has been formed. Fig. 344 shows how the sprayed shell is incorporated in a chase, cooling coils are added, and the chase is filled with poured metal to complete the mold. Total time required for this mold, about 21 man-hours. (Courtesy, Cerro de Pasco Corporation.)

Fig. 342

Fig. 343

Fig. 344

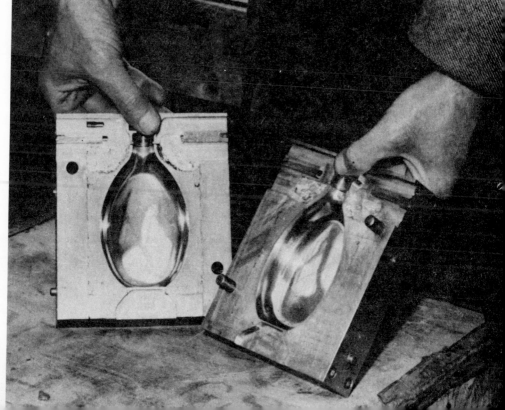

Fig. 345. The gun used in the flame-plating process consists of a barrel and a mechanism for loading precise quantities of oxygen, acetylene, and tungsten carbide powder into the firing chamber. It is aimed and fired by remote control from outside the firing chamber. The tungsten carbide powder is hurled at ten times the speed of sound at the workpiece surface. (Courtesy, Linde Air Products Company.)

Fig. 346. Wire-forming mandrels with their wearing surfaces flame-plated with tungsten carbide last 10 times longer than hardened steel parts. (Courtesy, Linde Air Products Company.)

8

Ultrasonic Machining

This is a new method that has been developed primarily for machining very hard materials, such as tungsten carbide, glass, quartz, and ceramics that are extremely difficult to work by other processes. It is based on the property of certain materials (in this case a rod of nickel alloy) to change dimension slightly when they are placed in a strong magnetic field. When the nickel rod is placed in a magnetic field that fluctuates rapidly, it changes its length slightly (in this case about 0.004 in.) in accordance with the field passing through it. This property of the nickel rod is known as magnetostriction. The alternating electric current used to vary the magnetic field in ultrasonic machining is about 25,000 to 30,000 cycles per second, which is well above the frequencies that can be heard as sound by the human ear.

If a hole of irregular shape is required in a block of carbide or other hard material, a rod of brass or soft steel of the same shape as the desired hole is attached to the nickel rod. This is simply rested on the workpiece and an abrasive and water mixture is flowed over the point of contact. The extremely rapid vibration drives the abrasive into the material and causes the shaped rod to work its way through the piece, leaving a clean hole of the desired size and shape. The action is amazingly rapid and tolerances of ±0.0005 in. can be held with a 10- to 15-μin. surface finish. The same principle is modified to give a milling or sawing action. An expensive electronic power supply is required to drive the ultrasonic tool, which makes the cost of the machine quite high. The process is used mostly for making carbide dies for extrusion, drawing, stamping, or powder metallurgy, and for highly specialized cutting operations.

A variation of the same principle is being used, with promising results, for the drilling of teeth in dentistry. The drilling is claimed to be painless.

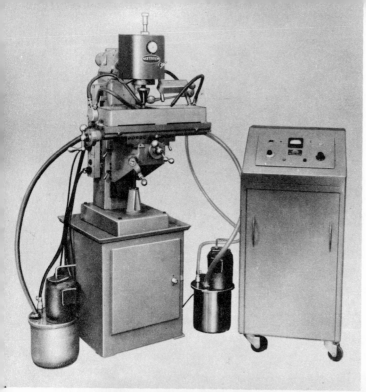

Fig. 347

Figs. 347–348. An "impact grinder" for ultrasonic machining. The two abrasive pumping units are for two sizes of abrasives, such as roughing and finishing grits. Fig. 348 shows a closeup of the cutting tool and work with the abrasive puddle covering both tool and work. (Courtesy, Raytheon Manufacturing Company.)

Fig. 348

Fig. 349. A group of carbide and Rexalloy dies formed by ultrasonic machining. These would be extremely difficult and expensive to make by conventional grinding methods. (Courtesy, Raytheon Manufacturing Company.)

Fig. 350. A ceramic spacer, 0.020 in. thick, with 150 0.005-in. holes drilled simultaneously by the ultrasonic tool shown. Drilling time is about 40 sec each. (Courtesy, Raytheon Manufacturing Company.)

Fig. 351. Synthetic sapphires and ruby drilled and engraved by ultrasonics. (Courtesy, Raytheon Manufacturing Company.)

9

Electrical-Discharge Machining

This is another new process, similar in some if its applications to ultrasonic machining but operating on an entirely different principle, since the work is done by electrical bombardment and no mechanical action is involved. It is limited to cutting electrically conductive materials, while the ultrasonic process can be used with either conductive or insulating materials. The action of the electrical discharge, or metal disintegrating processes as it is sometimes known, is much faster and is well adapted to machining flat surfaces as well as drilling.

In this process also, the cutting tool is a soft brass rod, but no mechanical contact and no abrasive are used. Instead, a rapid series of electrical arcs serves actually to disintegrate and vaporize the hardest metals at the tip of the cutting tool. The action is controlled accurately, either by maintaining a constant, very close spacing between the cutting tip and the work, in combination with a high-frequency power supply, or by rapidly vibrating the tip in synchronism with the alternations of the electric current. A coolant flowed between the tool and the work prevents either from heating excessively.

The low-frequency method, with the arc maintained and controlled by vibrations of the tip, synchronized with the electrical impulses, requires relatively simple equipment, and is used for drilling holes in hardened material to remove broken drills, taps, reamers, and studs. For this purpose, high accuracy and fine finish are not required.

For precision applications such as forming dies in carbide or hardened steel, machining flat or formed surfaces, sharpening carbide tools, or shaping very hard materials for jet-engine parts, the high-frequency method is used. A vacuum tube supply is used to furnish the high-frequency current. By control of the power supply, the cutting action can be varied from a rapid cut with a rough surface to a very light cut with 8- to 10-μin. finish and accuracy comparable with that of grinding. For flat surfaces, sharpening carbide tools, or shaping forming tools, a brass wheel is used, turning at relatively low speed. There is no contact between the wheel and the work, the electrical discharge doing the cutting. For the drilling or the sinking of dies, shaped tools of brass are used, as shown in Figs. 353 to 359.

Both ultrasonic and electrical discharge machining are extremely useful tools in the working of carbides and other very hard materials. So far, their use has been confined largely to the toolroom and the die shop rather than to production manufacturing. New developments and larger power supplies promise to open the production field in the machining of difficult materials.

Fig. 352. A machine and power supply for precision electrical-discharge machining with high-frequency current. (Courtesy, Elox Corporation of Michigan.)

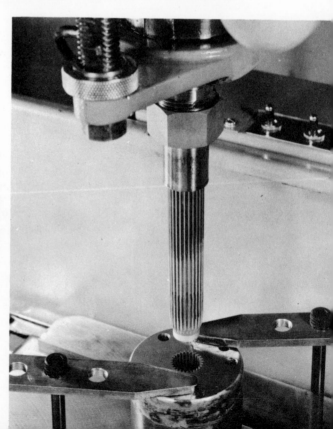

Fig. 353. A spline form die cut by electrical discharge with the brass tool or electrode shown above it. Heat treating of the steel die block was done before machining to avoid distortion after forming. The time on this job was 1 hr and 50 min against 40 hr for conventional machining. (Courtesy, Elox Corporation of Michigan.)

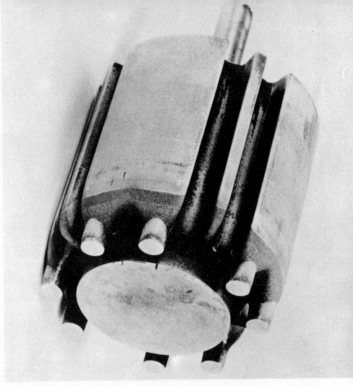

Fig. 354

Figs. 354–355. The electrode (Fig. 354) and the finished die (Fig. 355) for an automotive hub cap stamping. (Courtesy, Elox Corporation of Michigan.)

Fig. 355

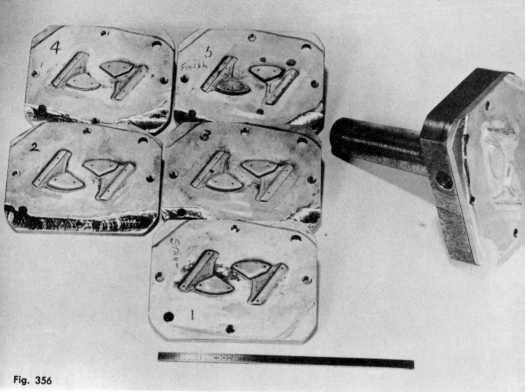

Fig. 356

Figs. 356–357. The five electrodes (Fig. 356) used to form the forging die (Fig. 357) by electrical discharge. (Courtesy, Elox Corporation of Michigan.)

Fig. 357

Fig. 358. The electrode and the finished cold heading die for a ¼-in. bolt produced by electrical discharge. (Courtesy, Elox Corporation of Michigan.)

Fig. 359. Showing how the shaped brass electrode, by electrical discharge, penetrates the hardest metals like this carbide block. (Courtesy, The Method X Company.)

10

Abrasive Blast Cutting

This is another process of considerable promise, but, so far, of limited applications. The use of sand blasting and related processes for cleaning, finishing, and de-burring is well established and widely used (see Chap. 16). Abrasive blast cutting is a highly refined development of the same principle. Fine abrasive particles are mixed with air or inert gas under pressure and blown against the work with considerable force in a very fine stream or jet. The nozzle may be held by hand or mounted on the carriage of a lathe or other machine. While the action cannot be controlled as accurately as that of the ultrasonic or electrical discharge methods, it can be used for etching, cutting, shaping, or drilling very fragile materials that would be extremely difficult to work by other methods, and for controlled removal of deposited surface film. Examples of its application are: cutting of external or internal threads on glass tubing, drilling and shaping of quartz crystals, and cutting of spiral grooves in a deposited carbon film to form precision resistors.

A method has also been developed to use an abrasive jet in electronic manufacturing for reducing printed circuit resistors, which are normally subject to wide variations, to an accurately controlled value. For this purpose, the conductive ink which forms the resistor is applied slightly heavier than is actually required by the needed resistance value. This gives a somewhat lower resistance than desired. The coating is then reduced in thickness by the abrasive blast until the desired resistance value is reached. Controls have been devised to perform this operation on a completely automatic basis.

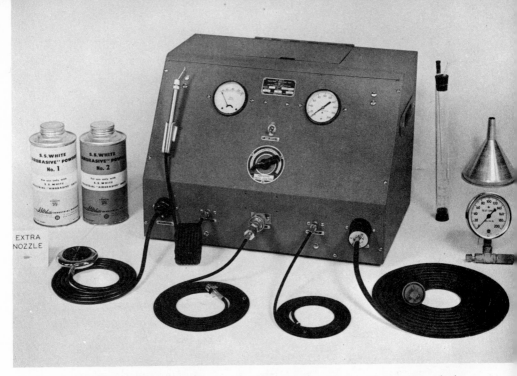

EXTRA NOZZLE

Fig. 360. A complete "Airbrasive" unit for abrasive blast cutting. A gas cylinder and dust-collecting system are also required. (Courtesy, The S. S. White Dental Mfg. Co., Industrial Div.)

Fig. 361. The abrasive blast unit in a hand operation. (Courtesy, The S. S. White Dental Mfg. Co., Industrial Div.)

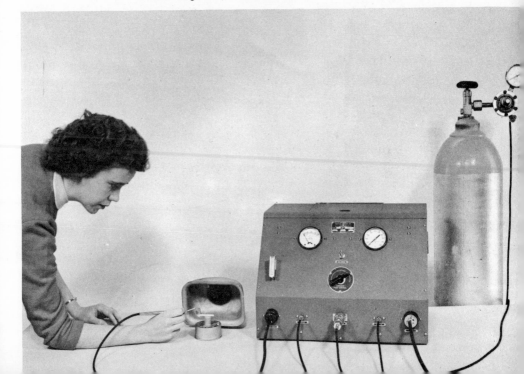

Fig. 362

Figs. 362–363. The abrasive blast nozzle mounted on a lathe cuts external and internal threads on glass tubing. The external thread shown is about 0.005 in. deep and 0.006 in. wide. (Courtesy, The S. S. White Dental Mfg. Co., Industrial Div.)

Fig. 363

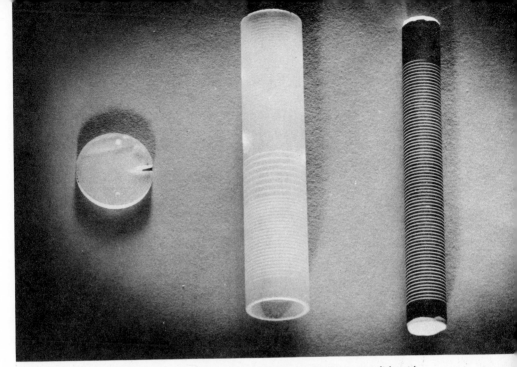

Fig. 364. Typical applications of abrasive blast cutting. (*Left*) A quartz disk with contact depressions, 0.030 in. diameter, 0.005 in. deep. (*Right*) A carbon film resistor with a spiral groove 0.007 in. wide. (Courtesy, The S. S. White Dental Mfg. Co., Industrial Div.)

Fig. 365. Use of the "Airbrasive" unit for abrading printed circuit resistors to a fixed value. The ohmmeter indicates the resistance value as the work progresses. (Courtesy, The S. S. White Dental Mfg. Co., Industrial Div.)

11

Welding and Brazing

Welding and brazing are no longer just methods of repair or for rough structural fabrication, but are highly developed manufacturing processes, widely used in the aircraft, the automotive, and the machine-tool industries. Other important fields of application are shipbuilding, the manufacture of farm and construction machinery, building construction, and the manufacture of steel tubing. The old-time blacksmith forge and anvil long ago gave way to the oxyacetylene torch and, more recently, the electric arc. These are still the most important methods of welding and brazing, and they have been highly developed to do work of high quality and reliability under closely controlled conditions. Another important brazing method is furnace brazing, which can be used for high-production work of great uniformity and reliability.

Welding is the process of joining two pieces of metal by melting them directly together, with or without the addition of more material of a similar nature and melting point. Brazing joins the two pieces by means of a lower melting point metal which flows between them and bonds to them without melting the base metal itself. Soldering is the same as brazing, but uses much lower melting point and lower strength alloys for the joining. In silver soldering, the alloys are intermediate in melting point between those used in soldering and brazing, but the process itself resembles brazing and is more properly called silver brazing.

FLAME WELDING AND CUTTING

This process uses a combination of two gases, usually oxygen and acetylene, but sometimes oxygen and hydrogen, to create a flame of high intensity. The temperature of this flame is around 6300 F, which is far above the melting point of iron or steel. The gases are usually stored in tanks under high pressure, and a regulator on each tank reduces this to a closely controlled low pressure for use in the torch. The torch mixes the two gases in the proper proportion and, by means of individual valves in the oxygen and acetylene lines, controls the size and the shape of the flame.

Much flame welding is done with the torch held by hand, and a skilled operator can do work of high quality by this method. For certain specialized welding jobs, such as the welding of long seams in pipe or tubing, both torch and work are held mechanically and the work progresses at a constant and closely controlled rate. Very smooth and uniform work is obtained in this way.

Various types of welded joints are used according to the requirements and the nature of the work. In most of these, additional material is added to the joint in the form of a rod of metal, similar to the base metals being joined. Enough of this material is added to build up a rounded bead along the joint to reinforce it. In welding castings, this bead can be ground off, if desired, and still leave a joint comparable in strength with that of the original parts, but in joining wrought metals, such as sheet or structural shapes, the bead usually is left on since otherwise the joint would form a weak spot. This is because the metal in the weld is similar in nature to cast metal, which is not as strong as the wrought metal unless further processing is used to "hot work" and anneal the weld.

Most types of iron and steel can be welded, but there are some exceptions. Malleable iron is one of them, although this can be brazed successfully. The welding of high carbon steel is seldom practical without special precautions because the material in the weld air hardens upon cooling and becomes brittle. In flame welding large castings, it is often necessary to preheat the entire casting and to cool it slowly after the welding to prevent stresses and cracks due to the intense localized heating at the point of the weld.

Only certain aluminum alloys are classed as weldable, since others have the property of losing all strength and collapsing, considerably before the actual melting point is reached. Only alloys 2 S, 3 S, 52 S, and 61 S are considered weldable. Special aluminum welding rods and fluxes are used with these, and good results are secured.

Cast iron can be welded but is often brazed with a lower melting point alloy to avoid the necessity of preheating the entire casting and to minimize the danger of distortion and cracking due to uneven heating. Copper and copper alloys and magnesium can be welded by the use of the proper welding rods and flux.

Sometimes dissimilar metals can be welded successfully, but this depends on the relative melting points and the reactions of the two metals. Each such application should be investigated individually.

In almost all production welding, the pieces to be joined are held in jigs or fixtures that not only maintain the proper position and alignment, but also hold the work in a convenient position for the operator. Fixtures should also be designed to dissipate the heat and to prevent distortion of the work. The rate of manual welding depends to a very large extent on the operator and also on the nature of the work, but it should average around 20 ft to 30 ft per hour in thin sheet metals to around 3 ft per hour in ¾-in. plate. Welding with the work horizontal and the operator above it is by far the easiest and most satisfactory. Gravity helps the melted metal, at the point of welding, to flow into the joint, and promotes a sound weld at maximum rate without operator fatigue. Welding on a vertical seam can be done where necessary without too much difficulty, but at a reduced rate. Overhead welding from the bottom of a horizontal piece should be avoided if it is at all possible, although it can be done where it is necessary, as in pipe-line work and certain structural and shipyard operations.

In the process of welding, oxides and nitrides are formed in the molten metal which cause brittleness and weaken the weld. Various methods are used to exclude the air from the point of the weld, and one of these should always be used where welds are required to carry heavy stresses or where corrosion resistance is needed. With gas welding, the shielding of the weld is usually done by surrounding the weld with an inert gas or by the use of a flux in powder or paste form applied ahead of the welding point. A coating on the welding rod is sometimes used in conjunction with the flux.

Much cutting of heavy steel is done most economically by means of the cutting torch. This is similar to the welding torch except that the flame is actually a group of four jets with an additional jet of pure oxygen, under the control of the operator, in the center of them. When the four flames have melted the base metal at a given spot, the operator turns on the jet of oxygen, which actually vaporizes the melted metal, forming a hole through the work. As the torch is moved along the cutting line, a slot is made through the metal until the cut is completed. The action is quite rapid, and steel plates up to 12 in. or 18 in. thick are readily cut with standard torches and up to 60 in. with special equipment.

Where a number of identical pieces are to be cut, machines are used which are operated either manually or automatically in guiding the cutting torch by means of a pattern or template. The edges of the machine-cut pieces are much smoother than those cut by hand, although the cut edges are always much rougher than sheared edges or those formed by various machining processes. With cutting machines, dimensional tolerances of the order of $\pm \frac{1}{32}$ in. can be held. The cutting speed varies with the thickness of material. In steel $\frac{1}{4}$ in. thick, it is about 20 in. per minute, 1 in. thick about 14 in., and 10 in. thick about $3\frac{1}{2}$ in. per minute. Cast iron and stainless steel can be flame cut, but they require special techniques and reduced cutting rates.

If a large number of pieces of the same shape are to be cut from thin material, such as sheet steel up to $\frac{1}{2}$ in. thick, several sheets may be stacked on top of each other and all cut together. With special techniques and care, good results can be obtained by this method. For multiple cutting in heavier materials, machines are available that guide several torches in identical paths from a single pattern or template, thus making several pieces at each operation and substantially reducing the cutting cost.

In simple machines, the pattern is simply a full-scale drawing, and the operator moves a stylus around the desired outline by hand. The torch follows the same outline at a remote point in the machine by means of a pantograph or other mechanical linkage. With more elaborate machines, the tracer is moved mechanically at a predetermined rate, and metal templates are used. The tracer point is often held against the template magnetically, in which case the template is usually made of steel about $\frac{1}{2}$ in. thick, as shown in Fig. 368.

A new improvement on the magnetic tracing machine, which requires a heavy metal template, is a photoelectric tracer which requires only a full-size line drawing. A spot of light in the electronic tracing head picks up the black outline and follows it accurately, at a predetermined rate, guiding one or several cutting torches in exactly the same path. Standard speeds of travel range from 5 in. to 30 in. per min, with slower speeds, down to $1\frac{1}{2}$ in. per min, provided for cutting very thick material. Figure 369 shows such an electronic tracer and Fig. 370 shows a multiple cutting unit guided by it. These units allow very economical cutting of single parts or large quantities of parts with very low pattern cost.

ELECTRIC-ARC WELDING

The work done by arc welding is similar in many respects to that done with the gas torch in flame welding. However, the heat needed for fusing the metals is generated by an electric discharge or arc instead of a gas flame. The most commonly used process is metal-arc welding, where the work forms the grounded side of the electric circuit and a metal welding rod forms the other side. An arc is started between the welding rod or wire and the work, which melts a small portion of the work and the tip of the rod. Small globules of the melted rod are deposited in the melted portion of the base metal as the work progresses.

Either alternating current (a.c.) or direct current (d.c.) may be used for arc welding. For most applications, either a.c. or d.c. may be used with good results. There are certain specialized applications where one type or the other must be used, but the choice should be left to the welding engineer. The current used may vary with the size and the type of work, from 25 to 600 or 800 amp.

An important variation of the metal-arc process is shielded-arc welding. When steel is in a melted condition, it combines easily with the oxygen and the nitrogen in the air, forming oxides and nitrides which tend to weaken the steel and to increase corrosion. If the molten metal at the point of the arc can be shielded from the air by an inert gas, this undesirable chemical reaction can be prevented. This is what is done in shielded-arc welding. The welding rod, forming the electrode, is coated with a material that gives off large quantities of an inert gas when it is subjected to the heat of the weld. The remaining material from the rod coating forms a slag which floats on top of the weld and protects the metal from the air while it is cooling. When the weld has cooled, the slag may be removed easily. Welds made with the shielded arc cost somewhat more than the open-type welds, but they are 20 percent to 50 percent higher in tensile strength, much more ductile, and more corrosion resistant.

Another form of arc welding is the carbon arc, in which only direct current is used. In this process, the arc is formed between the work and a carbon rod which does not melt from the heat of the arc. The extra metal needed in the weld is added by means of a welding rod or wire which does not form a part of the electric circuit. Carbon-arc welding is used mostly for aluminum and copper base alloys and for certain applications in automatic machines. If shielding is required with the carbon-arc process, a powder or paste may be applied at the point of the weld which serves the same purpose as the coating on the shielded arc rods.

Tungsten-arc welding is similar to the carbon-arc process in that the electrode is not consumed in the welding, but it can be used with either a.c. or d.c. and is usually performed with a shielding atmosphere of inert gas. Here also extra metal is added from a separate rod. It is used primarily on aluminum or magnesium but can be used also on copper base alloys and stainless steel or other materials.

Atomic hydrogen welding makes use of two tungsten electrodes, and the arc (a.c. only) is formed between them. The work does not form part of the electrical circuit, but a jet of hydrogen surrounds the arc and a chemical reaction takes place in the arc which transfers a very intense heat to the metal being welded. Metal is added from a separate rod. The hydrogen also serves to shield the weld from the air, with the result that very clean, smooth welds are formed, with exceptionally uniform structure. Although it is more expensive than other welding methods, it does work of the highest quality in practically all materials. It is used for repair work on molds and dies, for hard surfacing, and for production welding of heavy and light plates and sheets.

The arc-welding processes are more easily adapted to automatic machine welding than the gas flame. The welding head in these machines carries one electrode and moves along the work at a continuous rate. The welding rod, usually in the form of a wire, is fed into the arc at a predetermined rate and the shielding material may be applied through a tube to the weld. Very fine uniform work is obtained in this way.

HARD FACING

This is a welding process whereby a very hard and wear-resistant surface is built up on the surface of a softer base material, usually iron or mild steel. The material can be applied either by flame welding, which gives a better bond and a smoother surface, or by electric welding, which is faster. Although this process is used to a certain extent for production purposes, its primary use is on excavating and construction machines. Here the cutting edges of power-shovel teeth, rock-drilling bits, and similar items that have become worn can be built up and at the same time provided with a combination of the toughness of the softer steel base material and wearing surfaces that are superior to those of the original parts.

THERMIT WELDING

This is intermediate between a casting and a welding process. Molten iron or steel at extremely high temperature is formed in a crucible by means of a chemical reaction between powdered aluminum and iron oxide. Alloying elements are added if required and the superheated metal is poured into a mold which surrounds the parts to be joined. It fuses with the base metal to form a very strong, sound weld. The work cools slowly, so distortion is minimized. The process is obviously much more limited in its application than flame or arc welding, but it does find use in joining square edges of heavy material for repair work or fabrication in shipyards, steel mills, and railroad repair shops.

RESISTANCE WELDING

In resistance welding, the pieces to be joined are pressed together and a heavy flow of current is passed through them to heat the point of contact to welding temperature. The combination of heat and pressure makes a true weld that is comparable in strength with that of the base material welded. This is the same principle used by the blacksmith in welding with the forge and the anvil.

Spot Welding. Spot welding is the most widely used of the resistance welding processes. The two or more sheets of metal to be joined are pressed together between the points of a pair of copper or copper alloy electrodes, mounted on the arms of the spot-welding machine. When the pressure has reached the proper point, a switch is closed and a heavy current at low voltage is passed through the material for a short time. The voltage across the electrodes may vary from a fraction of a volt to a few volts and the current from a few thousand to several hundred thousand amperes. The time should be controlled accurately; usually it is a small fraction of a second for each weld. The pressure is continued for a short time after the current is shut off to allow the weld to cool. Sheet steel from the thinnest gages up to 2 in. thick may be spot welded with standard equipment.

With material more than ⅛ in. thick, so-called "pulsation" welding is usually used. This makes use of a series of pulses of electric current while the parts are held together under continuous pressure. If this is not done, the welding electrodes tend to overheat, even if they are water cooled, and their life is very short. Three or more sheets of the thinner materials can be spot welded together at a single operation. Under certain conditions, sheets of different materials may be spot welded together, although special techniques must be used if the electrical conductivity of the two metals differs greatly, such as aluminum and steel.

The spot welding of aluminum requires very heavy current for a very short time. If this were obtained directly from the electric line through a step-down transformer as in a standard type of spot welder, it would require special electric lines and more power than is available in most localities during the fraction of a second when the current flows. To avoid this condition, "stored-energy" spot welders are used which utilize the time between welding contacts to store up power from the electric line in large capacitors or inductors. This stored energy is released through the welding electrodes at the proper time in the form of a very heavy surge of current which completes the weld. These stored-energy spot welders are large and expensive machines, with accurate controls to enable them to do work of consistent high quality. The operation is rapid, so a considerable amount of work must be available for them to justify their purchase. If only occasional jobs require aluminum spot welding, it will be found more economical to subcontract it to shops specializing in this work.

Spot welding is used widely as a low-cost method of joining sheet metal to form such things as boxes, furniture, automobile body assemblies, and even aircraft components. For production work, simple fixtures are usually used to hold the work in alignment and to locate the welds. For large production, special machines can be made with multiple electrodes to form as many as 100 or more spots simultaneously or in rapid sequence. For simple spot welding of sheet steel in the common gages, the machines are relatively inexpensive and they are easy and rapid to use. The welds are neat and inconspicuous, usually requiring no special finishing operations.

Seam Welding. The seam welder is similar in operation to the spot welder except that the electrodes are in the form of wheels or rollers and they form a series of closely spaced spot welds as the material to be joined is passed between them. The rotation of the wheels is continuous, with the spots formed by intermittent pulses of electric current. These spots may be spaced so closely that they overlap and form a pressure-tight joint, or they may be spaced out to form a series of separate spots. In some types of heavy seam-welding machines for joining the edges of sheets, the overlap between the sheets to be joined is reduced to about one and a half times the thickness and the pressure increased so that the joint is both welded and rolled into a thickness not much greater than the original sheets. This is sometimes called crush or mash welding. In all spot and seam welding, the materials to be joined should be reasonably clean and free from scale and paint, which can prevent proper adhesion of the welds.

Projection Welding. Projection welding is another variation of resistance welding. Instead of the welding current being concentrated in a small spot by the shape of the electrodes, as in spot welding, small projections are stamped out on the surface of one of the pieces to be joined and electrodes of much larger area are used. The projections concentrate the current and fuse to form the weld. Since the projections determine the size and the shape of the welds, they must be designed properly for the thickness and the type of material to give the greatest strength to the welded joint. Projection welding is used most commonly where at least one of the parts to be joined is a stamped or formed piece so that the projections can be formed as part of the stamping operation. Much greater pressures are required than in spot welding, but the resulting joints are very uniform and the process is much used in mass production of fabricated assemblies.

A variation of projection welding is the joining of crossed wires by means of pressure and electric current. This process is very widely used to form lampshade frames, wire baskets and racks, and certain types of wire mesh. A wide range of special studs with projections on the heads are made for attachment to flat surfaces by means of projection welding. Nuts are also available with projections on one side which may be welded to thin material to form a strong thread for some later assembly.

Flash and Butt Welding. Flash and butt welding are also forms of resistance welding. They are used to join together the ends of sheets or bars without the overlap required in spot or seam welding. In butt welding, the pieces to be joined are clamped between the electrodes and pressed firmly together. A heavy current is applied and the pressure continued to fuse the parts together. A fairly large ring of material is squeezed out or "upset" around the line of the weld. The ends of strips or bars that have been bent around to form wheel rims or rings are often joined in this way, as are the ends of bandsaw blades. In flash welding, the parts to be joined are brought together only lightly or are slightly separated at the time the current is applied. This forms a flash or arc and the parts are then moved together to complete the welded joint. Less upset is formed than in butt welding, and the joints are generally stronger. Light-gage materials are easier to weld by the flash method, as well as dissimilar metals of different melting points.

Stud Welding. In stud welding, a stud with a tapered or conical end on the contact surface is held in a special gun and welded by a process similar to flash welding. This process is explained and illustrated in Figs. 394, 395, and 396.

BRAZING AND SOLDERING

While welding involves the actual fusion of the two or more pieces to be joined, brazing joins them by means of a lower melting point alloy which bonds to the base metal. The heat for brazing may come from a gas torch of the type used for flame welding, a carbon arc, an electric induction heater, a furnace, or a bath of the melted brazing alloy or flux.

Torch brazing is used commonly for making single units, for repair work, for small production jobs, or for work that cannot be placed conveniently in a furnace. The parts to be joined are fitted together or clamped in position, a flux is applied to the joint, and it is brought up to the proper heat with the torch. The brazing rod, which is usually a copper base or silver alloy, is then applied, and, if the joint has been prepared properly and the temperature is correct, it will flow smoothly into the joint and make a firm bond. The purpose of the flux is to dissolve the oxides that may be present on the metal surfaces and to prevent the formation of additional oxides during the heating. The melting point of the brazing medium must always be considerably lower than that of the materials being joined.

Most production brazing is done either by electric induction (see Chap. 17) or furnace brazing. For these methods, the higher cost silver alloys are often preferred because their lower melting point permits the use of lower temperatures, with consequent reduction of distortion and oxidation of the work. Where copper or brass is used as a brazing medium, it is often necessary to use a furnace with a hydrogen or other inert gas atmosphere to prevent undue oxidation.

Both induction heating and furnace brazing are often set up as continuous production processes, with the work carried through the heating coil or furnace on conveyors. Usually the brazing medium is applied in the form of a preformed ring or other shape which fits around the joint and provides the proper amount of material at the proper place when the melting temperature is reached.

Another method of applying heat for brazing that is used for production work is the salt-bath or chemical-bath method. The parts to be brazed are clamped in position with the brazing metal in the proper place and are then immersed in a tank of molten flux. This transfers the heat rapidly to the work and excludes the air. It is used successfully for aluminum brazing.

The parts to be joined should be designed properly to provide as much area as possible at the point of brazing, and they must be fitted together properly. The closeness of the fit will depend on the brazing medium used. For copper brazing, no clearance is required and the parts are often made a press fit, since the copper is fluid enough to penetrate even such a joint. For silver or brass brazing, a clearance of 0.001 in. to 0.003 in. between the parts is usually used. Joints with excessive clearance or poor fitting will not be satisfactory under any conditions. Properly designed brazed joints are strong and reliable. While the strength of the brazing medium is less than that of steel, usually the joint can be designed so that the area at this point is large enough to make this at least as strong as other parts of the completed piece. A good example of this is hydraulic cylinders made of steel tubing with steel ends silver brazed to it. In this case, the steel tubing will burst long before the brazed joint will fail.

Iron and steel are brazed easily with any of the brazing mediums, and brass, copper, and bronze can be brazed with the lower melting point alloys. Some aluminum alloys, especially 2 S, 3 S,

53 S, 61 S, and casting alloys 406 and X 612, can be brazed by
the use of special brazing mediums and fluxes. Special aluminum
"brazing sheets" are available which are coated with the low melting point alloy on one or both sides. These simplify the assembly
in certain types of work, especially where the chemical-bath heating method is used.

Soldering is identical in principle to brazing except that alloys
with a low melting point of below 800 F are used as the joining
medium. These are usually mixtures of tin and lead in various proportions. These solders are identified by the proportions of tin and
lead, the tin being given first. Thus 40/60 solder is 40 percent tin,
60 percent lead; and 60/40 solder is 60 percent tin, 40 percent lead.
The most commonly used solders use from 20 percent to 70 percent tin. The melting point varies from 532 F for the 20/80 solder
down to 356 F for the 63/37 solder, which is known as the eutectic
alloy, and then back up to 365 F for the 70/30.

Soldering fluxes are needed to make the solder adhere to most
metals. Acid fluxes are the most effective for use on iron, steel or
zinc, but they should never be used for electrical soldering because
of their corrosive action. Rosin or rosin and alcohol solutions are the
only fluxes safe for electrical or other delicate work.

Production soldering of such parts as cans and flanges can be
done by furnace or induction heating as in brazing, although, of
course, lower temperatures are required. Because of the low temperature required, soldering also can be done by means of a heated
copper or "soldering iron." This method is widely used in the assembly and the wiring of radio and electronic equipment; the subject is treated more fully in the chapter on assembly methods.

The strength of soft solder alloys is very low and the method
should not be used where any great mechanical strength is required. To obtain the maximum strength in a soldered joint, the
areas should be as large as possible and the clearance to be filled
by the solder should be from 0.001 in. to 0.008 in. Soldered joints
cannot be used where temperatures over 350 F are encountered,
as their strength above this is practically zero.

Because of the oxide which forms almost immediately on aluminum when it is exposed to air, it has long been considered almost impossible to solder this material successfully. A new technique is now available which removes this limitation. This makes
use of ultrasonic electric power, an alternating current with fre-

quencies above the range of hearing (about 20,000 cycles per second). (See Chap. 8 for the use of ultrasonics for machining and Chap. 16 for its use in metal cleaning.) This ultrasonic current is used to vibrate the tip of a soldering iron at high frequency and the iron is used in much the same way as a standard type of iron. The high-frequency vibration, transmitted through the melted solder, breaks up the aluminum oxide and allows the solder to adhere, even without any flux.

COLD WELDING

A process developed in England and recently introduced into this country makes it possible to weld together soft metals such as aluminum and copper, by means of pressure alone, without the application of heat. The pressure is applied by means of simple tools, which, in the case of thinner materials, can be hand-operated like a pair of pliers. The punches which apply the pressure must be of the proper shape and size to cause the metal to flow together under pressure, but, when these conditions are met, a true weld is obtained which is as strong as or stronger than the metals which are joined. A rather deep indentation is left at the point of pressure, which might be objectionable in certain applications. The process is in limited use though no doubt it will be developed further as new uses for it are found.

WELDED ASSEMBLIES vs. CASTINGS

There are certain parts (like machine bases, brackets, and levers) that can be made either as iron or steel castings or as welded assemblies of standard sheet and rolled steel. Many examples are cited by the proponents of one process or the other to prove the superiority or the lower cost of the particular method. Several examples are illustrated here where weldments were preferable and where castings worked out better. It is impossible to state just where the dividing line should be drawn; in cases of doubt, quotations should be obtained and characteristics compared using both methods. In general, cast-iron parts will be heavier and more rigid than welded steel. This might be an advantage in certain machine bases where vibration damping is important or where parts are to be held in close alignment. The welded steel parts would be much tougher and less brittle, which would be an advantage where break-age from impact is a factor. They would also be lighter, where portability is required. Factors of appearance and cost of machin-ing should be considered also for they might favor either one or the other method. It is certain that no one method is best for all applications and all factors should be considered before deciding which to use. Often combinations of castings and welding may pro-vide the answer, as shown in Figs. 421 and 422.

Fig. 366. Tack welding of joints and location of joints near corners help prevent distortion as in this flame-welding job on an aluminum tank. (Courtesy, Aluminum Company of America.)

Fig. 367. Sprockets flame-cut from steel plate. (Courtesy, Air Reduction Sales Company.)

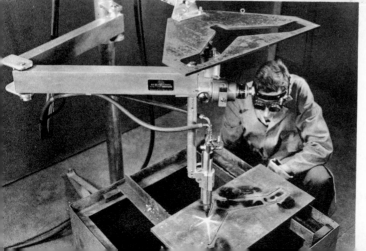

Fig. 368. A cam-controlled flame-cutting machine. A magnetized roller secures itself to the edge of the template above and guides the cutting torch. (Courtesy, Air Reduction Sales Company.)

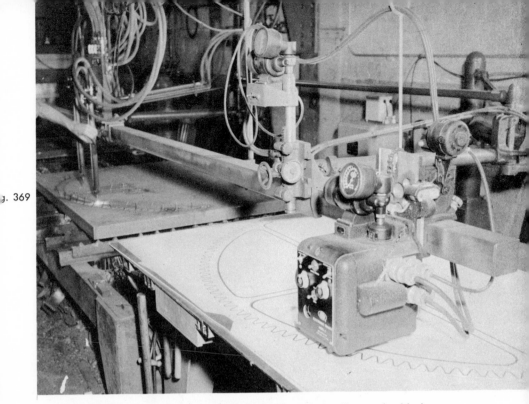

Fig. 369

Figs. 369–370. An electronic cutting torch control guides itself around a black outline on a white sheet of paper and (Fig. 370) a group of cutting torches follows accurately in the same path. (Courtesy, Air Reduction Sales Company.)

Fig. 370

Fig. 371. An a-c transformer welder with a current range of 25 amp to 295 amp.
(Courtesy, General Electric Company.)

Fig. 372. A d-c motor generator welding set being used to weld food machinery.
(Courtesy, The Lincoln Electric Company.)

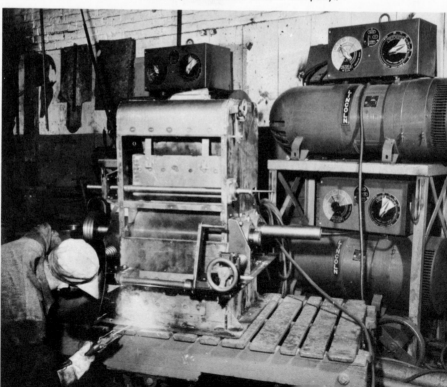

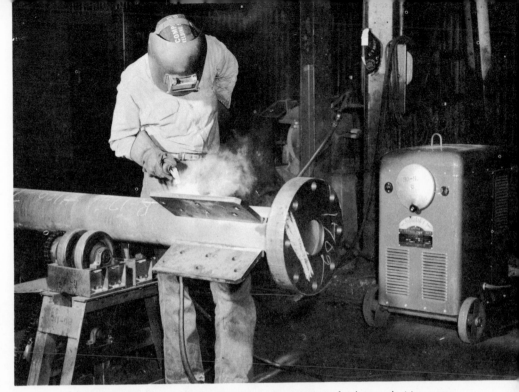

Fig. 373. An a-c transformer welder in use on a section of a large television tower. Note the work-holding fixture which allows turning the work for the most convenient welding. (Courtesy, The Lincoln Electric Company.)

Fig. 374. Welding a diesel engine exhaust manifold by the shielded manual arc-welding process. A new type of coated electrode is used in which the coating contains a large percentage of iron powder, permitting substantially increased welding speeds. (Courtesy, The Lincoln Electric Company.)

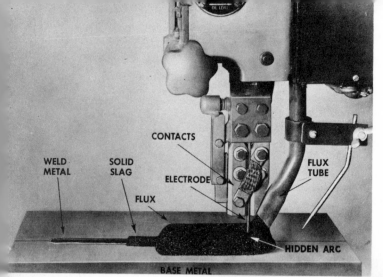

WELD METAL SOLID SLAG CONTACTS FLUX TUBE

ELECTRODE FLUX

HIDDEN ARC

BASE METAL

Fig. 376. Manual use of the submerged-arc process with semi-automatic equipment. The wire is fed automatically and the gun is guided manually over the seam. The work can be rotated to the most convenient position for each weld. (Courtesy, The Lincoln Electric Company.)

Fig. 377. An application
submerged-arc welding with
head stationary and the w
rotated beneath it. (Courte
The Lincoln Electric Company

Fig. 378. Inert gas, consumable electrode welding on a tank head of 3 S aluminum. (Courtesy, Aluminum Company of America.)

Fig. 379. These 11 ft aluminum reels for use on mine sweepers are made by inert gas arc welding. (Courtesy, Air Reduction Sales Company.)

Fig. 380. All of these aluminum utensils have welded joints on spouts, handle sockets, leg sockets, or handles. (Courtesy, Aluminum Company of America.)

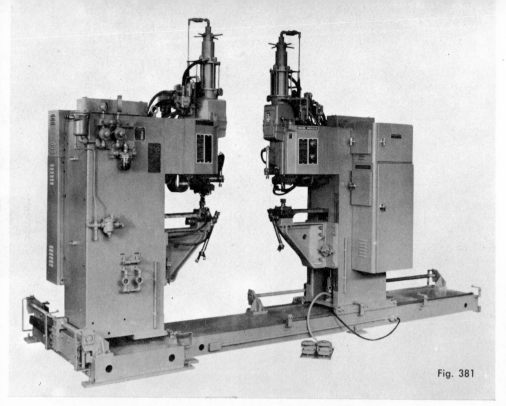

Fig. 381

Figs. 381–382. Two standard 75-kva resistance welders mounted on an adjustable base for production welding of ornamental iron work, as shown in Fig. 382. (Courtesy, The Taylor-Winfield Corporation.)

Fig. 382

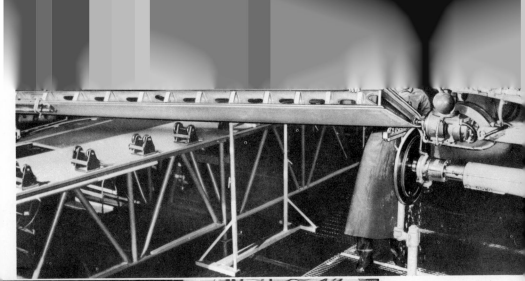

Fig. 383

Fig. 384

Fig. 385

Figs. 383–385. The resistance welding of this large aircraft fuel tank required special tooling and fixtures. Figs. 383 and 384 show the seam welding of the liner and rib to the skin. An exceptionally small wheel is required to operate in the confined space. Fig. 385 shows the spot welding of the ribs which requires a special horn to reach inside the narrow tank. (Courtesy, Sciaky Bros., Inc.)

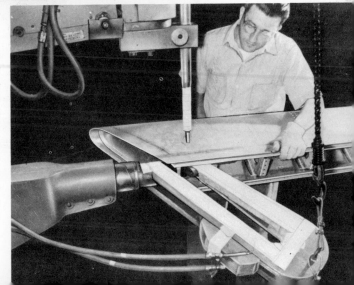

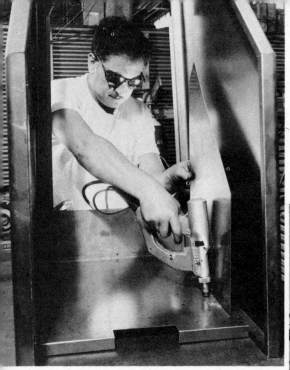

Fig. 386. A spot-welding gun that works from one side of the pieces to be joined, uses the principle of the shielded arc. It can be used in places where conventional spot-welding equipment would not be practical. (Courtesy, Air Reduction Sales Company.)

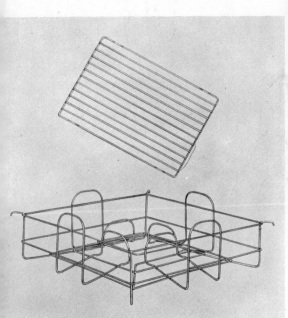

Fig. 387. These two sink wells are jointed means of crush or mash welding to make a si unit. They are flooded with water for cooling ing welding and a single 250-kva welder out 900 per 8-hr day. The only finishing requ is a single pass with a hand belt grinder. (C tesy, Sciaky Bros., Inc.)

Fig. 388. These aluminum wire articles are made by spot welding. (Courtesy, Aluminum Company of America.)

Fig. 389. A 200-kva flash butt welder economi-
lly joins the mitered corners of extruded alumi-
m window frames on a mass-production basis.
ourtesy, Sciaky Bros., Inc.)

Fig. 390. Flash welding of an
aluminum ring showing the water
cooling lines to the electrodes,
which also act as clamps. (Courtesy, Aluminum Company of
America.)

Fig. 391. A setup for flash
welding of heavy, hot rolled
steel bars in a T form. (Courtesy,
Thomson Electric Welder Company.)

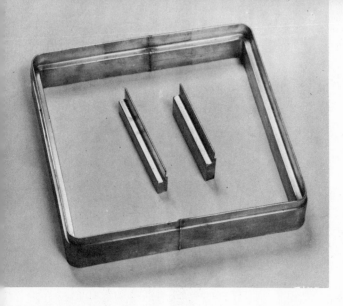

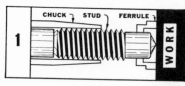

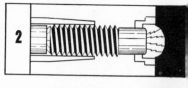

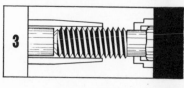

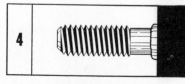

Fig. 392. A difficult job of flash welding because of the two welds and the thick and thin sections of the aluminum extrusions, but it was successfully done on a production basis by a 250-kva "Synchro-Matic" welder. (Courtesy, Thomson Electric Welder Company.)

Fig. 393. A big field for flash welding is the mitered corners of aluminum window and door frames. (Courtesy, Thomson Electric Welder Company.)

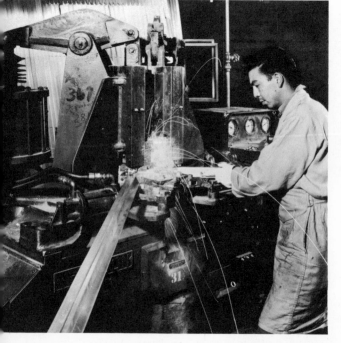

Fig. 394. Steps in the stud-welding process. (1) The stud is pressed against the work with a ceramic ferrule around the point of contact. (2) When the gun's trigger is pressed, the stud is withdrawn automatically, creating an arc and melting a portion of the stud and the plate. (3) After a controlled interval, the stud is pressed into the molten pool of metal on the plate. (4) The gun is removed and the ferrule broken off. The entire operation requires less than a second. (Courtesy, Nelson Stud Welding, Div. of Gregory Industries, Inc.)

Fig. 395. The stud welding gun in operation. (Courtesy, Nelson Stud Welding, Div. of Gregory Industries, Inc.)

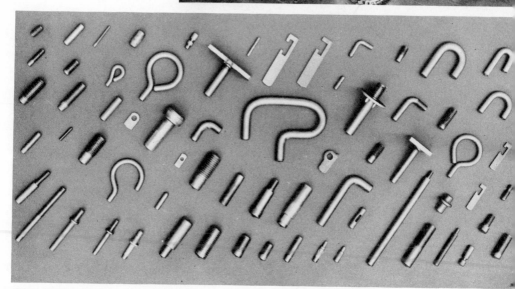

Fig. 396. A group of standard and special welding studs. (Courtesy, Nelson Stud Welding, Div. of Gregory Industries, Inc.)

Fig. 397. Basic joint designs for brazing. (Courtesy, Handy & Harman.)

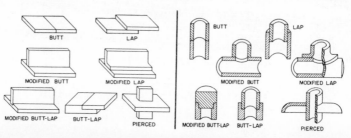

BUTT

LAP

MODIFIED BUTT

MODIFIED LAP

MODIFIED BUTT-LAP

BUTT-LAP

PIERCED

BUTT

LAP

MODIFIED BUTT

MODIFIED LAP

MODIFIED BUTT-LAP

BUTT-LAP

PIERCED

Fig. 398

Fig. 399

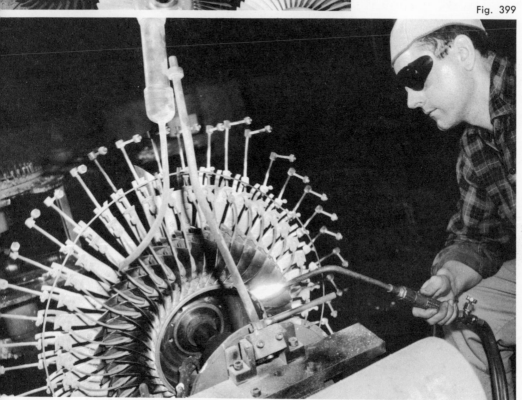

Figs. 398–399. A rotor assembly fabricated by silver brazing by torch in the special fixture shown in Fig. 399. (Courtesy, Air Reduction Sales Company.)

Fig. 400. This lightweight motorcycle frame is silver brazed with high-strength lap joints. (Courtesy, Handy & Harman.)

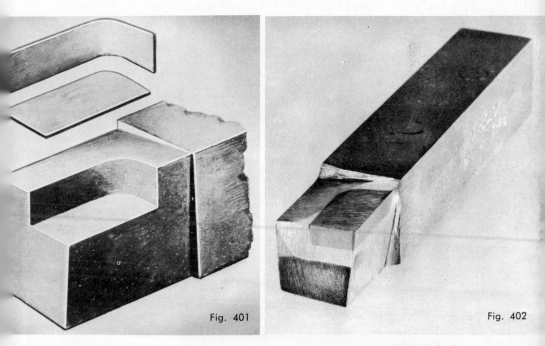

Fig. 401

Fig. 402

Figs. 401–402. A carbide tip silver brazed to the steel shank of a lathe tool. The strips of brazing alloy, 0.003 in. thick, are precut and placed in position. (Courtesy, Handy & Harman.)

Fig. 403. A gas-fired muffle-type furnace with a wire-mesh belt conveyor for continuous brazing, sintering (see Chap. 4) and other processes requiring temperatures up to 2050 F. (Courtesy, The Electric Furnace Company.)

Fig. 404. Three-piece pulley assemblies coming from the discharge end of a brazing furnace. (Courtesy, The Electric Furnace Company.)

Fig. 405. The spud is silver brazed in this automobile oil pan by induction heating. Two men do 1000 in an 8-hr day. (Courtesy, Handy & Harman.)

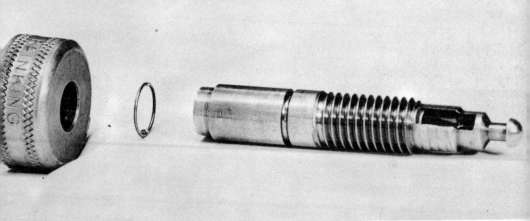

Fig. 406. These hoze nozzle parts are assembled with the ring of silver alloy and furnace brazed on a large production basis. (Courtesy, Handy & Harman.)

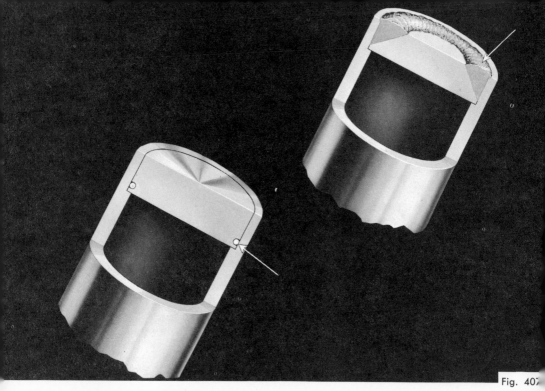

Fig. 407

Figs. 407–408. Changing from welding to induction silver brazing cut costs 50 per cent on these hydraulic cylinders and caps. Time was cut from 15.3 min to 2 min on a 5¼-in. cylinder and no machining is required. Fig. 407 shows a cutaway view of the welded and brazed ends. Fig. 408 shows the induction brazing setup for this job. (Courtesy, The Ohio Crankshaft Co.)

Fig. 408

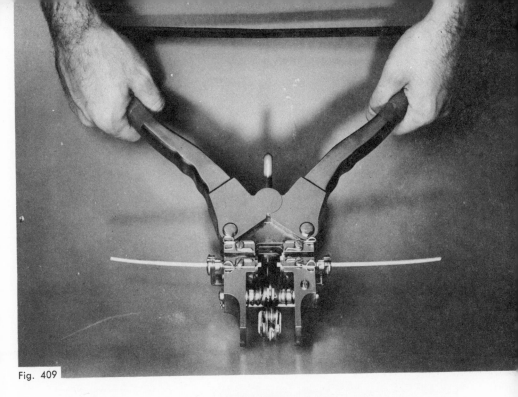

Fig. 409

Figs. 409–410. A hand tool for cold butt welding of copper and aluminum wire and (Fig. 410) a hydraulic machine for performing the same operation on rod up to ⅜ in. diameter. (Courtesy, Utica Drop Forge & Tool Corp.)

Fig. 410

Fig. 411. A group of cold welds made on these machines, before and after trimming of the flash, between copper and copper, copper and aluminum, aluminum and aluminum. Under tension, the wire will break before the cold welded joint. (Courtesy, Utica Drop Forge & Tool Corp.)

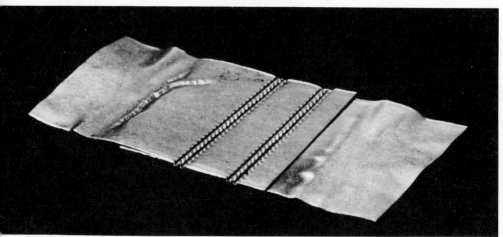

Fig. 412. A cold-welded lap joint between aluminum sheet. Various patterns of embossing can be used. (Courtesy, Utica Drop Forge & Tool Corp.)

Fig. 413

Figs. 413–414. A small foot-operated press converted from cast iron to welded steel with a 50 percent reduction in both cost and weight. (Courtesy, The Lincoln Electric Company.)

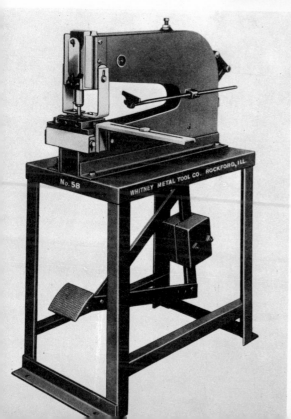

Fig. 414

Fig. 415. This machine base was converted from cast iron to welded steel with a 50 percent saving, increased rigidity, and easier installation. (Courtesy, The Lincoln Electric Company.)

Fig. 416. Another machine base where a conversion from a casting to a weldment saved 50 percent of the weight. (Courtesy, The Lincoln Electric Company.)

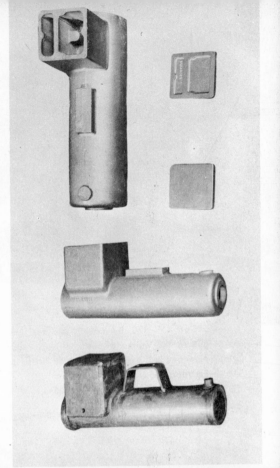

Fig. 417. This industrial oil burner part was converted by York-Shipley, Inc. from the weldment at the bottom, used on the pilot models, to the cored gray iron casting shown in the two upper pictures. The casting is pressure tight and a saving of 25 percent was made in addition to improved appearance. (Courtesy, Reading Gray Iron Castings, Inc.)

Fig. 418. The conversion of this trailer hitch from a welded assembly (*left*) to a malleable casting (*right*) resulted in reduced cost, greater strength, and improved appearance. (Courtesy, Malleable Founders' Society.)

Fig. 41

Figs. 419–420. By making this steel casting in three pieces and welding them together, the weight of the core was reduced from 308 lb to 3 lb, and this design permitted a 30 percent reduction in the total weight of the casting. (Courtesy, Steel Founders' Society of America.)

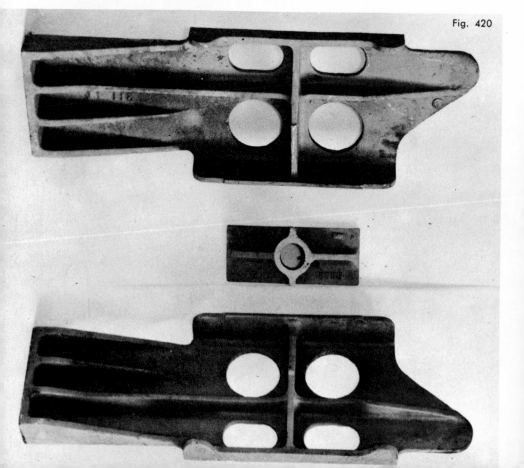

Fig. 420

Fig. 421. Another good example of how casting and welding can complement each other. In this 19,000-lb pump body, the blades inside at the front are cast steel, welded in place. The base consists of both castings and ¾-in. thick plate welded together and welded to the main body which is cast with a wall thickness of 3 in. to 4 in. (Courtesy, Steel Founders' Society of America.)

Fig. 422. An excellent example of a composite fabrication where castings, stampings, tubing, and rolled plate were all welded together to form a single piece. (Courtesy, Steel Founders' Society of America.)

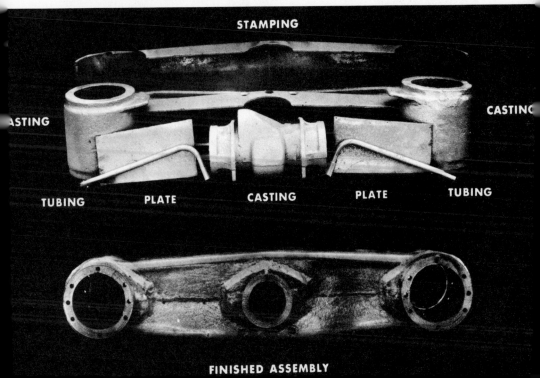

12

Assembly Processes

Processes for making parts such as castings, stampings, or plastic moldings have received much more attention than the methods of assembling them together, yet in many industries the assembly accounts for by far the greater part of the labor cost and offers the greatest opportunities for savings. Perhaps one reason that more has not been written about assembly processes is the fact that each operation on the assembly line is a problem in itself and it is very hard to lay down general principles for reducing assembly labor costs. Factors of the basic product design enter into this, as well as plant layout, production methods, and material handling.

One basic principle that has made mass production possible is the interchangeability of parts. This makes it possible for unskilled help to assemble extremely complex devices, since no individual fitting of parts is required on the assembly line. It is here that the correct specification of tolerances on the parts shows up. For example, if two stampings are to be assembled together with several screws, difficulty will be experienced if the spacing of the holes is not held to close enough tolerances so that the holes line up properly. On the other hand, the tolerances in the spacing of holes can be broadened if the holes themselves can be made somewhat oversize to compensate for some misalignment and still permit the screws to fit easily into place. In some cases, slots can be provided to compensate for still greater variation in hole spacing. Practical shop experience is of great help to an engineer in specifying tolerances that make a workmanlike job without slowing up assembly or adding unreasonably to the cost of making the parts. It is often helpful to have both the design engineer and the production supervisor go over these points together before the drawings are released. Purchasing agents should encourage consultation between suppliers of component parts and the engineering and production personnel to avoid tolerances or design features that increase costs or that may cause trouble in assembly.

Once it has been determined that all parts of an assembly can be fitted together consistently and easily, a careful analysis of each step in the assembly operation should be made and a method established that permits the operation to be done with the absolute minimum of wasted motion. The location of the working stock of parts with relation to the operator is most important, and extended reaching for material or tools should be avoided carefully. Wherever possible, both hands should be utilized simultaneously in bringing material to the point of assembly and in the actual assembly itself. Time standards should then be established and the operator carefully trained to follow the established procedure. Operators should not be allowed to depart from the established procedure without authorization from their supervisors, but they should be encouraged to make suggestions for improving the methods and, if possible, should be rewarded for constructive suggestions that are adopted and that prove to be time- and money-saving. An intelligent operator who is doing a job day after day will often see chances for improvement in methods that otherwise would be overlooked.

SPECIAL FASTENERS

There are many methods of joining mechanical parts into assemblies and finished products and these methods should be analyzed carefully before a final design is approved. The right method can often show tremendous savings in assembly labor cost.

The first method of joining parts that comes to mind is the use of a screw or a bolt with a nut and a lock washer to prevent the nut from loosening in service. This is still a very widely used method, but its use should be scrutinized closely, for it involves the handling of three separate pieces in addition to holding the workpieces themselves. Ordinarily, the screw is picked up and inserted with the left hand. The lock washer is then applied over the screw with the right hand. Then, while the left hand is holding these in place, the right hand reaches out, picks up a nut, starts the nut on the thread (often with some difficulty) and after running it down as far as possible by hand, reaches for a wrench and completes the tightening. It is often necessary for the left hand also to reach for another wrench or a screwdriver to hold the screw from turning. Obviously this is a very inefficient operation, but it is amazing how often it is seen on production lines.

A big improvement can be made by designing a simple fixture that holds the work and that also holds a number of screws in place and prevents them from turning. Such fixtures are often easily built and are inexpensive. Both hands can then be used to drop lock washers in position and to start nuts on the threads. A single electric or air-operated wrench or screwdriver then runs the nuts down and tightens them to a predetermined tension. Often these simple tools and fixtures can reduce the time on an assembly operation to one quarter or less of what otherwise would be required.

Further savings can often be made by the use of special types of screws and fasteners. Self-tapping screws are one of the commonest of these and they are made in a wide variety of types and sizes for use in sheet metal, ferrous or nonferrous castings, or plastic moldings. Manufacturers' literature can be a big help in selecting the proper type and size and in determining the correct hole size to permit easy insertion and still give good strength. The use of self-tapping screws eliminates the nut or a tapping operation in one of the parts and usually eliminates the need for a lock washer, since the friction of the thread prevents loosening. Usually they are driven in by power tools, and they have made tremendous cost reductions in such items as automobile bodies, all types of home appliances, and radio and television sets.

Still further cost reduction is often possible by the use of spring type fasteners that require only a simple push with a hand tool or an arbor press to set them firmly in position. These spring fasteners are made in numerous standard styles and in almost innumerable special varieties for use on a particular job. One commonly used type is made of spring steel in rectangular shape. It is formed into an arch shape and in the center is a rectangular hole with sharp edges that bite into a plain stud over which it is pressed. The spring tension holds the assembly tightly together and presses the prongs into the stud. These spring fasteners are not designed for heavily loaded parts but are great time savers for assembling parts that are not subjected to great strain—for example, the chrome-plated molding attached to automobile bodies and the ornamental dial plates on radio and television sets.

Taper pins have long been used as a means for fastening such parts as collars, pulleys, and gears to shafts, but these are expensive and require an accurate reaming operation on a previously drilled hole. A less expensive fastening that is equally satisfactory for many purposes is a special pin that is formed by rolling a piece of flat steel into a cylinder with a slight gap at the joint. These are made slightly oversize for the hole in which they are to be used and are driven or pressed into place. They are heat-treated to make them retain their tension which holds them firmly in place in spite of normal variations in the drilled holes. They cost less than taper pins and eliminate the reaming operation.

Cotter pins have also been standard practice for preventing shafts and pins from shifting endwise where no end thrust was involved. These require a drilled hole, and often a saving can be made by replacing this with a narrow groove that can be cut during other machining on a lathe or screw machine, and replacing the cotter pin with a spring "C" washer (Fig. 430) or wire "hairpin" clip which can be installed much more quickly than the cotter pin.

In assemblies subjected to severe vibration, it has been common practice to use castle nuts with a cotter pin inserted through a drilled hole in the bolt and the notches in the nut. Many types of lock nuts (Fig. 440) are now available which are completely satisfactory in most of these applications and which save the drilling operation, the cotter pin, and considerable assembly time. The choice of lock nut depends on the application and the requirements of heat, vibration, and frequency of disassembly.

Other special connectors that can prove to be cost savers in certain applications are machine screws and nuts with lock washers preassembled on them for ease of assembly. Also, there are stamped nuts made of thin steel, shaped to fit standard machine screw threads, which cost less than standard nuts and require no lock washer. These are designed for light loads only.

Another group of fasteners are nuts and studs designed to be attached to sheet metal or plates by means of projection welding (see Chap. 11). These provide a strong thread in thin metal assemblies and often simplify further assembly operations.

Other special nuts attach to holes in sheet metal by a simple pressing operation. They are so shaped that the pressure locks them firmly, both from coming out and from turning. Like the projection welding types, they provide a strong thread in thin material and provide for easy assembly.

In sheet-metal assemblies it is often desirable to have a nut held in place for assembly but free to shift slightly to align itself with the bolt or screw. This is provided by retainer nuts in which a sheet-metal housing, slightly larger than the nut, is attached to the sheet metal with the nut free to shift slightly inside it but not free to turn or to get too far out of place. These retainers may be spot welded in place or they may be held in a rectangular hole by spring tension. On assemblies where one side is inaccessible or difficult to reach, these captive nuts are a great time-saver and often make it possible for one operator to make assemblies that otherwise would require two.

It has long been recognized that the slotted head used on wood and machine screws is far from an ideal method of driving them. Although many slotted-head screws are still used, many improved types are now available. Most widely used is the Phillips or cross-recessed head screw. Others are the Clutch head; the Allen head, with a hexagon socket; the Bristol head, with a splined socket; and the Reed and Prince head, with a cross recess slightly different from the Phillips. All of these cost more than slotted-head screws but due to easier location of the driver and reduced danger of slippage they often show substantial savings in labor and material spoilage that far outweigh this. They are especially advantageous on finished work where a slip of a screwdriver could do much damage and on any applications where power-driven screwdrivers are used.

The Allen and the Bristol head screws are made not only in the smaller sizes, where they compete with slotted-head screws, but also in the larger bolt and cap screw sizes, where hexagon or square heads are standard. Their advantage in this field is chiefly in space-saving, since no wrench clearance is required around the head.

RIVETING

Another common method of holding parts together in mechanical assemblies is the use of rivets. These may be the huge iron or steel rivets that are inserted in holes through steel plates and hammered over while red hot to hold great structural steel assemblies or the plates for ships or boilers. At the other extreme they may be the tiny pins that hold the hinges on your eyeglass frames. They may be solid, tubular, or split, according to the application and the load carried.

Solid rivets are used in heavily loaded parts such as structural steel work and aircraft assemblies. A solid rivet has a head on one end and a straight, solid shank. It is inserted through holes in the parts to be joined and held in place by a solid block or anvil held against the head, while the opposite end is formed into a second head on the other side of the work by means of a series of hammer blows, usually from an air-operated hammer, which upset the hot or cold metal into the desired shape. The parts are held tightly together under considerable tension and a very strong joint is formed. Aluminum solid rivets are widely used in the aircraft industry but they are now meeting some competition from resistance-welded joints (see Chap. 11) and adhesive-bonded joints (Chap. 15).

Where the load is not so great and faster assembly is required, tubular rivets or eyelets are used. Tubular rivets have a head on one end and a shank that is drilled part way through to form a tubular section that is rolled over to form the holding member. Usually they are inserted by means of semiautomatic machines which hold the parts in alignment, insert the rivet, and clinch it by one quick blow of a specially shaped punch. The machines may be foot-operated or motor-driven, and the rivets are fed automatically from a hopper. They are widely used by the electronics industry for assembling sockets and other components to metal chassis bases. Eyelets are used in the same way but they are formed from tubing, so that the hole goes all the way through and is seen on both sides of the work. Eyelets cost less than rivets and are quite satisfactory where their appearance is not objectionable and where the somewhat greater shear strength of the rivets is not needed.

Split rivets have a wedge-shaped slot in the end opposite the head. They are used in leather work or in assembling hardware to luggage, where they are driven through the leather or wood without the need for drilling a hole. The prongs strike a shaped anvil on the back side of the work and this rolls them outward and clinches them tightly in place. They also are usually inserted very rapidly by means of power-driven or foot-operated, automatically fed machines.

The ordinary types of rivets require access to both sides of the work to drive and clinch them. In many applications this limits their usefulness, and various types of "blind rivets" have been developed for use under these conditions. These are all considerably more expensive than plain rivets, but they make possible the simplification of many assemblies with large savings in assembly labor. One type of blind rivet carries a small chemical charge in a cavity inside the body which expands upon the application of heat. When the rivet is set in place, heat is applied to the head, causing the charge to expand and set the rivet firmly in place, as shown in Figs. 448 to 452.

STAKING

Staking is a variation of the riveting process in which a portion of the metal in one of the pieces assembled is cold worked by punching or rolling to spread it out and hold the other piece of the assembly to it. For example, a stamped gear is to be assembled to a hub which has been made on a screw machine. The hub has been formed with three steps on its outside diameter. The first is the full diameter of the original stock. Then comes a shoulder somewhat smaller in diameter and slightly longer than the thickness of the stamped gear. The balance of the length of the hub is turned down to a still smaller diameter. The hole in the stamped gear is a close fit on the middle diameter of the hub over which it is placed. A round tool with chisel-shaped edges is brought down over the small diameter and under pressure expands the edges of the shoulder so as to clamp the gear firmly in place. If it is tightly staked and the load is light, the friction may be sufficient to keep the gear from turning on the hub. If a more positive drive is desired, a flat may be cut on the hub where the gear fits, with a corresponding flat in the gear hole, or the gear may be forced over straight knurls or serrations in the hub, or the hole in the gear may be made with notches in it and the metal of the hub may be forced out into these notches in the staking operation. Staking forms a quick and economical method of assembly when the parts are adapted to it.

METAL STAPLING

A very rapid method of assembling sheet metal together, where the load is not heavy and appearance is not important, is known as metal stapling. A power-driven machine drives special steel staples through the two pieces of metal to be joined and clinches them on the reverse side in one quick stroke. Mild steel up to 0.050 in. or aluminum to 0.093 in. thick (each sheet) can be joined by this method at very low cost. It is also used for attaching felt, rubber, fabric, or other soft material to metal.

ELECTRICAL WIRING METHODS

The joining of two pieces of metal by the use of a low melting point solder has been discussed in Chap. 11 on Welding and Brazing. Another use of the soldering process falls into the category of an assembly process and will be covered here. In the assembly of radios, television sets, and electronic equipment, soldering is the major operation. The solder not only reinforces the mechanical joints between the wires and the sockets and other lugs, but also insures a good and permanent electrical connection. In military equipment it is standard practice to wrap the wires one and a half turns around the lug before soldering. This makes a good mechanical connection with the solder performing mostly an electrical function. In much commercial equipment, however, the wires are simply inserted through holes in the lugs and bent over to form a half turn, in which case the solder is depended on for both a mechanical and an electrical purpose.

The heat for this type of soldering is almost always furnished by electrically heated soldering irons with copper tips which must be well tinned and kept clean to do good work. The tip of the iron is held against the joint until the temperature is high enough to melt the solder and make it flow smoothly around the connection. The solder is applied manually in the form of a hollow wire with the necessary flux in the center.

Various fluxes are available, but for electrical work rosin is the only one that is recognized as being completely noncorrosive. An acid flux should never be used on any wiring work because the residue that remains on the joint will eventually cause corrosion, and it is almost impossible to be sure that this residue is completely removed.

Hand soldering of this type is a relatively fast operation and much radio and television equipment is still made by this method. New developments in the use of printed wiring, in which the entire assembly, which may have several hundred connections, is dip soldered at one operation, seem likely to replace hand soldering in most production work. These are discussed more fully in Chap. 21 on Printed Circuits.

Other methods of wiring that compete with soldering in certain applications are the use of crimped-on terminals (see Fig. 460) and solderless wrapped wire connections. The wrapped wire method was developed in the Bell Telephone Laboratories and is being used quite largely in switchboard wiring. Special terminals of square or rectangular cross section are used and a simple tool operated by hand, electricity, or air makes four or more tight turns of the solid wire around the terminal. Actual compression of both the wire and the terminal occurs at each corner point of contact which excludes the air and forms a permanent, low-resistance contact. Tube sockets, relays, controls, and some other electronic components are now available with these special terminals, and the method is coming into quite general use in industrial electronics and computer work (see Figs. 461, 462, 463).

MATERIAL HANDLING

The handling of raw materials, component parts, and work in process is a vital part of the assembly process and has an important bearing on costs. An efficient material control system is also essential to insure a smooth flow of material to the assembly lines, without shortages, which cause expensive delays, and without excessive inventories at any point. This applies to small plants with only a few people just as strongly as to large, automated factories. The importance of material control and handling is more often overlooked in the small- and the medium-size plant, and large savings can often be made by a careful analysis of these phases of the operation.

Plant layout has an important bearing on material handling and it is well to review this from the ground up at regular intervals. Outside consultants can often be used to good advantage to work with supervisory and management personnel in making these reviews. As a starting point, it is well to assume that you are just moving into a new plant with no fixed locations for partitions, machines, or departments. From this beginning it is interesting to see how closely you come to your existing layout as an arrangement of maximum efficiency. Sometimes a complete rearrangement is justified and shows large savings in operation.

Space does not permit mentioning more than a few basic principles of plant layout here. The movement of material from receiving through incoming inspection, stockroom, processing, assembly, packing, and shipping should be planned for as smooth a flow as possible with a minimum of back tracking and cross movement. A straight-line movement from one end of the plant to the other would be ideal, but the conditions are usually not that simple. Most plants have a variety of products and numerous operations to worry about, but careful planning will simplify the movement to as great an extent as possible.

Supplies of parts needed in assembly should be stored as close to the point of use as possible. If the main storage has to be located some distance away, these working stocks should be adequate to avoid any danger of tie-ups. Heavy material can often be stored on pallets from the time it is received so that it can be handled by a lift truck with a minimum of hand labor. This applies to the "job shop" type of factory as well as to mass production.

On the assembly line itself, conditions vary so much that it is hard to generalize. If the operation is large enough and well enough standardized to consider a moving conveyor belt, serious thought should be given to both the pros and the cons before an installation is made. The increase in production is often greater than anticipated, since the human element is reduced, and the output comes closer to the theoretical ideal. However, flexibility is sacrificed, model changes become more difficult and expensive, and delays, due to material shortages, mechanical difficulties, or the "bugs" that develop in even the best run plants, are likely to cause more serious disruption.

Regardless of the size of the plant, it is of the utmost importance to analyze each operation and to be sure that the time of production people is not being wasted in transporting material. This means not only the obvious waste of walking across the room for a part, but also the less obvious cases where unnecessary stooping or reaching are required.

It can be seen from the few points mentioned here that the study of material movement and handling and of assembly methods can be both interesting and fruitful in any manufacturing business. It is equally important that the design engineer should have a thorough understanding of assembly methods and problems since it is only by co-ordinating design and manufacturing that the greatest economy and efficiency can be achieved.

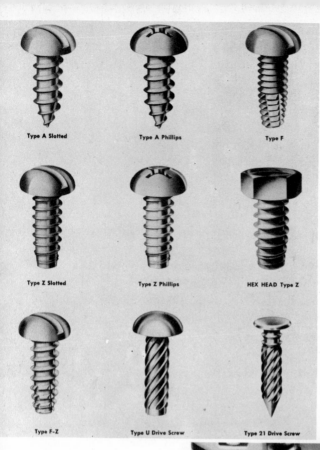

Type A Slotted

Type A Phillips

Type F

Type Z Slotted

Type Z Phillips

HEX HEAD Type Z

Type F-Z

Type U Drive Screw

Type 21 Drive Screw

Fig. 423. Self-tapping screws such as these are used widely in all industries for fastening in sheet metal, plastics, or castings. They save on tapping and assembly time and often result in substantial savings. (Courtesy, Parker-Kalon Div., General American Transportation Corporation.)

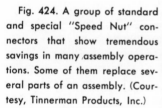

Fig. 424. A group of standard and special "Speed Nut" connectors that show tremendous savings in many assembly operations. Some of them replace several parts of an assembly. (Courtesy, Tinnerman Products, Inc.)

Fig. 425. Fasteners of the type illustrated in Fig. 424 showed a saving of 75 percent in the mounting of this automobile radio loud speaker. (Courtesy, Tinnerman Products, Inc.)

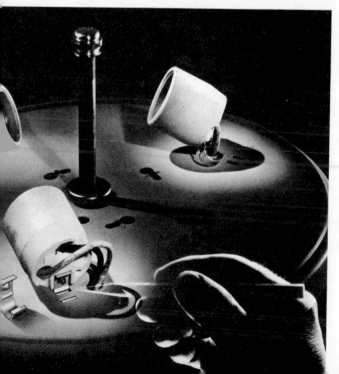

Fig. 426. A special spring fastener saved 80 percent on assembly time in attaching this lamp socket to a lighting fixture. It snaps into place by hand and replaces a screw, a nut, and a special tapped bracket. (Courtesy, Tinnerman Products, Inc.)

Fig. 427. Two tubular spring clips replace a long bolt, centering washers, lock washer, and nut in this resistor mounting on an indicator light. A saving in space requirements also resulted. (Courtesy, Tinnerman Products, Inc.)

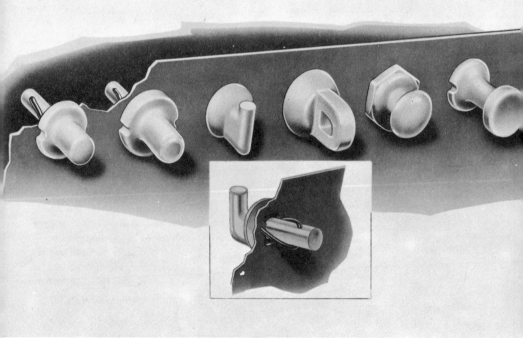

Fig. 428. These plastic shelf supports have a steel insert and a spring that locks them in position by a half turn. They are used in most home refrigerators. (Courtesy, Simmons Fastener Corp.)

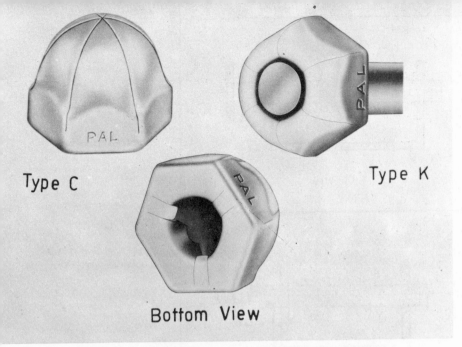

Type C

Type K

Bottom View

g. 429. These "PUSHNUT" ® fasteners are for rapid assembly and are applied by pressure only. (Courtesy, The Palnut Company.)

Fig. 430. Types of "Truarc" retaining rings and their uses. (Courtesy, Waldes Kohinoor, Inc.)

function	basic types				for taking up end-play				
nomenclature	basic		inverted		bowed		beveled		bowed e-ring
series no.	5000	5100	5008	5108	5001	5101	5002	5102	5131
application	Internal for Housing Bores	External for Shafts	Internal for Housing Bores	External for Shafts	Internal for Housing Bores	External for Shafts	Internal for Housing Bores	External for Shafts	External for Shafts
range — in.	.250-10.0	.125-10.0	.750-4.0	.500-4.0	.250-1.456	.188-1.438	1.0-10.0	1.0-10.0	.110-1.375
range — mm.	6.4-253.8	3.2-253.8	19.0-101.5	12.7-101.5	6.4-37.0	4.8-36.5	25.4-253.8	25.4-253.8	2.8-35.0
features	Tapered design principle permits rings to maintain constant circularity and pressure against bottom of groove.		Inverted construction provides uniform protruding shoulders while maintaining constant circularity when installed in groove.		Bowed construction permits resilient take-up of end-play.		Beveled construction permits rigid take-up of end-play.		Radially applied. Provides large shoulder on small shaft diameter. Bowed construction permits resilient take-up of end-play.

function	for radial assembly			self-locking types					
nomenclature	e-ring	crescent	interlocking	circular self-locking		triangular self-locking	triangular nut	grip-ring	locking prong
series no.	5133	5103	5107	5005	5105	5305	5300	5555	5139
application	External for Shafts	External for Shafts	External for Shafts	Internal for Housing Bores	External for Shafts	External for Shafts	With Threaded Screw	External for Shafts	External for Shafts
range — in.	.040-1.375	.125-2.0	.469-3.375	.312-2.0	.093-1.0	.062-.437		.077-.755	.094-.438
range — mm.	1.0-35.0	3.2-51.0	11.9-85.7	7.9-50.8	2.4-25.4	1.55-11.1	●		2.4-11.1
features	Radially applied. Provides large shoulder on small shaft diameter. (see 5131)	Applied radially over shaft. Secure against impact and vibration.	Two-piece ring applied radially. Secure against extremely high r.p.m.'s and heavy thrusts.	Installed axially. Requires no groove. Recommended for permanent assemblies exposed to relatively moderate thrusts, impacts or vibrational loading.		Low cost retainer. Makes possible tight assemblies free of end-play on relatively soft shafts.	Flattens under torque. Secures equal load distribution. Replaces lock washer on screw.	Applied axially on shaft. Requires no groove. Exerts considerable frictional hold against axial displacement.	Radially applied. Locks positively in groove. Can be used as shoulder against rotating parts. Replaces nuts and bolts, springs, washers.

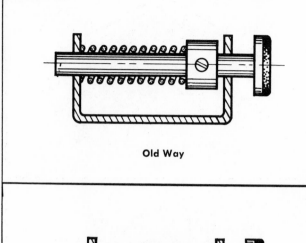

Old Way

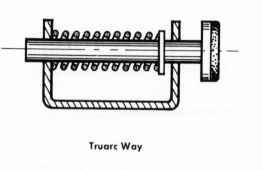

Truarc Way

Fig. 431. A retaining ring (series 5555 in Fig. 430) is used to replace a collar and set screw in a pressure pad assembly for a tape recorder with a saving of 2 cents per unit and reduced size. (Courtesy, Waldes Kohinoor, Inc.)

Fig. 432. Two retaining rings (series 5139 in Fig. 430) are used to replace nuts, lock washers, and spring washers. This reduces the shaft length and eliminates the threading operation. This type of ring is bowed to take up end play. (Courtesy, Waldes Kohinoor, Inc.)

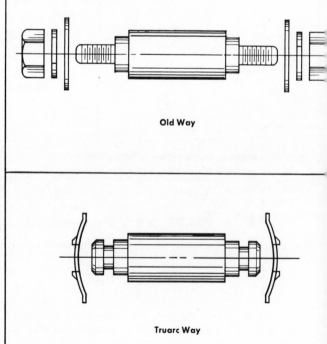

Old Way

Truarc Way

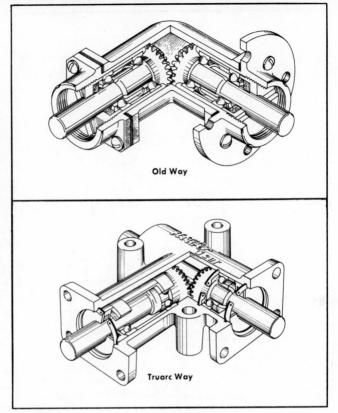

Old Way

Truarc Way

Fig. 433. This shows the tremendous savings made possible by an examination of assembly methods. The angle drive at the top was costly to make and difficult to assemble. A redesign at the bottom eliminates 21 parts and uses three retainer rings (two series 5008 and one series 5000 in Fig. 430), to position the bearing and shaft assemblies and lock the bearings in place. The saving in cost was $6.75 per unit. (Courtesy, Waldes Kohinoor, Inc.)

Fig. 434. A group of standard and special spring washers suggesting their many applications for maintaining tension, removing end play, makng electrical contact, etc. (Courtesy, Wallace Barnes Company.)

Fig.

Figs. 435–437. Plastics and light metals are fine for many things but tapped holes in them do not have the strength of steel. These helical inserts of diamond-shaped wire make up for that by providing internal threads of stainless steel or phosphor bronze in almost any material. They are easily inserted by simple hand or power tools. They are also excellent for repairing stripped threads as shown in the series of pictures in Fig. 436: (A) drill out the stripped thread, (B) tap oversize, (C) install "Heli-Coil" insert, (D) result—a thread stronger than the original. Fig. 437 shows a special screw-locking version of this insert. (Courtesy, Heli-Coil Corporation.)

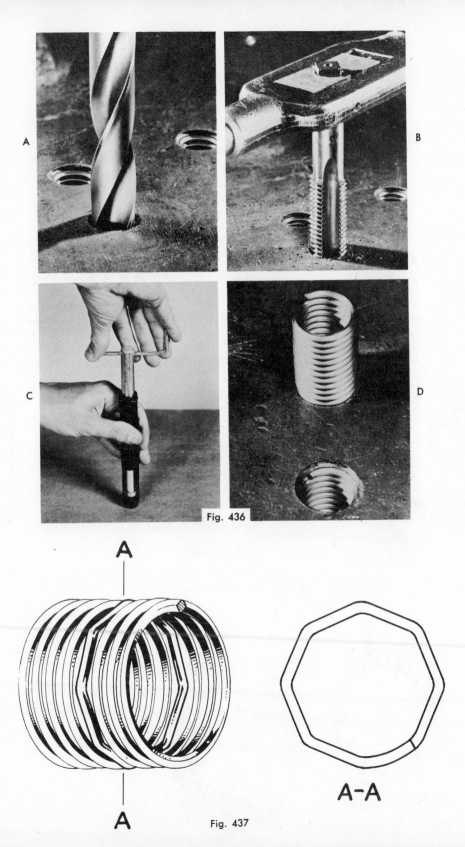

A

B

C

D

Fig. 436

A

A

A-A

Fig. 437

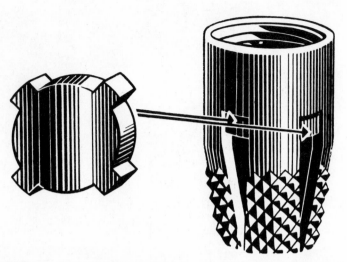

Fig. 438. Threaded metal inserts are often required in molded plastic parts. To place these during the molding reduces the production from the press considerably. The self-locking inserts shown here are placed automatically or manually at the time of assembly in plain holes in the plastic. The screw forces the spreader ahead of it and expands the insert tightly in place. (Courtesy, The Phelps Manufacturing Co.)

Fig. 439. Internal and external "Shakeproof" ® lock washers and a dished type for maintaining tension. (Courtesy, Shakeproof Div., Illinois Tool Works.)

Fig. 440. This gives an idea of the wide variety of lock nuts available for various light and heavy applications. (Courtesy, Industrial Fasteners Institute.)

Fig. 441. A group of high-temperature lock nuts for jet engine and aircraft applications. (Courtesy, Elastic Stop Nut Corporation of America.)

 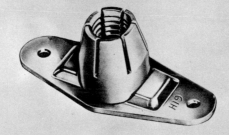 

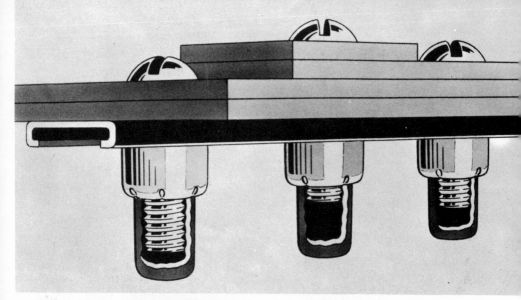

Fig. 442. Special channel lock nuts with a high nylon cap that seals the end and covers the bolt ends. (Courtesy, Elastic Stop Nut Corporation of America.)

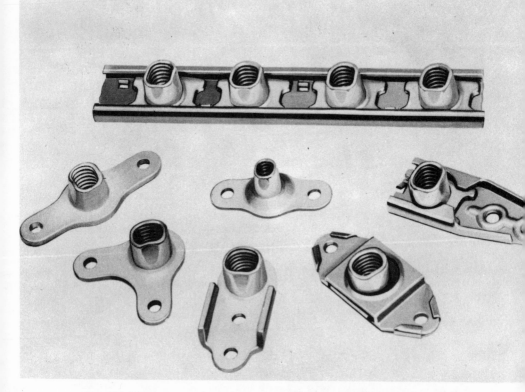

Fig. 443. Various types of stainless-steel anchor and channel lock nuts for use up to 800 F. (Courtesy, Elastic Stop Nut Corporation of America.)

Fig. 444. Lock washers assembled to screws (known as Sems) and to nuts ("Keps" ®) are often great time-savers on assembly operations. (Courtesy, Shakeproof Div., Illinois Tool Works.)

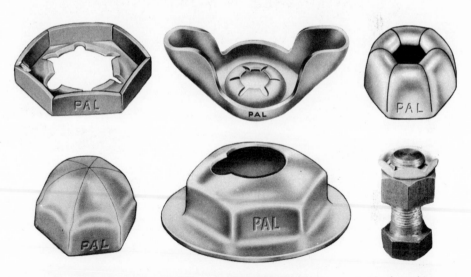

Fig. 445. A group of stamped steel "PALNUTS" ® for use on standard machine screws. They are self-locking and, for heavily loaded parts, are often used as lock nuts on top of a standard nut as shown at the lower right. (Courtesy, The Palnut Company.)

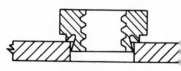

Insert Fastener squarely in sheet

Apply pressure to head of Fastener

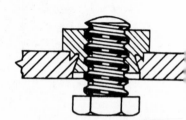

Install screw or bolt from side opposite to the head of the Fastener.

Fig. 446. "Pem" self-clinching nuts are attached easily, as shown in the line drawings, and give a load-carrying thread in thin sheet metal. (Courtesy, Penn Engineering & Manufacturing Corp.)

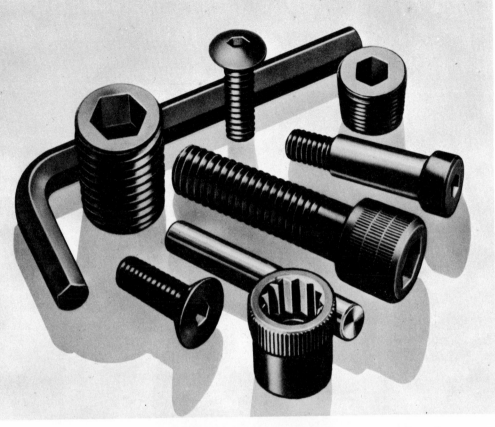

Fig. 447. A group of recessed hexagon head screws and the type of wrench used with them. These are used widely in the machine tool and many other mechanical industries. (Courtesy, The Allen Mfg. Co.)

Fig.

Figs. 448–452. A type of blind rivet for application from one side of the work is shown here. It is made with a hollow shank filled with a small chemical charge that expands upon the application of heat. The rivet is set by simply applying heat to the head by means of an electric tool similar to a soldering iron. This not only forms a head on the opposite side of the work, but also expands the shank to make a tight fit in the hole. Fig. 448 shows a group of these rivets; Fig. 449 shows a cross-section after they are expanded and Fig. 450 shows the method of applying them. Figs. 451 and 452 are typical applications. This type of rivet is used widely, both for original construction and for repair in both aircraft and industrial uses. (Courtesy, E. I. du Pont de Nemours & Company.)

Fig. 449

Fig. 450

Fig. 451

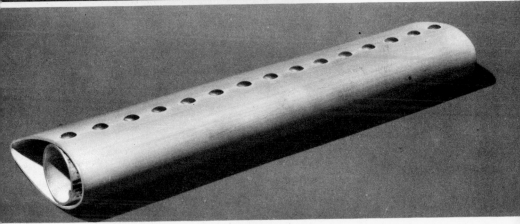

Fig. 452

Fig. 453. The "Rivnut" combines the functions of a blind rivet with a threaded connector. It is applied with simple hand or power tools like the one shown. (Courtesy, The B. F. Goodrich Company.)

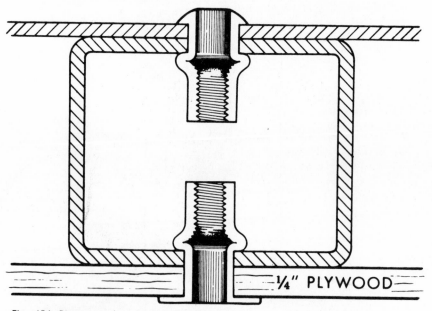

¼" PLYWOOD

Fig. 454. Rivnuts used to fasten plywood and steel to a steel tube and provide a thread for other assembly. (Courtesy, The B. F. Goodrich Company.)

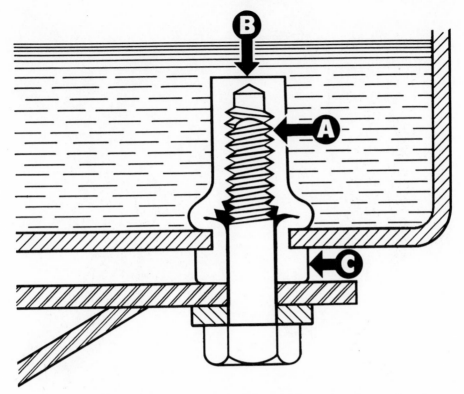

Fig. 455. A closed-end Rivnut replaced a brazed nut plate on this oil reservoir tank; it is installed in one tenth the time. (Courtesy, The B. F. Goodrich Company.)

Fig. 456. Another type of Rivnut provides a secure fastening in wood. The splined shank prevents turning. (Courtesy, The B. F. Goodrich Company.)

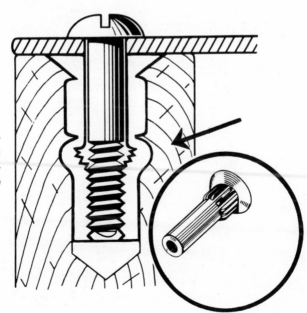

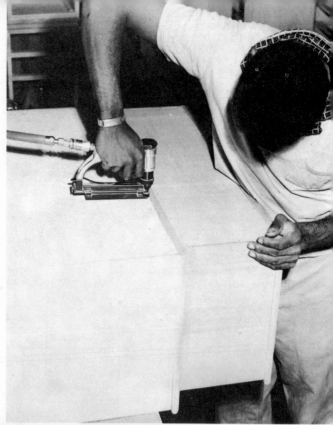

Fig. 457. Staples driven by hand- or air-operated machines are rapid and efficient for many light fastening jobs. Here an air-driven tool is fastening the back in a chest of drawers in a furniture factory. Rosin-coated staples are used for greater holding power. (Courtesy, Fastener Corporation.)

Fig. 458. The hammer type of hand stapler is used to fasten rust-inhibitive paper to an export crate. (Courtesy, Fastener Corporation.)

Fig. 459. The air stapler used to fasten fabric to a sofa bed. (Courtesy, Fastener Corporation.)

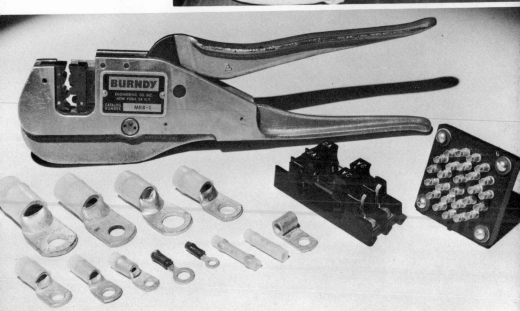

Fig. 460. Crimped-on terminals such as these are widely used on electric wires of all sizes from small radio wires to large power cables. They make a good connection without solder and are attached by simple hand tools like the one shown or by power-operated production machines. (Courtesy, Burndy Engineering Company, Inc.)

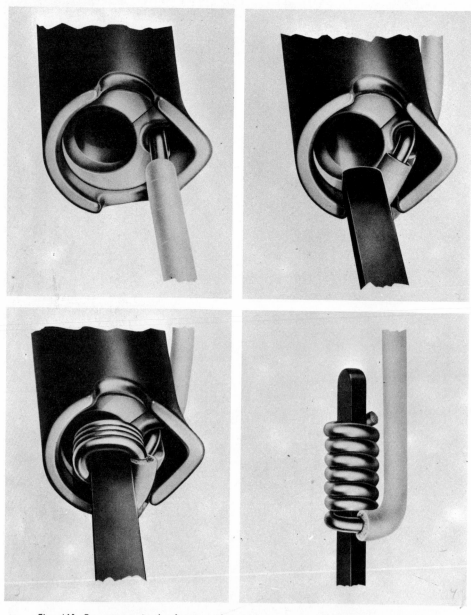

Fig. 461. Four stages in the forming of a solderless wrapped connection. (Courtesy, Keller Tool Div., Gardner-Denver Company.)

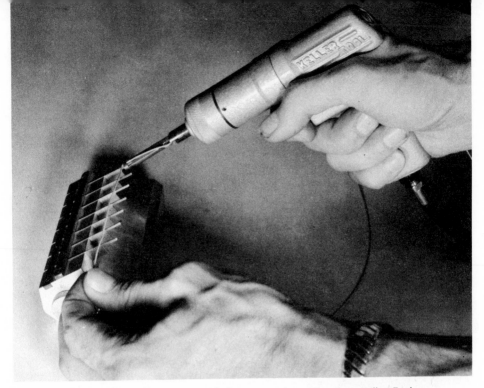

Fig. 462. A wrapping tool for forming solderless connections. (Courtesy, Keller Tool Div., Gardner-Denver Company.)

Fig. 463. A complex relay assembly being wired with solderless wrapped connections. (Courtesy, Keller Tool Div., Gardner-Denver Company.)

Heat Treating and Case Hardening

It is beyond the scope of this book to give any detailed directions for heat treating, since volumes have been written on this subject and it is still almost as much of an art as a science. Modern control instruments and controlled atmosphere furnaces have taken much of the guesswork out of the process since the days when the heat treater judged temperature solely by color, and the schedules for a particular steel were guarded as personal secrets.

Steels are heat-treated to develop required characteristics of hardness, ductility, and strength. Variations in the heat-treating schedule can bring out the best possible balance of these characteristics for each specific use. Heat treatments may be used not only to increase its hardness or strength but also to soften a metal, as by annealing, to adapt it for easier machining or cold forming; or by normalizing, to relieve strains. The term "heat treatment" may be extended also to include "cold" treatments at several hundred degrees below zero Fahrenheit for artificial aging and for making shrink fits.

Practically all steels can be heat-treated to a greater or less extent, although the higher carbon and alloy steels respond much more to heat treatment. Cast iron can be hardened by chilling in the casting process but it is not, strictly speaking, heat-treatable. Some bronze alloys can be heat-treated, as can some aluminum alloys.

The heat treating of steel usually involves heating to a high temperature that may range from 1400 F to 2400 F and cooling it rapidly by quenching in water or oil. This leaves the steel hard and brittle, and, for most purposes, this hardness must be reduced by a drawing or annealing process to provide greater toughness. The drawing consists of heating the piece to a much lower temperature of 300 F to 1300 F and allowing it to cool slowly, often over the course of many hours or days. The rate of heating and cooling is important in both the hardening and the drawing, and these rates vary according to the particular alloy being treated and the final characteristics desired.

Water quenching gives the most rapid cooling but it is the most likely to set up strains or develop cracks in the work. The design of the piece has much to do with whether these strains are serious or not. Parts for water quenching must be designed so that they will cool uniformly and will not have sharp corners or abrupt changes in cross section where stresses can concentrate or strains develop. Many parts are of such a shape that they cannot be hardened successfully by this process.

Oil quenching cools at only about one fifth the rate of water and its action is therefore less drastic. The hardness is likely to be less, but there is also much less strain and distortion and less danger of cracking. Tool and die steels are usually classed as "water-hardening" or "oil-hardening" according to which process is recommended for use with them. Oil is probably the most common quenching medium.

Air-hardening steels are highly alloyed to require only an air blast for hardening. These are more expensive steels, but they can be hardened with a minimum of distortion and danger of cracking so they are often preferred for complex tools and dies.

Annealing is the process of reducing the hardness of a metal to make it machine or form more readily. In the case of steel, it is done by heating to a high temperature and cooling slowly, either in air or in an insulating material such as fine ashes which slow down the cooling and make the annealing more effective. Most steels, except the very low carbon or "free machining" types, require an annealing operation before any extensive machining can be done on them. They are then rehardened after machining.

Normalizing and stress relieving are closely related to annealing, but are done primarily to relieve stresses caused by previous hot or cold working. Forgings are almost always normalized before machining or heat treating.

Some special alloy steels are available which can be machined in a heat-treated condition with approximately 320 Brinell hardness and 170,000 lb tensile strength. This often eliminates the need for heat treating of the finished piece. Parts requiring hardening and fine finish are usually machined to shape but left slightly oversize so that a light grinding operation after hardening can remove the distortion and the oxidation or scaling that often take place in the heat-treating process. The distortion can be minimized by careful controls during the heating and the quenching, and scaling can be almost eliminated by the use of controlled atmosphere furnaces where inert gases replace the oxygen of the air, which causes oxidation.

The hardness is measured in Rockwell or Brinell units, and Table 1 shows approximate corresponding figures of hardness and tensile strength. The tensile strength is given by the load in pounds required to break a 1-in. square test bar by means of a straight pull or tension. Two significant figures are usually given for this test, one being the yield point at which the test bar is permanently stretched or elongated and the other being the point at which it breaks. The difference between these figures is an indication of the toughness, although toughness is actually a combination of several characteristics. A piece of very hard steel, such as a file, might have a high ultimate tensile strength of 350,000 psi, but the yield point would be very close to the same figure since little elongation would take place before the piece broke. On the other hand, a tough piece of steel might have a lower tensile strength or breaking point but the yield point would be much lower than the ultimate tensile strength. In other words, it would stretch more before it broke and would have more toughness and ductility. Ductility is measured by the elongation that takes place between the yield point and the breaking point and also by the reduction in area that occurs during this elongation.

It is evident that no one characteristic of a steel part can be used to specify its suitability for a particular application. The specifications should include tensile strength, yield point, elongation, reduction in area, and hardness. If the user is not equipped to determine just what his requirements are, it would be best for him to consult with a reputable supplier regarding the application, and to rely on his advice.

With plain carbon steels, hardness is obtained only at a sacrifice of ductility, and vice versa. While they cost more, the more highly alloyed steels containing such other elements as nickel (abbreviated Ni), tungsten (W), cobalt (Co), molybdenum (Mo), chromium (Cr), vanadium (Va), and manganese (Mn) permit much better combinations of the desirable characteristics and are widely used for highly stressed parts, especially where the parts have thick cross sections that require deep hardening. The selection of a steel giving

TABLE 1. HARDNESS CONVERSION TABLE (APPROXIMATE ONLY)

| Brinell Hardness Number | Rockwell | | Shore Scleroscope Number | Tensile Strength 1000 psi |
	C Scale 150 kg 120 Diamond Cone	B Scale 100 kg 1/16 in. Ball		
780	70	..	106	384
745	68	..	100	368
712	66	..	95	352
682	64	..	91	337
653	62	..	87	324
627	60	..	84	311
601	58	..	81	298
578	57	..	78	287
555	55	..	75	276
534	53	..	72	266
514	52	..	70	256
495	50	..	67	247
477	49	..	65	238
461	47	..	63	229
444	46	..	61	220
429	45	..	59	212
415	44	..	57	204
401	42	..	55	196
388	41	..	54	189
375	40	..	52	182
363	38	..	51	176
352	37	..	49	170
341	36	..	48	165
331	35	..	46	160
321	34	..	45	155
311	33	..	44	150
302	32	..	43	146
293	31	..	42	142
285	30	..	40	138
277	29	..	39	134
269	28	..	38	131
262	26	..	37	128
255	25	..	37	125
248	24	..	36	122
241	23	100	35	119
235	22	99	34	116
229	21	98	33	113
223	20	97	32	110
217	18	96	31	107
212	17	96	31	104

TABLE 1. HARDNESS CONVERSION TABLE (APPROXIMATE ONLY) (*Continued*)

Brinell Hardness Number	Rockwell		Shore Scleroscope Number	Tensile Strength 1000 psi
	C Scale 150 kg 120 Diamond Cone	B Scale 100 kg 1/16 in. Ball		
207	16	95	30	101
202	15	94	30	99
197	13	93	29	97
192	12	92	28	95
187	10	91	28	93
183	9	90	27	91
179	8	89	27	89
174	7	88	26	87
170	6	87	26	85
166	4	86	25	83
163	3	85	25	82
159	2	84	24	80
156	1	83	24	78
153	..	82	23	76
149	..	81	23	75
146	..	80	22	74
143	..	79	22	72
140	..	78	21	71
137	..	77	21	70
134	..	76	21	68
131	..	74	20	66
128	..	73	20	65
126	..	72	..	64
124	..	71	..	63
121	..	70	..	62
118	..	69	..	61
116	..	68	..	60
114	..	67	..	59
112	..	66	..	58
109	..	65	..	56
107	..	64	..	55
105	..	62	..	54
103	..	61	..	53
101	..	60	..	52
99	..	59	..	51
97	..	57	..	50
96	..	56	..	49
94	..	52	..	..
92	..	50	..	..

the required strength and hardness at minimum cost and the establishment of a heat-treating schedule to bring out these characteristics is the job of the metallurgist.

Where a hard outer layer is required on a piece, with a softer and more ductile center or core, case hardening or carburizing is used. The part is heated to high temperature, usually for an extended period of time, in contact with one of a number of materials from which the steel absorbs more carbon or nitrogen. Thus the outer layer becomes a higher carbon steel than the core. Usually the part is quenched immediately after case hardening. Case hardening is usually applied to the lower carbon steels, with the result that the outside layer is very hard and wear-resistant while the body remains tough to prevent breaking under impact. Examples of case-hardened parts are wrist pins and spring shackle bolts in automobiles and the races of ball and roller bearings.

INDUCTION HARDENING

Another method of selectively hardening the outside of a steel piece is by means of induction heating, which is covered more fully in Chap. 17. When a piece of metal is placed in a strong, alternating current magnetic-field "eddy currents" are induced in its surface and cause heating. The higher the frequency of the alternating field, the more the eddy currents tend to flow only on the surface, and the shallower is the heating action. By properly selecting the frequency (which may run from 3,000 to 1,000,000 cycles per sec) and the power, and by quenching the piece before the heat has had time to be conducted to the center, surface hardness is obtained while the center is left soft and ductile. The design of the coils which couple the work to the high-frequency generator is very important in utilizing the power efficiently and in confining the heat to the desired area. The high-frequency power may be supplied by a motor generator if the frequencies are in the lower range, while electron-tube oscillators usually are used for frequencies above about 10,000 cycles. The lower frequencies penetrate more deeply and the higher frequencies confine the heat more to the surface. Hardening can be localized not only in the surface but also in any localized areas, such as the teeth of gears and ratchets, the edge of shear blades, and the wearing surfaces of shafts and cams. It is a widely used and economical process for such applications.

FLAME HARDENING

Another method of obtaining surface or localized hardening is by means of an intense flame applied to the points where hardening is required, followed immediately by quenching before the heat has had time to penetrate far below the surface. This may be done manually with very simple equipment or it may be done under closely controlled conditions in automatic equipment. By the latter method it is a widely used and successful method of hardening gears, splines, ratchets, and similar parts.

COLD TREATMENT

It used to be considered necessary to age castings that were to be used for critical uses (such as machine tool beds and engine cylinder blocks) for a season or more out of doors. The yards of foundries were piled up with these castings, where they were submitted to 0 F temperatures in the winter and 100 F temperatures in the summer. This did have the effect of relieving strains so that the parts when machined would remain dimensionally stable. It has now been found that the same results can be obtained in a few hours by subjecting the parts to extreme cold, of the order of −200 F to −250 F, followed by heating to moderate temperature.

These very low temperatures are also most useful in production for obtaining shrink fits of machine parts. A shrink fit of a collar or a flange on a shaft can be obtained either by expanding the outer member by heat until it will slide over the shaft, or by shrinking the shaft by extreme cold. Often the latter is preferable, especially in cases where the outer part might be damaged by the heating or where it is large and difficult to heat.

CLASSIFICATION OF STEELS

The composition of steel usually is designated by a four-digit number based on a system developed by the American Iron & Steel Institute. The last two digits of these numbers indicate roughly the percentage of carbon in "points" or hundredths of 1 percent. The first two digits designate the general alloy classification of the steel. For example, 10 designates plain carbon steels; so, 1020 is a carbon steel with 0.20 percent carbon while 1030 has 0.30 percent carbon.

With slight variations, this system is also used by the Society of Automotive Engineers to designate their SAE standard steels.

The general classifications are as follows:

10—Plain Carbon Steels
11—Free Cutting Steels
13—Manganese Steels
23—25—Nickel Steels
31—33—Nickel-Chromium Steels
40—41—43—48—Molybdenum Steels with varying proportions of Nickel and Chromium
50—51—52—Chromium Steels
61—Chromium-Vanadium Steels
86—87—Nickel-Chromium-Vanadium Steels
92—Manganese-Silicon Steels
93—94—98—Nickel-Chromium-Molybdenum Steels

HEAT TREATING NONFERROUS METALS

Most copper base alloys and aluminum alloys become hard and brittle when they are severely cold worked by forming processes such as deep drawing and extruding or rolling. They can then be annealed or softened, but only certain aluminum and bronze alloys can be rehardened by heat treatment. Heat-treated aluminum in sheets or bars has the treatment or condition indicated by a letter following the alloy designation. A 32 S sheet in its fully hardened condition would be 32 ST, in the annealed state it would be 32 SO and in its "as quenched" condition 32 SW.

This latter terms requires some explanation. Aluminum alloys harden by what is known as "precipitation." After heating to the proper temperature and quenching in water, it is very soft. The hardness develops during an aging period, which for some alloys is several days at room temperature while for others it is a matter of hours at temperatures of 290 F to 360 F. Where it is desired to cold form the material in its soft, or W, condition before it hardens, and this cannot be done immediately, the aging can be arrested or retarded by storing the material at low temperatures of around −40 F. Usually this is necessary only with the room-temperature hardening alloys since those requiring heat can be stored at room temperature for a matter of days or weeks without serious effect.

This cold storage is often done with rivets which should be used in a soft condition and allowed to air harden after they are in place.

Of the copper base alloys, only a few of the bronzes can be hardened by heat treatment. Of these, the most important are aluminum bronze and beryllium bronze, or beryllium copper as it is often called. Excellent characteristics are obtainable from both of these materials, with strength comparable to that of good alloy steels. The aluminum bronze is used in castings and forgings for such things as gears and bearings requiring good hardness and wear resistance. Beryllium bronze is cast for heavy-duty bushings, and in its wrought form is an excellent material for springs, being the best of all nonferrous materials for this purpose.

Fig. 464. The heat-treating department in a large gear plant, consisting of (A) two liquid carburizing furnaces for large and small parts, (B) a neutral salt bath furnace for controlled temperature quenching after carburizing, (C) a hard quenching furnace to control distortion, core, and case hardness, (D) a wash after hard quenching, (E) a furnace for tempering to desired hardness. (Courtesy, The A. F. Holden Company.)

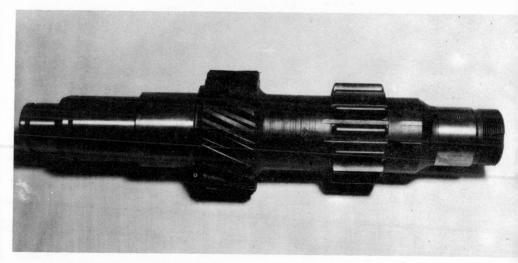

Fig. 465. Typical gear heat-treated in this setup, showing smooth finish and absence of scale. (Courtesy, The A. F. Holden Company.)

Fig. 466. An aluminum brazing and heat-treating furnace with three separate chambers for brazing, solution treatment, and forced cooling. (Courtesy, The Electric Furnace Company.)

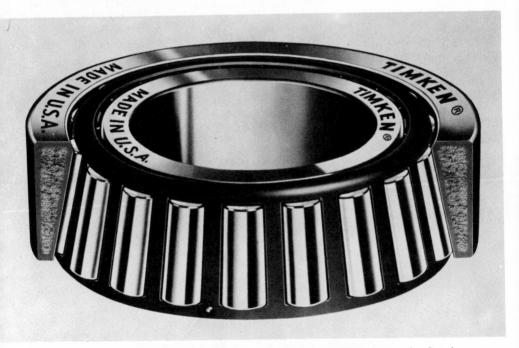

Fig. 467. A cut-away view of a tapered roller bearing showing the case-hardened outer race with a hard dense case and a softer tough core. (Courtesy, The Timken Roller Bearing Company.)

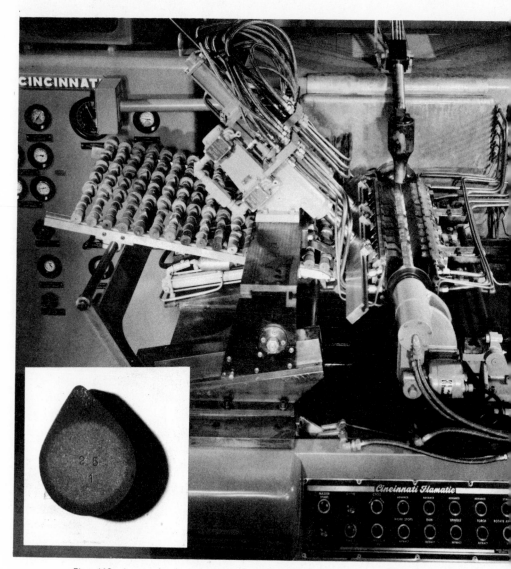

Fig. 468. A completely automatic flame-hardening machine for automobile cam-shafts. The insert is a cross section of one cam showing the hardened exterior and the softer center. (Courtesy, The Cincinnati Milling Machine Co.)

14

Plastics and Their Fabrication

TYPES OF PLASTICS

Within a relatively few years, plastics have taken their place as one of the most important materials of modern production. From their use in a few Celluloid combs and ornaments, they have progressed to the enormous variety of materials now available for everything from fabrics to machine tool parts, from delicate electronic components to 36-ft hulls. So many types and variations of plastics are available, and the field is developing so rapidly, that it is impossible to do more here than outline the principal types of materials and methods of fabrication. Companies having possible applications for plastics would do well to keep in touch with the suppliers of the basic resins and the molders and fabricators of plastic parts for the new developments, which come on almost a day-to-day basis. Plastics are no longer a "substitute" but an important and growing group of basic new materials for industry.

Plastics can be divided into two general groups, *thermoplastic* and *thermosetting*. The thermoplastic materials are those which can be resoftened repeatedly by the application of heat after hardening. In this group are the cellulosics, the styrenes, the vinyls, the acrylics, polyethylene, nylon, and Teflon. Thermosetting materials change chemically during the curing process and cannot be resoftened by additional heating. Thermosetting plastics are the phenolics, the epoxies, the ureas, melamine, and polyester. A list of some of the more commonly used plastics, with an indication of their application, follows:

Cellulose nitrate, sold under the trade names of Celluloid and Pyralin, was the first of the plastics, dating back to 1868. It is tough and can be made in a wide variety of beautiful colors. However, its high flammability seriously limits its usefulness.

Cellulose acetate is another of the older plastics and is still used widely in jewelry, cases, and novelties, where its excellent appearance and wide color range are features and where its inability to stand high temperatures or humidity are not serious drawbacks.

Cellulose acetate butyrate is similar to cellulose acetate but will stand up better under higher temperatures and humidity. It has found wide application as a general-purpose material for parts requiring toughness and high impact strength at moderate temperatures and humidity. It is the only cellulosic material recommended for outdoor use.

Ethyl cellulose is similar in characteristics to butyrate. It is more resistant to acids and alkalis, and, while its resistance to high temperatures is not quite so good, it retains its flexibility and strength at very low temperatures. It is often used for transparent boxes and for wire insulation. Its toughness and impact strength adapt it for certain types of forming dies for sheet metal.

Nylon, which has been used for some time as a textile material and for brush bristles, has now become an important molding and extruding material. It can be used at very high temperatures (300 F to 350 F) and is the toughest of all plastics. These qualities make it ideal for small gears and mechanical parts and for bearings, where it requires little or no lubrication. Its limited color range (usually milky white or black) and its high cost are limiting factors to its wider use.

Methyl methacrylate (trade names, Lucite, Plexiglas) is the clearest of all plastics and has the best light transmission. It also retains this quality very well on aging. It can be molded or cast and is available in standard rods and sheets which can be formed easily at relatively low temperatures. It will not stand high temperatures and becomes brittle at low temperatures, but has found wide use in transparent brush backs, plastic lenses, signs, and for casting around ornamental objects. It is also used for transparent windows and domes on aircraft and the only reason it has not substituted more widely for glass is its cost and its ease of scratching.

Polystyrene has become almost standard for many uses as insulation in radio, television, and electronics because of its excellent electrical characteristics at both low and high frequencies, as well as its low moisture absorption. It has also found wide application in tableware, refrigerator panels, and containers, where its dimensional stability, good color range, and moderate price have made it attractive. A high-impact styrene is also an excellent general-purpose material. The styrenes can be molded and extruded and are available in standard size sheets, rods, and tubes. Clear polystyrene is almost as transparent as methyl methacrylate, but it yellows slightly with age and on exposure to sunlight.

Vinyls are another group of plastics that are used widely in the electrical and electronic industries and as garden hose, phonograph records, and wall and floor coverings. In addition to excellent electrical properties, they are highly resistant to chemicals and to aging. They are used in a flexible form for extruded insulation on wire and for insulating tubing. An extruded vinyl filament is woven into window screening and fabrics. The flexible form is also used for coating fabrics to make artificial leather and similar products and for coating metals with attractive colors and textures that are tough enough to stand severe forming operations. The rigid form is molded into insulators and mechanical parts, such as dials and panels. It is relatively low in cost. A form of vinyl known as *polyvinyl chloride* (PVC) is finding wide use in pipe and fittings for water and oil lines or for use with corrosive liquids.

Fluorocarbons (trade names, Teflon and Kel-F) are among the newer plastics and are outstanding for use in extremes of high and low temperatures. Their moisture absorption is practically zero and their electrical characteristics, especially at high radio frequencies, are excellent. The Teflon type can be used in temperatures from −100 F to 550 F and the Kel-F type from −320 F to 390 F. They are highly resistant to chemicals, and, in addition to their electrical and electronic applications, are used for valve seats, diaphragms, gaskets, and bearings. Teflon resins can be used also to formulate a highly effective release agent which has found use in bakeries and commissaries, since pans and cutters coated with these materials do not require greasing, and dough or other food will not adhere to them. They are difficult to mold and to cement to other materials, and are one of the most expensive of plastic materials. A hazard involved in the machining of Teflon is not as widely known as it should be: when this material is burned, it gives off fumes that can cause serious illness or even death. Normal machining temperatures are not high enough to cause trouble, but if the Teflon dust settles on cigarettes which are smoked later, the results can be serious. All personnel in areas where the material is being machined should be warned about this and no cigarettes should be carried or left exposed where they can become contaminated. Teflon scrap or shavings from machining should not be burned.

Polyethylene has proved to be the fastest growing of all the new plastics. It is a flexible material with a waxy feel and is most familiar in the widely used squeeze bottles. It is also used for plastic pipe, tableware, and flexible sheeting. Its usual color is a milky white; when it is colored, it has a tendency to be streaky, with a dull surface. It retains its flexibility over a wide range of temperatures, from —70 F to 212 F, and is low in cost. A new technique has been developed and is in laboratory use which irradiates polyethylene plastic with high-voltage x-rays to produce an entirely new material of considerable promise. Whereas polyethylene melts at about 230 F, the new material (trade name, Irrathene) will not melt at any temperature, although the strength decreases at high temperatures and eventually it will char and burn. It retains substantial strength up to 390 F, and resists certain solvents that dissolve the original material. It is too early to tell what applications may be found for irradiated polyethylene, or where the technique may lead when applied to other materials.

Silicones are a group of new materials, introduced in 1943, that offer outstanding improvements over other materials in many respects. They withstand higher (about 500 F) temperatures than any of the other plastics except Teflon, which is about equal in this respect. They are highly water-repellent and even small amounts of silicone fluids used in coatings give this characteristic to the coated material. They also form a film that prevents adhesion of other materials, even at high temperatures, and this property is used in a variety of release agents for coating molds used in metal casting and plastic molding. Silicone rubber combines the properties of rubber with the heat resistance of the silicones. Silicone greases retain their lubricating properties at high temperatures. The resins can be molded or extruded, but more often they are used as binders for glass fiber, asbestos, or mica. The electrical characteristics are excellent at high and low frequencies and the material is highly resistant to moisture and most chemicals. Their many excellent properties have found the silicones many uses in spite of their high cost and difficult molding characteristics.

All of the above have been thermoplastic materials. Following is a listing of the more common thermosetting plastics:

Phenolics are the most widely used of all the thermosetting plastics, and are sometimes referred to as the workhorse of the plastic family. They are molded into radio and television cabinets, radio tube bases, appliance handles, clock cases, electrical sockets and insulators, and thousands of other parts that are familiar in our everyday lives. They are hard and rigid and have good heat resistance up to 300 F or more if special fillers are used. While the common phenolics are rather brittle, special high-impact types are available that are excellent in this respect. They are good electrical insulators at low and medium frequencies, and special low-loss types, using powdered mica as a filler, are good at high frequencies. The resin is also used as a binder for laminating paper or fabric to form the sheet material that is a standard component of electronic circuits and is the base for most of the new printed circuits. Electrically, its only weak point is its low resistance to arcing and the fact that it forms a conducting path after an arc has once broken it down. From the point of view of appearance, the phenolics have a good surface finish and luster, but can be made only in the darker opaque colors. A phenolic casting resin is made which is available in all colors. Cast phenolics are also used to make forming dies for sheet-metal work, in which field they share the honors with the much newer (and more expensive) epoxies. Another important application for phenolic resins that is increasing in importance is their use as binders for sand in the shell-molding process of casting metals (see Chap. 1). The molds made from this resin-sand mixture retain their shape even when they are subjected to the heat of the melted metal, which is far above the working temperature of the plastic itself.

Epoxies are some of the newest of plastics. They are used primarily as adhesives, for which purpose they are excellent. They are used as binders for glass fibers or other materials to make a base material for electronic printed circuits (see Chap. 21). They are also used as a binder for metal powders to form plastic fixtures and dies, for which purpose their ability to cure or harden at room temperature is a big advantage. As casting resins, the shrinkage is very low, which has led to their use in plastic forming dies and for embedding electronic components. However, they are expensive, and this has discouraged their wider use.

Alkyds were used originally as resins for synthetic enamels and lacquers, but they are now used also for molding. Their principal use is for electrical insulation, where their excellent electrical properties and high-temperature resistance are important. They stand up exceptionally well in outdoor applications.

Aminos; urea and melamine are used widely in making plastic dishes, buttons, bottle caps, and similar products, where their bright colors and hard, glossy surface give them great eye appeal. They are also used for various types of housings and lighting fixtures, and for laminated table tops. Their low-temperature performance is good and they are good for continuous operation up to 170 F for urea and 210 F in the case of melamine. With inorganic fillers such as asbestos or glass fibers, this may be extended to 350 F or 400 F. The electrical characteristics are good and melamine especially is finding considerable use in this field, where its superior arc resistance has caused it to be substituted for phenolic material. The cost is considerably more than that of phenolics. The resins of urea and melamine are used to make excellent waterproof glues for plywood and marine use.

Polyesters are used primarily as binders for low-pressure laminates to form such products as automobile bodies, boat hulls, building panels, lamp shades, and aircraft parts. For this purpose, the liquid resins are used to impregnate sheets of glass fiber which are then pressed into place over molds or forms to make the desired shape. The resulting pieces are strong and tough, with good surface hardness. Pieces up to 500 sq ft or more in area are made in this way. The water resistance and weathering properties are good, and a wide variety of colors is available. Polyesters are used also with high percentages of fillers for molding compounds which have excellent electrical properties and moisture resistance. The resins are also used for casting and encapsulating, and they may be mixed with short fibrous fillers to make a putty-like mixture for low-pressure molding. In fiber form, polyester resins are sold under the trade name Dacron and in the form of a thin film as Mylar. Polyurethane is a form of polyester that shows excellent possibilities of wider use, especially in coatings and as a soft or rigid foam.

Glass-bonded mica (trade name, Mycalex) is an inorganic material intermediate between a plastic and a ceramic. It is molded like a plastic but has many desirable properties that make it unique among plastics. It can be used at temperatures up to 700 F, which is far above the range of organic plastics. Its electrical characteristics are excellent at both high and low frequencies, and it also rates very high in moisture and solvent resistance, arc resistance, and dimensional stability. In spite of high cost and difficult machining, it has found wide use in electronic equipment for tube sockets and insulators.

Cold-molding plastics are another group of inorganic materials. They are mixtures of asbestos, cement, or clay with water and are molded cold under pressures of 2,000 psi to 10,000 psi and are then cured under steam pressure. They are hard and brittle and have very high moisture absorption unless they are impregnated. They are used mostly for insulation in electrical fixtures.

From the point of view of poundage used, four classes of plastics—the styrenes, the vinyls, the alkyds, and the phenolics—divide almost three fourths of the total plastic market between them. In an industry that is developing as fast as this one, however, these percentages will no doubt change as some of the newer materials are reduced in cost and as new applications are developed for them. It is also probable that alloys of two or more plastics will be developed, just as they have been in metals, and that these alloys may exhibit properties that are superior to any of the single materials from which they are compounded. Mixtures of styrene or phenolic with rubber are in wide use and have outstanding toughness and shock resistance.

PLASTIC PRODUCTION METHODS

Compression molding is the method used most commonly for forming the thermosetting plastics. It is seldom used with the thermoplastics. The plastic resins are supplied in the form of a powder or granules. A measured quantity of this material is placed in an open mold. The mold closes and the plastic is forced under heat and pressure into the shape of the mold. The pressure is held long enough for a chemical change to take place which converts the powder, first into a fluid, and then into a permanently hard, homogeneous material. The pressure, the temperature, and the time vary greatly, according to the shape of the piece and the material used. The size of piece that can be made in a given press is determined by the pressure available, and presses usually are rated in this way. A few presses up to 1500 tons are in use, but these would be economical only for molding very large pieces, such as console television cabinets and air-conditioner housings. In general, temperatures of 270 F to 360 F are used and pressures of 300 psi to 8000 psi, with about 3500 psi being used commonly. The time cycle may be from a few seconds to several minutes for each piece or group of pieces formed in the die. At the end of the cycle, the die opens and the piece is ejected by means of knockout pins or air pressure. Since the pieces are still hot and relatively soft, usually it is necessary to support them in some sort of fixture while they are cooling and the cure is being completed. Metal inserts can be located in the mold by means of pins or recesses and these inserts become a part of the molded piece. With complex pieces, the mold may open in several directions, and cores may be inserted either manually or automatically to form holes or recesses at various angles to the pressure. These cores and the supports for the inserts must be fairly substantial or they will be broken or distorted by the pressure on the powdered resin before it reaches its fluid state.

Transfer Molding. This process, a form of which is known as *plunger molding*, has been developed to minimize the condition just described. It is done on the same type of press as compression molding but the die is made in two sections. The first section or loading chamber is an open die into which the proper amount of powder resin is placed.

The powdered material is often preformed into pellets of the right volume for the piece to be formed and these pellets are heated before being placed in the mold to reduce the time required for the cycle. This chamber is heated, and, as the plunger closes into it, the material is converted into a fluid form. The continued movement of the plunger forces the fluid resin through a small passageway into the final mold, where the cure is completed. By this method, it is possible to form more intricate pieces with inserts and cores more fragile than would be possible with straight compression molding. The molds are, of course, more complicated and expensive, and the cycle is longer.

Injection Molding. This is the process generally used for forming the thermoplastic materials. The granulated resin is placed in a hopper from which a measured quantity is transferred at each stroke of the plunger to a heating chamber. Here the material is melted and then forced out into the closed mold, which has been brought into contact with a nozzle on the end of the heating chamber. The mold is relatively cool (being water cooled if necessary) and the plastic hardens very quickly after the mold has filled. The mold then opens and the finished piece is ejected, usually by means of ejection pins. The pressures used in injection molding are higher than those used for compression molding, being 12,000 psi to 30,000 psi. The time required for each cycle is less, from 3 to 6 complete cycles per minute being the usual rate. Each cycle may form one or several pieces, according to whether a single cavity or a multiple cavity mold is used. Because the cycle is much shorter for injection than for compression molding, the production from each cavity in the die is much greater and the piece cost is considerably less, provided that the thermoplastic materials give characteristics that are satisfactory for the piece being molded. The size of injection presses is usually given by the number of ounces that can be handled at each stroke. Presses range from 2 oz to 48 oz in capacity. Operation of the press may be manual, semiautomatic, or completely automatic.

With all types of plastic molding, the molds are expensive and the piece cost is low, so basically they are quantity production processes. Tolerances vary so much, according to the design of the piece, the material, and the production method, that it is impossible to give general figures that have any meaning. Each project should be discussed with reliable suppliers to make sure that the piece is suitable for the material and the method selected.

Extrusion. The process used to form thermoplastic materials into continuous rods, sheets, tubes, or special shapes is extrusion. The granular material is transferred from a hopper through a long heating chamber by means of a continuously rotating screw. At the end of the heating chamber the now fluid plastic is forced out through an opening of the size and the shape of the piece desired. This ribbon of soft plastic is carried away by a slowly moving conveyor belt, where it is cooled by air or water and cut into the desired lengths. Insulated wires are often made by this process with the wire being passed through the center of the die and the plastic being extruded around it. Many standard shapes are available as extrusions and the dies for special shapes are relatively inexpensive. However, the setup of the machine requires time, and, since the process is very rapid when it is started, usually it is not practical to extrude a special shape unless a considerable quantity is required.

Casting. Casting can be used to form parts of either thermoplastic or thermosetting materials. The material in a liquid or syrupy form is poured into simple molds and cured either by heating or by chemical action. In the case of the thermoplastic materials, they may be poured hot in a melted condition and harden upon cooling. Sheets, rods, and special shapes are often formed by casting, and small production runs of radio cabinets and the like for samples or prototypes can be made in inexpensive lead or plaster molds, or in flexible molds made from plastisols (see p. 309). Plastic forming dies for sheet metal are often cast from phenolic or epoxy or cellulose resins. Ornamental objects can be embedded in blocks of clear acrylic material by a variation of this method. Pressure is not used, but in some cases a vacuum may be applied to the mold, during or after pouring, to eliminate bubbles and voids in the piece.

High-Pressure Laminating. This process is used for making the sheets of insulating material so commonly used in all electrical and electronic equipment. These are formed from sheets of paper, fabric or other base material which have been impregnated with a plastic resin, usually of the phenolic type. These sheets are laid on top of one another until the desired thickness is obtained, after which it is placed between polished steel sheets. A stack of these sandwiches is placed in a hydraulic press and cured under heat and pressure of 1000 psi to 2000 psi. If the material is to be used for printed circuit work, a layer of copper foil is bonded to one or both sides of the plastic while it is being formed. The commonest of these laminates are the paper-base phenolic grades X, XP (the "P" indicates suitability for punching), XX, XXP, XXX, and XXXP. These are of successively better electrical quality. The XXXP with copper foil is the most widely used printed-circuit material. The fabric base grades C, CE, L, and LE are also used widely for their superior mechanical strength, although they have greater moisture absorption. Some of these laminates are made in thicknesses from 0.005 in. up to 10 in. or more. High-pressure laminates can be formed into curved or irregular shapes by laying the impregnated sheets of paper or fabric on a form of the desired shape and applying pressure and heat through a rubber bag, backed up on all sides so that heat and pressure in the form of steam or hot water can be forced in under considerable pressure to squeeze the laminates against the mold and complete the cure. Shaped pieces can also be formed in matching metal dies. The epoxies, the melamines, and some other plastics are also used as high-pressure laminating resins. Many other laminates are made with various base materials and resins for requirements of decorative, electrical, or mechanical properties.

Low-Pressure Laminating. Laminates formed under pressures from zero (no pressure) to 400 psi are low-pressure laminates. Early experiments with low-pressure laminates using phenolic, urea, and melamine resins were not completely successful because these resins require solvents, and, unless the process was controlled very carefully, blisters developed and imperfect adhesion resulted. The polyester and the epoxy resins, on the other hand, can be made as liquids that cure into 100 per cent solids, so practically no shrinkage occurs and there are no solvents to be trapped. This has led to the much wider use of the process in forming boat hulls, automobile bodies, structural panels, aircraft parts, luggage, housings, and many other parts. The reinforcing material may be glass fibers in the form of mats or fabric or it may be various other fibers or paper. It may be in the form of sheets or loose fibers which are saturated with the resins and in some cases are preformed by suction or centrifugal force into roughly the shape required. This is later formed into the final shape in the mold. Excellent strength to weight ratio is obtained and parts of large size can be formed. The molds can be very simple wood or plaster forms for small production, although, for larger production and more accurate parts, matched metal molds are preferable. In the metal molds, and where rubber bags are used to provide a certain amount of pressure, heat is usually applied to cure the resins, but special accelerators and catalysts are available that will permit curing in air at room temperature. So far, the process has been largely a hand operation and the piece cost is high, but, in the production of corrugated structural panels for home and industrial use, it has been made largely automatic. In the production of automobile sport bodies, progress has also been made toward mechanization, with consequent cost reduction. The cost of the plastic bodies is still much higher than metal and probably will continue so unless the cost of the material can be drastically reduced, but the die cost is so much less that it has been found economical for models where the anticipated production is low. On the basis of present costs, it has been estimated that the cross-over point between metal and plastic bodies would be around 15,000 units.

Post-Forming of Thermoplastic Sheets. Several methods for forming are coming into general use for making fairly simple parts of
uniform cross section out of thermoplastic sheets from 0.010 in.
to ⅝ in. or more in thickness. The sheets are heated until they are
soft enough to form easily and are then forced into the desired shape
by one of several means. The three commonest methods are: (a)
the use of a pair of matched molds, (b) a male or female half mold
with air pressure either directly on the plastic or through a rubber
bag, and (c) vacuum or suction forming over male or female molds.
The first two are used where thick material is to be formed or where
the forming is quite severe, requiring deep draws and sharp detail
and forming into undercut recesses. Vacuum or suction forming has
developed rapidly as an inexpensive method of making fairly large
parts out of the thinner sheeting materials from 0.010 in. to 0.300 in.
thick.

The development of high-impact styrene sheets with smooth
white or colored surfaces has greatly broadened the scope of vacuum
forming for three-dimensional displays, refrigerator door panels.
television cabinets and tube masks, and plastic containers. Formable
sheeting is made also from the butyrates, the acetates, the vinyls,
polyethylene, and the acrylics. The acrylics are especially useful in
applications requiring transparency, such as pilot domes on aircraft.
Since the vacuum is only equivalent to 14.7 psi of air pressure, it is
limited in what it can do but within its capacity is very economical;
and simple, low-cost machines have been developed to take advantage of its possibilities. The air pressure and the matched mold
methods are used to form aircraft noses, radomes, and the like and
for luggage and carrying cases. In any of the forming processes the
sheet is usually clamped around the edges, and it is necessary to
trim the piece by means of simple steel-rule dies after it is formed.
Any holes are usually punched after forming because of the distortion that occurs during the forming operation.

Plastisols. These are combinations of plastic resins and plasticizers
in the form of a liquid or a paste. They can be cured by heat to a
tough, rubbery material, and since there are no solvents, little or no
shrinkage occurs in the curing process. The vinyls are used most
commonly as plastisols. They can be cast in molds but are used
more commonly for coatings and for slush molding and dip molding.
For coatings, the plastisol may be applied by spray or dipping, and
it is commonly used for such articles as wire dish racks, egg baskets,

and racks for electroplating and for coating the inside of drums and tanks. Dipping is the most common method of application and the piece is usually heated prior to dipping to partially cure the resin and to give a heavier coating. The thickness of coating may be controlled by the viscosity of the compound, the temperature of the article dipped, and the length of the immersion. Thicknesses of $\frac{1}{16}$ in. to $\frac{3}{32}$ in. are obtained easily at a single dip. If good adhesion is required, a primer is used prior to dipping. The dipping is easily mechanized, a conveyor carrying the parts through a preheating oven, the dipping tank, and a curing oven. The cure requires only 5 min to 15 min at 350 F to 400 F, depending on the type of piece and the coating thickness. Plastisols are available in clear and in all colors.

Plastigels are plastisols whose consistency has been modified by the addition of gelling agents to produce liquids with a more jelly-like consistency or soft putty-like compounds. These make it possible to obtain thicker coatings or to form extrusions or molded parts that retain their shape during the curing process without the need for supporting molds.

Slush Molding and Dip Molding. These processes are really variations of the coating process. In *slush molding*, a female mold is used which is heated, filled with plastisol, and a short period allowed for a layer of the plastisol to form on the inside of the mold. The remaining liquid plastisol is poured out and the cure of the adhering layer is completed in an oven. The cured piece is then stripped from the mold. The outside surface of the finished piece reproduces the mold detail very well, and the process is used for such things as doll heads, storm boots, sparkplug covers, and novelties.

Dip molding is very similar except that a male mold is used and the coating is formed on the outside of the mold by dipping the heated mold in the plastisol. When it is removed, a partially cured layer adheres and the cure is completed in an oven. After curing, it is stripped off the mold. The mold detail is reproduced on the inside of the finished piece although often the piece can be turned inside out to reverse this. Dip moldings are often used as molds for casting other plastic parts and their flexibility enables the castings to be removed from a single piece mold even if there are considerable undercuts in the piece.

Rotation Molding. A variation of slush molding, rotation molding is preferable in many applications. A closed female mold is used, usually made in two halves, and a measured quantity of the plastisol is placed in it. The mold is then closed and rotated in two planes to distribute the plastic evenly over the inside surface of the mold while heat is applied to effect the cure. The parts are more uniform in weight and thickness than those made by slush molding.

Plastisols can also be cast into solid parts with sections up to 2 in. thick in metal molds into which the plastisol may be poured or forced under low pressure. Provision must be made to vent the mold to release entrapped air and to insure sound castings, and also to provide for the expansion and then the contraction of the plastisol that occurs during the curing cycle. This process is especially adapted to small quantities, since the molds are relatively inexpensive and the curing cycle is quite long. In large quantities, injection molding would be cheaper.

Hot-Dip Plastics. These are used primarily for the protection of tools and finished metal parts against rust and mechanical damage in shipment or handling. The resins used are usually of the cellulosic type and are blended with oils and waxes to make them form a heavy coating that can be stripped easily from the coated part. In use they are heated in thermostatically controlled kettles to a temperature of 325 F to 375 F. The piece to be coated is dipped at room temperature into the melted resin and immediately removed. The resin cools almost instantaneously into a soft rubbery coating which does not adhere to the metal but can be easily slit, even with the fingernail, and peeled off. The plastic can be remelted and used repeatedly. The color of the coating varies from clear, which permits markings to be seen underneath, to dark brown. The color tends to darken after long heating. Many taps, drills, reamers, cutting tools, and gages are protected in this way at the factory, and many tool and gage rooms keep a kettle at the window and make a practice of dipping all tools and gages before they are placed in stock. It is especially useful on carbide tools, after grinding, to prevent nicking during handling or storage. It is also often used to protect gears and similar machined parts in the stockroom and for shipment as spare parts.

Foamed Plastics. Foamed plastics are a new development that is finding many uses where extremely light weight and good heat- and sound-insulating properties are advantageous. Many plastics can be used for this purpose, the styrene, the phenolics, polyurethane, and the silicones being in common use. The material may be in the form of beads which expand to many times their original volume upon heating and join together to form a closed cellular structure. Another method is the use of a liquid resin to which a foaming agent is added. This can be formulated to cure at room temperature or by the application of heat. The resulting material may have a density of 2 to 35 lb per cu ft and can have either closed or interconnected cells according to the formulation and the end use. It may be either a rigid material of considerable strength which will support as much as 150 psi to 750 psi, according to the density, or it can be soft with a consistency like sponge rubber, which it is replacing in many applications. The rigid material is used as a core for sandwich construction panels with faces of sheet plastic, metal, or paper. These panels have an extremely high strength to weight ratio and are used primarily for aircraft work. The foaming may be made to take place in simple molds, from which the material can be removed after hardening. In this way, it can form molded insulation around pipes and valves or it can be used to encapsulate electronic assemblies where heavier solid resins might be objectionable because of weight or the danger of disturbing delicate parts. It can also be formed inside irregularly shaped parts like refrigerator doors by simply placing a measured amount of the liquid with the foaming agent, or the beads, in the enclosed space, and allowing it to expand to fill the entire space, after which it is cured in place. It would find even wider use if the cost were not fairly high compared with that of other insulating and structural materials.

Webbing Plastics. Another interesting development which so far has found only limited application is the webbing plastics—liquid plastics of the vinyl type containing solvents and a webbing agent. When sprayed from a standard or special spray gun, the material forms long filaments of the consistency of cobwebs which bridge over considerable distances and form a web-like envelope over an object. It was first used by the Navy to protect guns and exposed machinery on ships that were being put in "mothballs" for storage. After forming the web coating, a heavy coat of liquid plastic is sprayed over the webbing to form a closely fitted air-tight envelope. The material can be formulated to adhere to the coated object or to be easily strippable. It has also been used commercially to form lamp shades over wire frames. It can be made in any color and can be formed over frames of a shape that would be very difficult to cover by other methods. The pattern of the webbing shows through the outer coating of plastic to give a pleasing texture. Modern chairs have been formed by spraying the webbing over a metal frame and then building up a strong thick coating by repeated layers of solid plastic, sprayed on top of the web. Its use has been suggested to form partitions and even small buildings by spraying over wire mesh, but so far the cost has made this a rather expensive way of building.

Plastic Tooling. Plastic tooling is rapidly becoming an important aid to short- and medium-run stamping and forming operations where the cost of permanent steel dies would be excessive. Phenolic or epoxy resins are usually used with or without reinforcement of glass fibers or metal powders. Their most common application is for dies for forming operations on aluminum or thin steel where the forming is not too severe. The mating part may be of steel, plastic, or rubber. The plastic die may be cast in a mold of plaster or lead alloy or may be machined from a solid block much more rapidly than could steel. The cost of plastic dies is often one third or less that of steel, and they are entirely satisfactory for many jobs. They are widely used in the aircraft industry, where they first found acceptance, and are now even being used for certain automobile body parts. In addition to their lower cost, plastic dies have other advantages, such as lower weight and the fact that they do not scratch or score the metal being formed. Since they can be made more quickly than steel dies, tooling time is reduced and production can get under way faster.

Several mixtures of plastic resin and steel powder, of putty-like consistency, are available which can be molded into the desired form and cured to give excellent strength and hardness. These are often time-savers in making special work-holding fixtures, drill jigs, and the like.

Fig. 469. The toy industry is one of the largest users of acetate molding material. This little ballet dancer is a good example. (Courtesy, Celanese Corporation of America.)

Fig. 470. Good examples of acetate toys are these realistic model cars with lacquered authentic two-tone color combinations. Toughness, durability, and lustrous finish of the acetate are important here. (Courtesy, Eastman Chemical Products, Inc.)

Fig. 471. The housing of thi A. C. Gilbert mixer is molded o cellulose acetate because of it high impact strength and lus trous finish. (Courtesy, Celanese Corporation of America.)

Fig. 472. Frames for eyeglasses in many attractive colors and styles are made from extruded sheets of "Lumarith," a special acetate material developed for this purpose. (Courtesy, Celanese Corporation of America.)

Fig. 473. For dealer displays, these giant replicas of the General Electric appliances in the foreground are made from acetate sheeting finished by vacuum metallizing (see Chap. 16) to closely resemble the chrome finish of the originals. (Courtesy, Celanese Corporation of America.)

Fig. 474. This "Hi Prancer" hobby horse will take considerable abuse. It is injection molded of butyrate plastic, complete with saddle and bridle in two opposing halves and permanently cemented together. The red saddle and black trim are painted after molding. High impact strength is a characteristic of butyrate plastics. (Courtesy, Eastman Chemical Products, Inc.)

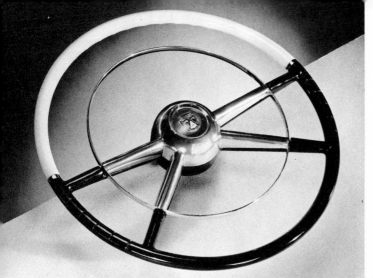

Fig. 475. Butyrate plastic is used for many automobile steering wheels, including this black and white accessory for Ford. It is injection molded in two operations over a steel core. Chrome metal rings, set flush with the plastic, cover the places where the two colors meet. (Courtesy, Eastman Chemical Products, Inc.)

Fig. 476. The colorful new telephones are molded of butyrate plastic, as the bases of the familiar black ones have been for some time. Two-tone color combinations are also available. (Courtesy, Eastman Chemical Products, Inc.)

Fig. 477. Butyrate pipe is used in the oil fields for sour crude oil and salt water disposal lines requiring corrosion resistance. It is light and easy to handle and delivers some 40 percent more fluid than a steel pipe of the same size. (Courtesy, Eastman Chemical Products, Inc.)

Fig. 478. Tough butyrate plastic is widely used for screwdriver and other tool handles. These "Hold-E-Zee" drivers have a screw-holding gripper that recedes into the handle when not in use. (Courtesy, Eastman Chemical Products, Inc.)

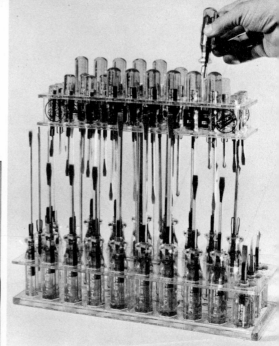

Fig. 479. A group of hospital utensils molded from "Zytel" nylon resins. They are extremely tough and resist sterilization and the chemicals encountered in the medical field. (Courtesy, E. I. du Pont de Nemours & Company.)

Fig. 480. The battery case for this miner's lamp is molded of nylon resin. It is light, tough, and resistant to the alkaline solution used in the battery. (Courtesy, E. I. du Pont de Nemours & Company.)

Fig. 481. Wire braider bobbin of nylon resin resists bending and breakage. (Courtesy, E. I. du Pont de Nemours & Company.)

Fig. 482. These eight cams molded of "Zytel" nylon resin are used to provide a variety of decorative stitches on this sewing machine. Cams and gears are important uses for nylon resins and require little or no lubrication. (Courtesy, E. I. du Pont de Nemours & Company.)

Fig. 483. Ornamental objects embedded in "Lucite" acrylic resin form these attractive book ends. (Courtesy, E. I. du Pont de Nemours & Company.)

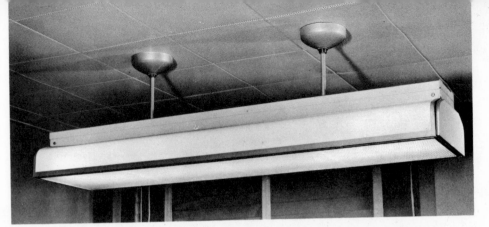

Fig. 484. "Lucite" acrylic resins have excellent light-diffusing properties that make them ideal for use in lighting fixtures. (Courtesy, E. I. du Pont de Nemours & Company.)

Fig. 485. Optical, mechanical, and electrical parts molded from styrene resins. (Courtesy, Catalin Corporation of America.)

Fig. 486. Good electrical and mechanical properties make styrene plastics the choice for these fluorescent light sockets, a group of which are shown as they come from the multiple injection molding die. (Courtesy, Catalin Corporation of America.)

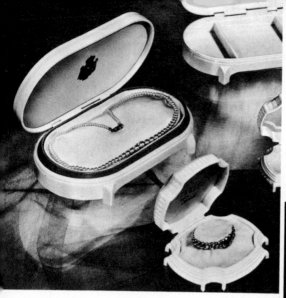

Fig. 487. Attractive color and texture are required for these molded styrene jewel boxes. (Courtesy, Catalin Corporation of America.)

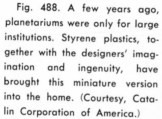

Fig. 488. A few years ago, planetariums were only for large institutions. Styrene plastics, together with the designers' imagination and ingenuity, have brought this miniature version into the home. (Courtesy, Catalin Corporation of America.)

Fig. 489. The flexible drain rail held in the man's hand is one of the largest injection molded vinyl parts made. Lack of odor and ability to retain flexibility at low temperature are important here. (Courtesy, B. F. Goodrich Chemical Company.)

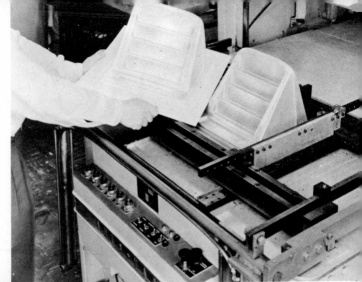

Fig. 490. A display rack formed of vinyl sheeting being removed from a vacuum forming machine. (Courtesy, Chemical Division, The Goodyear Tire & Rubber Company, Inc.)

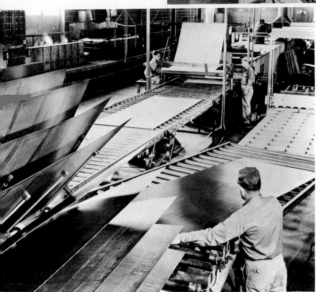

Fig. 491. Vinyl sheeting in a variety of colors and textures is bonded to metal sheets to make "Sullvyne-Clad" laminates. Goodyear resins are used and the bond is so strong that severe forming operations can be performed on the finished sheet to make television cabinets, business machine housings and similar products. (Courtesy, O'Sullivan Rubber Corporation.)

Fig. 492. The cabinet of this CBS television set is made of "Sullvyne-Clad" vinyl coated sheet with an attractive leather grain surface. (Courtesy, O'Sullivan Rubber Corporation.)

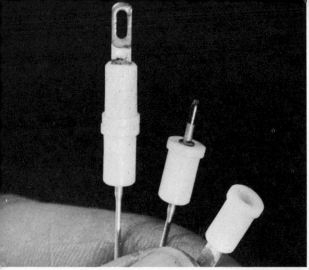

Fig. 493. Miniature insulated connectors made of "Teflon" resin have outstanding electrical characteristics and withstand temperatures as high as 550 F. (Courtesy, E. I. du Pont de Nemours & Company.)

Fig. 494. Polyethylene squeeze bottles for liquids and powders are increasingly popular and are finding many new applications. (Courtesy, The Dow Chemical Company.)

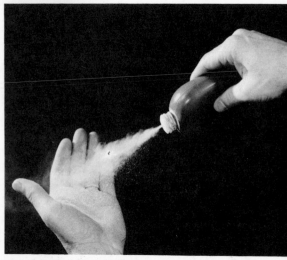

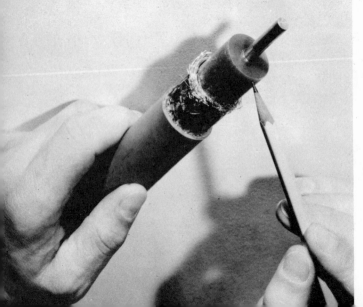

Fig. 495. Insulation on electrical and telephone cables is an important use for polyethylene. (Courtesy, The Dow Chemical Company.)

Fig. 496. This flashlight case molded of polyethylene resin is waterproof and virtually unbreakable. (Courtesy, E. I. du Pont de Nemours & Company.)

Fig. 497. Pipe made of polyethylene is widely used, especially where flexibility and chemical resistance are required. (Courtesy, The Dow Chemical Company.)

Fig. 498

Fig. 499

Fig. 500

Figs. 498–500. Silicone resins are the basis for a long list of water-repellent, heat-resistant, and adhesion-preventive coatings. Fig. 498 shows one for waterproofing leather; others are made for use on masonry and fabrics. Fig. 499 shows a silicone-treated tissue for polishing eyeglasses; others polish automobiles and furniture. Fig. 500 shows a silicone enamel finish (*right*) and a conventional enamel (*left*) on a garbage incinerator cover after a few weeks of service at around 500 F. Other silicone compounds are used for mold release agents and on baking pans and griddles. (Courtesy, Dow Corning Corporation.)

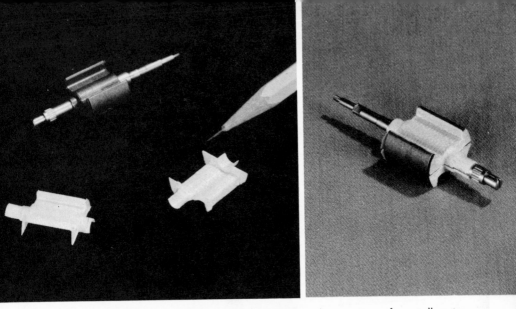

Fig. 501. Silicone glass laminate is used to insulate the armature of a small motor which operates at high temperature. (Courtesy, Dow Corning Corporation.)

Figs. 502–505. Typical parts molded from phenolic resins are radio cabinets (Fig. 502), camera cases (Fig. 503), bottle and jar covers (Fig. 504), and one-piece molded drawers for modern furniture (Fig. 505). (Courtesy, Bakelite Company.)

Fig. 502

Fig. 503

Fig. 504

Fig. 505

Fig. 506. Good mechanical and electrical properties, heat resistance, and glossy surface make phenolic plastics the most widely used for electric fixtures. (Courtesy, Bakelite Company.)

Fig. 507. Dimensional stabili and high impact strength mad phenolic resins the choice f molding this light-proof fil chamber. (Courtesy, Bakeli Company.)

Fig. 508. Attractive dinnerware like this made of "Melmac" melamine resins is now available with decorated surfaces. (Courtesy, American Cyanamid Company.)

Fig. 509. Costume jewelry takes advantage of the beautiful color effects and lustrous surface of melamine or a combination of melamine and urea plastics. (Courtesy, American Cyanamid Company.)

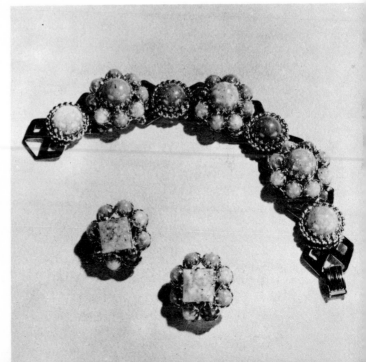

Fig. 510. This film-slide viewer is made of black and white urea plastic. It does not stain from handling and can be cleaned easily. (Courtesy, American Cyanamid Company.)

Fig. 511. This "Sweden Speed Juicer" uses the good features of several plastics. The 4-lb white automatic feed and cover unit is of "Beetle" ® urea molding compound. The 4½-lb base is a phenolic molding, the 1-lb juice bowl is acetate-butyrate, and the safety switch cam is of nylon resin. (Courtesy, American Cyanamid Company.)

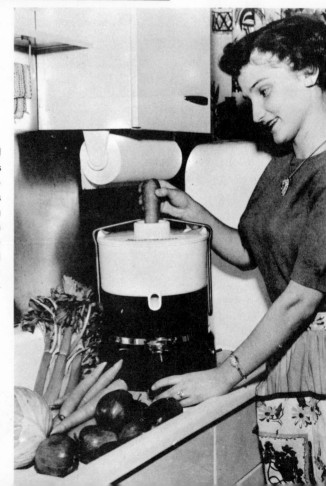

Fig. 512

Figs. 512–513. Glass-bonded mica is the only truly inorganic plastic and has many of the desirable qualities of both plastics and ceramics. These "Mycalex" parts are molded from this material, some with metal inserts. Fig. 513 shows some parts machined from standard sheets and rods. (Courtesy, Mycalex Corporation of America, Clifton, N. J.)

Fig. 513

Fig. 514. Removing plastic tumblers from a 150-ton semiautomatic compression molding press. (Courtesy, F. J. Stokes Machine Company.)

Fig. 515. This automatic injection molding machine requires no attention other than the loading of the hopper and the removal of finished parts. (Courtesy, F. J. Stokes Machine Company.)

Fig. 516. A plastic tube emerges from an extrusion press. (Courtesy, F. J. Stokes Machine Company.)

Fig. 517. Sections of typical rigid plastic extrusions showing wide variations possible in size, cross section, and surface finish. (Courtesy, Sheffield Plastics, Inc.)

Fig. 518. A 2000-ton press for the high-pressure lamination of paper- or fabric-base plastic sheets. The steam-heated platens are 42 in. x 83 in. (Courtesy, R. D. Wood Company.)

Fig. 519

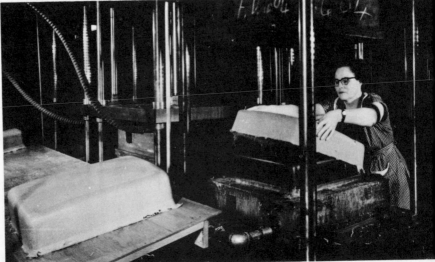

Fig. 520

Fig. 521

Figs. 519–521. This attractive line of "American Tourister" luggage is molded of glass and cellulose fibers and plastic resin binders. The material is preformed and then molded under high pressure in steel dies (Fig. 520). The covering is then bonded to the shell under heat and pressure in another die (Fig. 521). The complete line required a total of 81 dies. (Courtesy, American Luggage Works, Inc.)

Fig. 522. Boats like this 14-footer, mass-produced from glass fiber and plastic laminates, have much to do with the current wave of public interest in boating. (Courtesy, Winner Manufacturing Co., Inc.)

Fig. 523. An automatic machine for forming thermoplastic sheet by suction, vacuum, or mechanical methods. Sheets up to 24 in. x 60 in. and ¼ in. thick can be handled with fully automatic heating, feeding, forming, cooling, and ejection. (Courtesy, Borkland Laboratories, Marion, Indiana.)

Fig. 524. A semiautomatic suction or vacuum forming machine for sheets up to 24 in. x 24 in. and 0.040 in. thick. The feeding and the loading are manual; stroke and removal of part from die are automatic. (Courtesy, Borkland Laboratories, Marion, Indiana.)

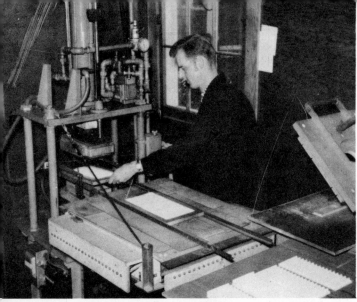

Fig. 525. A simple manual sheet forming machine for small work. The heating frame is at the right. (Courtesy, Borkland Laboratories, Marion, Indiana.)

Fig. 526. Displays of various types form an important application for suction or vacuum forming. (Courtesy, Borkland Manufacturing Co., Marion, Indiana.)

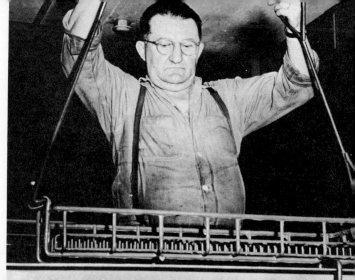

Fig. 527. A vinyl plastisol is used to coat this conveyor basket through a trichlorethylene degreasing bath. Electroplating racks are also commonly coated with this material. (Courtesy, B. F. Goodrich Chemical Company.)

Fig. 528. A vinyl plastisol compound in the form of a heavy liquid is used to seal the spot-welded joints in automobile bodies. The compound fuses and cures during subsequent paint-baking operations. (Courtesy, B. F. Goodrich Chemical Company.)

Fig. 529. A vinyl plastisol with a gelling agent makes a putty-like compound which is here being applied to a plating rinse tank for protection from corrosive chemicals. (Courtesy, B. F. Goodrich Chemical Company.)

Fig. 530

Figs. 530–532. Hot-dip plastics are used for temporary protection of tools and finished work. The compound is heated to around 350 F in thermostatically controlled kettles, at which temperature it is liquid. Parts dipped in it are covered with a thick coating (Fig. 531) which can be easily stripped off (Fig. 532). The material can be remelted and used over. (Courtesy, Chem Products, Inc.)

Fig. 531   Fig. 532

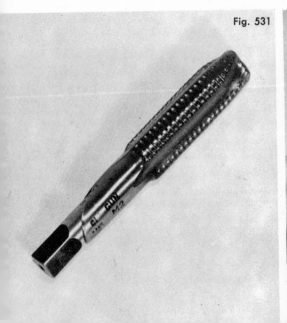

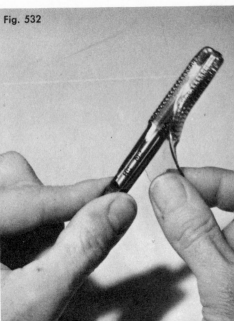

Fig. 533

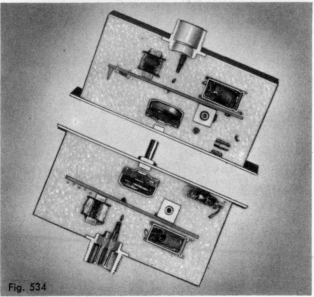

Fig. 534

Figs. 533–537. Polyester resins can be mixed with a foaming agent to form a lightweight foamed-in-place material for various insulating and stiffening purposes. Fig. 533 shows "Lockfoam" being used to encapsulate an electronic assembly. Fig. 534 is a cross-sectional view of this assembly, showing how the foam completely fills every crevice. Figs. 535 and 536 show the material used for heat insulation on a food container. Fig. 537 shows the cross section of an aileron with a rigid foam plastic used for stiffening. (Courtesy, Nopco Chemical Company, Inc.)

Fig. 535

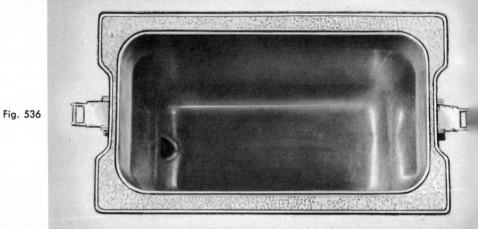

Fig. 536

Fig. 537

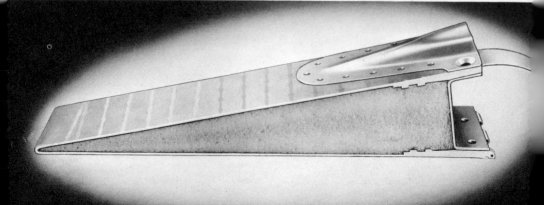

Fig. 538. The polystyrene beads on the scale at the left are expanded by heat alone to form the pile of expanded plastic blocks on the right, having exactly the same weight. (Courtesy, Koppers Company, Inc.)

Fig. 539. Expanded polystyrene beads are used for insulation on the bowl, hopper, and gear case of this counter type "Snow Ice" machine made by Brockman Tool and Manufacturing Company. The insulation is molded in place around the castings. (Courtesy, Koppers Company, Inc.)

Fig. 540. Plastic foam is both practical and attractive as a packaging material. (Courtesy, The Dow Chemical Company.)

Fig. 541. "Styrofoam" plastic foam is made in sheets and blocks for insulation of walls and under floors. It is here being cemented to an exterior brick wall. (Courtesy, The Dow Chemical Company.)

Fig. 542. A machine being prepared for storage with COCOON ® webbing plastic. Tape has been applied around the high points and the web is being built up with the spray gun until it forms a continuous coating, as shown at the lower right. (Courtesy, R. M. Hollingshead Corporation.)

Fig. 543. Machines, such as these, protected with webbing plastic, may be stored outdoors indefinitely and remain in perfect condition. (Courtesy, R. M. Hollingshead Corporation.)

Fig. 544. Dies for pre-production models in the automobile industry commonly are made from plastic to save time and cost. This draw die for a luggage compartment cover was made in 6 weeks from Rezolin die compounds based on Bakelite epoxy resins. (Courtesy, Bakelite Company.)

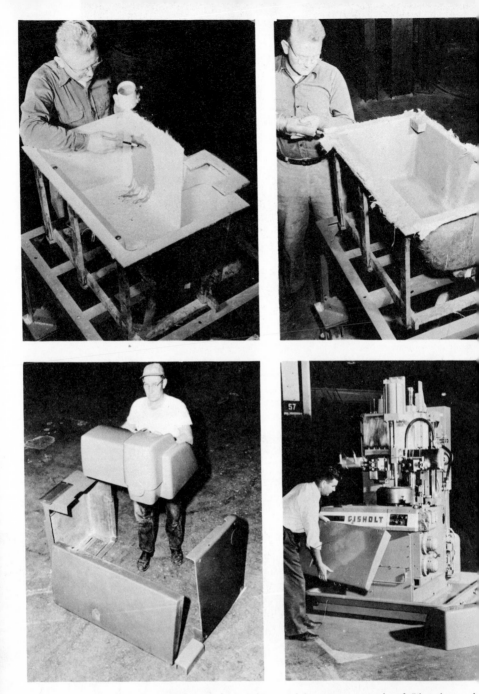

Fig. 545. Five sections of this machine tool housing are made of Fiberglas and polyester resins formed in plastic molds by a vacuum bag method. The mold is made of Rezolin Toolplastik compounds based on Bakelite epoxy resins. No finishing is required and a saving of 263 lb in weight is realized. (Courtesy, Bakelite Company.)

Fig. 546. Phenolic as well as epoxy resins are used for plastic tooling. This large forming die was made entirely from phenolic resins which cost much less than epoxy. Where sharp contours are required only in small areas, the phenolic is chipped away and inserts of the stronger epoxy material are cast in place. In some cases, an epoxy surface ⅛ in. to ¼ in. thick is cast over the entire surface of the phenolic. (Courtesy, The Marblette Corporation.)

Fig. 547. Phenolic casting resin is used to make a master for use in a three-dimensional pantograph machine (see Chap. 5) which is here cutting a multiple steel die for injection molding. The Marblette casting resin is poured over a lead original to form the master. (Courtesy, The Marblette Corporation.)

Fig. 548

Fig. 549

Figs. 548–549. Dies for vacuum forming of thermoplastic
sheets are made easily by casting in plaster molds. Fig. 548 is
such a die made from Marblette
phenolic resin and shows the
sharp detail obtainable. Fig. 549
shows the forming of displays in
a larger die of this type; note
that the sheets are printed in
colors before forming. (Courtesy,
The Marblette Corporation.)

15

Adhesive Bonding

The use of adhesives for the assembly of furniture, for bonding plywood, and in the manufacture of paper and cardboard products has been standard procedure for many years. The materials used for this work were mostly animal glues (fish, hide, bone, and sinew) and vegetable glues such as the starches. These were of adequate strength for the materials being joined, but had very poor moisture resistance. Also, their adhesion to nonporous surfaces is very low.

Great progress has been made in recent years in the development of new adhesives and their use, especially as a means of joining metal parts, where strengths approaching those of riveted or spot-welded joints are obtainable under favorable conditions of design. Even in aircraft construction, where the greatest strength and reliability must be obtained, cemented joints are being used with increasing frequency. Structural panels of great rigidity and very light weight are made by cementing sheets of aluminum to both sides of a honeycomb core made of cemented paper, plastic, wood veneer, or metal. In some cases, even parts of the fuselage and wing members are being joined by adhesives instead of the conventional welding or rivets. This makes possible reduced labor cost and less air resistance, due to the smoother surface and the absence of projecting rivet heads. Cemented joints must be designed properly and used only where the stresses are such that they adapt themselves to the strength and not the weaknesses that are characteristic of the method. Some of these considerations will be outlined later in this chapter.

The joining of metal to metal and porous substances to metal is done almost entirely by adhesives of the plastic and rubber types, and many resins have found application for these purposes. Because of the wide variations possible with each type of resin, it is difficult to generalize on the uses or the characteristics of a given type.

When a critical or difficult problem concerning adhesives is to be solved, manufacturers of various types of adhesive materials should be called on for recommendations and samples requested for test under the actual conditions involved.

TYPES OF ADHESIVES

The following is a brief outline of the more commonly used types of adhesives:

Animal glues are available in either the liquid form, for use at room temperature, or as granules or flakes, which are mixed with water and used hot. They are still used to a large extent in woodworking applications and for the manufacture of sandpaper and other coated abrasives, but are being supplemented in many applications by the various synthetic resins. This is not only because of the better moisture resistance of the synthetics but also because their much faster curing time fits in better with modern production schedules. This is especially true when heat is used in the curing process.

Vegetable glues, such as starches and dextrin, are cheap and are commonly used in the manufacture of paper products. They are also used occasionally for wood joining. Tapioca is a starch adhesive used on postage stamps.

Casein is another of the older adhesives and is derived from milk. It is used to quite a large extent in the woodworking and the paper industries. It has good adhesion to these porous materials and the moisture resistance is superior to animal glues but still far below that of the synthetic resin adhesives. All of the animal and vegetable glues are subject to attack by fungus under conditions of high temperature and humidity.

Sodium silicate is low in cost and has very high heat resistance. The adhesion to glass and paper is good, so it is often used for attaching labels to bottles and also for paper box work. Mixed with inorganic fillers such as fuller's earth, it forms a high-temperature cement for use on electric heaters and similar devices.

Natural and synthetic rubbers combined with solvents are used very widely for joining rubber, felt, or paper to metal, and have good adhesion to most porous or nonporous substances. However, they remain more or less flexible and do not develop the strength of some of the other plastic cements. An elastomer of phenolic resins has similar flexibility and greater solvent and heat resistance. It has good strength and is often used for metal to metal bonding.

Phenol-formaldehyde adhesives are among the most widely used of all the plastics and are available either as liquids or as dry sheeting. Some of the liquids cure at room temperature but most of these and the sheeting require heat and pressure. The latter gives by far the strongest and the most reliable bonds. They are used for bonding plywood and furniture and for rubber and plastics, but are not very good for metals or glass. Other phenolic compounds, such as phenol acetals and phenolic polyamide, are excellent metal adhesives, however. The phenolics are thermosetting materials, so they have good heat resistance. Their water resistance is also good.

Urea-formaldehyde resins are the base for a group of widely used adhesives. They make strong bonds with wood and porous substances, but are not good for metals or glass. These, as well as the phenolics, are used very generally for the bonding of plywood as well as for making assemblies of wood parts. They are less expensive than the phenolics.

Resorcinol resins make adhesives with excellent resistance to water and solvents, heat and cold. They also bond well with porous materials, but not with metal. They are more expensive than the phenolics or the ureas, but have better moisture resistance.

Alkyd resins make good adhesives for porous materials with fair adhesion to metal. The "Glyptol" cements are of this class and are widely used in the electrical and the electronics industries.

Vinyl resins, in wide variety, are used as adhesives, and some of them—notably vinyl acetate and vinyl butyral—have excellent adhesion to metal and glass. One of the largest uses is in the manufacture of safety glass. The vinyls have excellent electrical characteristics, and a vinyl solution is often used for coating and cementing coils for radio-frequency work.

Emulsions of polyvinyl resins in the form of a milk-white liquid glue have come into wide use as general-purpose wood adhesives where heat is not available for curing. They keep well, make a strong bond, and in most cases the work need be left in the clamps only 20 min or so.

The acrylics have characteristics similar to the vinyls but their adhesion to metal is not so good. These are the most transparent of all the plastics, and this is an advantage in some applications. Some of the acrylics are also used in pressure-sensitive adhesives.

Cellulose derivatives have been used for many years as adhesives with good results. One common example is the "Duco Cement" found in most household tool boxes which is based on cellulose nitrate resins. The adhesion to metal and glass is only fair, but for more porous materials it is quite good. It dries quickly by evaporation of the solvents and has good moisture resistance, but, like all adhesives based on thermoplastic resins, its heat resistance is low.

Melamine resins make excellent adhesives for porous materials with good resistance to water and solvents. The bond is exceptionally strong.

Polyester resins are used most generally as binders for glass fiber or other base materials in low-pressure molding, as discussed in Chap. 14 on plastics. In fact, these low-pressure moldings may be properly considered as fibers bound together with adhesives rather than reinforced plastics. Polyesters have the great advantage, for this and some other adhesive applications, that no solvents are necessary, so they cure almost without shrinkage. Their bond to metal is only fair, although an elastomer of this resin is excellent in this respect.

Polyurethane resins, which are among the newer forms of polyester, show most promising results as adhesives for metal and glass. They seem certain to find important uses in the near future.

Epoxy resins in the last few years have become very important as adhesives with outstanding characteristics. They show most excellent adhesion to almost all materials, including metal and glass, and are extremely resistant to water and solvents. Epoxy, like polyester, can be formulated without solvents, so practically no shrinkage occurs and even poorly fitted joints show good strength. The epoxies are used quite generally for bonding copper foil to plastic laminates for use in electronic "printed circuits" (see Chap. 21). Epoxies are still quite high in price.

Silicone is also used as an adhesive where heat resistance is a factor. It is the best of all plastic materials in this respect, although the cost is high.

APPLICATION OF ADHESIVES

In the design of adhesive bonded joints, especially in metals, several factors must be kept in mind. The joints are strongest in shear strength, weakest against a peeling strain. When lapped joints are used, between two metal sheets, the lap should be as wide as possible—preferably 1 in. or more. With all adhesives, the parts should be well fitted and the adhesive film kept as thin as possible. Joints bonded with plastic cements loose strength rapidly at high temperatures, especially when thermoplastic resins such as cellulosics, vinyls, and acrylics are used. Even with the thermosetting resins, such as the phenolics, the ureas, melamine, epoxy, and polyester, the temperature is a serious limitation to the use of adhesive-bonded joints for metal structures. The upper limit for useful strength with the phenolics is about 350 F, with the thermoplastics about 200 F, and up to 500 F with the silicones. The only adhesives that are good at higher temperatures are the silicates, especially sodium silicate (water glass). Its bond strength is not high compared with that of some of the plastics, but it holds this strength well, even up to 1000 F. Cements made of sodium silicate and inorganic fillers hold their strength at much higher temperature.

Shear strength up to 3000 psi are regularly obtained with lap joints between metal sheets using adhesives under carefully controlled conditions. This method is being used for attaching stiffening members to the inside of wing and fuselage sections in aircraft and for making extremely light and rigid panels of sandwich construction, with honeycomb cores, for use as floors and partitions in aircraft and in marine and automotive trailer construction. The preparation of the metal surface before application of the adhesives is extremely important. By careful attention to this factor, and under laboratory conditions, bond strengths up to 7000 psi have been obtained with epoxy adhesives.

Adhesive bonding is useful not only for the large area parts mentioned previously but also for the assembly of small, delicate instruments where other processes would cause damage to the components. With modern, high-strength adhesives, assembly of metal, plastic, and ceramic parts by this process is entirely practical and reliable. No doubt its use will increase as the possibilities become better realized and still further improvements are made in materials and techniques.

Since adhesives vary so much in their characteristics and uses, there is also a wide variety in the methods of applying them. Most common are spray or brush application and roller coating. Where heat and pressure are to be used for curing, the use of adhesive in sheet or film form, for insertion between the parts to be bonded, is also an excellent method. This is often used in the bonding of plywood. For the assembly of furniture and wooden cabinets where the adhesive must often be applied to tongue and groove, mortise and dowel joints, application by a hand gun with the adhesive under air pressure is often most efficient. Various nozzles and spreaders are available for these guns to control the flow of adhesive and to spread it just where it is wanted. Some adhesives are applied as a solution, the solvents are allowed to evaporate, and the actual bonding is done either by moistening the surfaces with a solvent, or by means of heat and pressure without solvents. The strongest joints are made by the latter method.

Thermosetting adhesives that are formulated without solvents or that depend on curing by chemical reaction rather than by evaporation, are usually furnished in the form of two liquids or a liquid and a powder that are mixed together just before use. These materials usually keep for months or even years before mixing, but the "pot life" after mixing is quite short. This varies, with the particular formulation, from a matter of minutes to a few days. In general, the faster curing materials have a short pot life, and vice versa. This factor should be considered in selecting a material and setting up a process for a production bonding operation.

Certain adhesive formulations involve hazards in the matter of flammability, and dangers to personnel through skin contact or inhalation of fumes that should be understood thoroughly before a procedure is established. Most of these are not serious if proper attention is given to ventilation, protection from ignition, and the use of gloves and masks for operators where they are indicated. The manufacturers of the adhesives used are well qualified to give advice about the precautions necessary, if any, and should always be consulted about this.

SEALANTS

Sealants are related to adhesives and it is often difficult to determine just where the line is drawn. The primary function of a sealant is to fill small crevices between parts of an assembly where other fastenings are depended on for mechanical strength. They are widely used in the automotive industry, where spot-welded body joints are made weatherproof by means of sealants, and in the aircraft industry, where pressurized cabins must be made air-tight.

Many of the same compounds that are used for adhesives are also used for sealants, but, in general, the formulation is modified to give a heavier body and to retain a certain amount of flexibility after hardening. Good adhesion to the base material is required, but no great strength within the material itself. Some sealants are designed to be applied to metal surfaces prior to spot welding. The welding current breaks through the sealant film to form the weld, but the material around and between the welded spots remains and fills the gap to form a water- and air-tight joint.

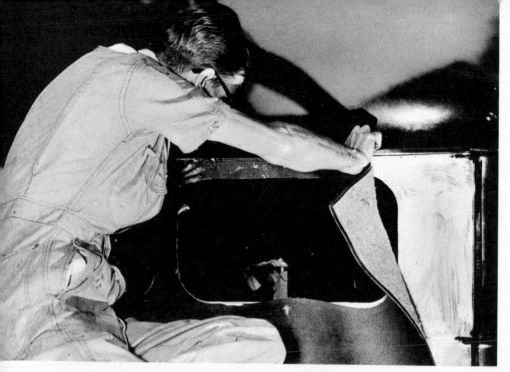

Fig. 550. A vinyl-coated jute lining is attached permanently to a truck cab by means of a water dispersion resin adhesive at the Diamond T. Motor Car Company. (Courtesy, Minnesota Mining & Mfg. Co.)

Fig. 551. Pressed fiber board is bonded to an enameled steel frame in a simple jig. Both parts are precoated with a contact adhesive. (Courtesy, Minnesota Mining & Mfg. Co.)

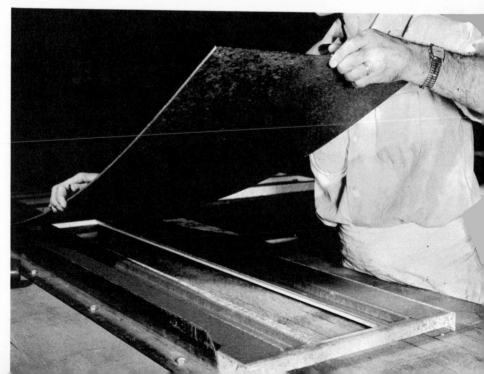

Fig. 552. A production bonding operation of fish paper grills to perforated aluminum strips at Dictaphone Corporation. (Courtesy, Minnesota Mining & Mfg. Co.)

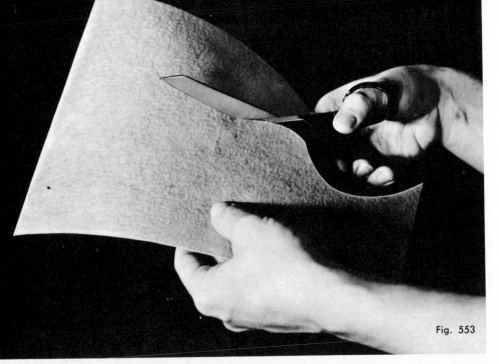

Fig. 553

Figs. 553–556. A new "Plymaster" adhesive film supported by glass mat can be cut with ordinary shears (Fig. 553). Placed between two sheets of aluminum (Fig. 554) or between sheets of polyester board, aluminum and vinyl (Fig. 555) and bonded under heat and pressure, it furnishes a most convenient method of making high strength joints. Fig. 556 shows a rigid, light-weight panel made by bonding an aluminum sheet to each side of an aluminum honeycomb core. Panels like this find wide use in the aircraft industry. (Courtesy, Rubber & Asbestos Corp., Bloomfield, N. J.)

Fig. 55

Fig. 555

Fig. 556

Fig. 557

Fig. 558

Figs. 557–559. Three steps in the making of copper-clad laminated plastic sheets for electronic printed circuits (see Chap. 21). A sheet of copper foil coated with adhesive, is laid on a polished press platen (Fig. 557). Layers of resin-impregnated paper are placed on top of this and another sheet of adhesive-coated copper foil (if required) on top (Fig. 558). These "sandwiches" are loaded into the press to be cured under heat and pressure (Fig. 559). (Courtesy, Rubber & Asbestos Corp., Bloomfield, N. J.)

Fig. 559

Fig. 560

Fig. 561

Figs. 560–562. Another new epoxy-based, metal-to-metal adhesive, in paste form, can be used just as it comes from the container (Fig. 560) without the addition of an accelerator or a catalyst. It is 100 percent solids and can be used to form thick or thin joints which cure by heat without appreciable shrinkage (Fig. 561). Fig. 562 shows a ceramic bushing bonded to a metal ring with this material. (Courtesy, Rubber & Asbestos Corp., Bloomfield, N. J.)

Fig. 562

Fig. 56[3]

Figs. 563–564. This aluminum radar unit trailer, built by Thompson Trailer Corp., requires all joints to be waterproof even when submerged. A sealant is applied, as shown in Fig. 564, before the skin panels are riveted in place. The sealant is flowed over the rivet holes so the rivets are sealed as they are forced through it. When the rivets are tightened, the sealant spreads and fills all voids between the metal surfaces. (Courtesy, Minnesota Mining & Mfg. Co.)

Fig. 564.

16

Finishing Processes

The finish of any products intended for sale to the public or to industry is much more important than is often realized. The first impression of a product is based on appearance, and if the appearance creates the impression of a finely made, quality product, the sale is often more than half made. On the other hand, if the finish is poor or unattractive, even though the device may be well designed and sturdily built, it requires a lot of salesmanship to overcome the first bad impression. In competitive products, sold to the public, appearance is very often the one deciding factor in a choice among several makes. It is not surprising, therefore, that great attention has been given to finishing methods and that the finishing often accounts for a large part of the total cost of consumer products. It is sometimes hard for engineers to realize the necessity of this emphasis on appearance, but everyone concerned with design, production, or sales should understand its importance and should be familiar with the latest developments in finishing processes.

CHEMICAL CLEANING

This is a very important preliminary to most of the finishing processes, especially on metal parts. If cleaning is not done properly, the finish will usually be a failure. Many variations are used, some of which are patented and available under license. The commonest basic methods are the use of solvents or alkali solutions to remove grease, and the use of strong acids to remove rust and scale. Often both an alkali and an acid dip are used with thorough rinsing between dips and after the last one.

The solvent cleaners are very effective in removing most oil and grease and may be either petroleum products such as naphtha and Stoddard solvent, or chlorinated solvents such as trichloroethylene.

The former are less expensive but involve a serious fire hazard. Either type may be used by simple immersion, by a pressure spray, or in vapor degreasing equipment. In the latter case, the pieces to be cleaned are placed in racks in open tanks over the heated solvent. The solvent vapor condenses on the cold workpieces and drips back into the tank, carrying the grease with it.

An expensive but highly efficient method of cleaning small, precision parts is by immersion in a tank of solvent that is agitated by means of ultrasonic waves (see Fig. 567). These waves are generated electronically and are similar to sound waves, but of much higher frequency, so they are inaudible to the human ear. When properly applied to liquids, they cause a "cold boiling" action that forces the solvent into every crevice of the work and loosens the dirt more effectively than any other method. (See Chaps. 8 and 11 for other uses of ultrasonics.)

The commonest and the least expensive method of removing grease and oil is by means of alkali solutions in water. The solution is usually heated to 150 F or 200 F and the work immersed in it. The solution is often agitated by air or mechanical means to reduce the cleaning time. Large parts or machines are often cleaned by means of jets of steam containing a weak alkali. This is usually done with a portable steam generator called a high-pressure Jenny, and the steam jet is directed by hand against the work.

In production, parts may be carried through a tunnel where the solvent or alkali solution is sprayed against them from all sides under considerable pressure. This is very effective in making the cleaning solution operate more rapidly.

Another method of making the alkali solution more rapid and effective in its action is electrolytic cleaning. An electric current is passed to or from the piece to be cleaned and an inert anode or cathode in the solution. This causes gas to be released from the metal with a bubbling action which is very effective in removing hardened grease and dirt. Care must be used with this process to avoid excessive etching of the surface.

With all alkali cleaning methods, care must be used to rinse the piece thoroughly after cleaning since any alkali left on the surface would interfere with the future finishing operations. Great care should be used in cleaning aluminum with an alkali solution since a strong alkali dissolves this metal very rapidly. Therefore, the solution must be relatively weak, not too hot, and its contact with the aluminum continued only long enough for the desired cleaning. The electrolytic process should not be used with aluminum.

Acids are used for a "pickling" operation to remove rust and scale from iron or steel parts, especially castings and forgings. The acids most commonly used are sulfuric and hydrochloric, usually in a hot solution. The operation must be controlled carefully to avoid excessive etching action on the metal, and also to avoid the embrittlement that is often troublesome on carbon steels. A number of commercial inhibitors are available which help control the action of pickling baths. Electrolytic methods of pickling are sometimes used, usually by one of several patented processes. They are especially effective on certain alloy steels that develop a scale that is very difficult to remove by other methods.

PLATING PROCESSES

Electroplating may be used for any one of several purposes: (1) appearance; (2) corrosion resistance; (3) electrical conductivity; (4) wear resistance.

For appearance, the most commonly used materials are nickel, chromium, gold, silver, and brass. These also serve to resist corrosion, but, where appearance is not the primary function of the plating, we also find more common use of cadmium, zinc, copper, and tin. For electrical and electronic purposes on switch contacts and conductors for high radio frequencies, where surface conductivity is important, silver is used most commonly. Sometimes a light plating of rhodium over nickel is used on switch contacts for a combination of wear and low contact resistance. For wear resistance on cutting tools and dies and wearing surfaces, chromium plating is very generally used.

All electroplating is done by passing a direct current of low voltage and high amperage from an anode or positive electrode, through a liquid solution, to a cathode or negative electrode which consists primarily of the piece to be plated. The plating metal comes from the anode or from metal salts in the solution or both. Metals vary greatly in the ease with which they can be plated, copper and silver being the easiest. A very light "flash" of copper or silver can even be obtained by dipping in a solution of the metal salts, without the use of electric current. The coating obtained in this way is so thin that it has very limited usefulness.

In most plating, anodes of the plating metal are immersed in a solution of the metal salts along with the piece to be plated. As the metal is deposited out of the solution, it is replenished by the dissolving of the anodes, due to the electrolytic action. In the case of chromium, inert lead anodes are used and all the metal from the plating comes from the chromic acid solution.

Certain inherent difficulties are present in all electroplating which must be recognized. The deposition of the metal depends entirely on the flow of electric current, and this flow depends on the distance between the anode and the workpiece at each point on its surface. Where this distance is less, the current flow is greater and the plating builds up faster. Where a plating of uniform thickness is required, it is necessary to make the distance between the cathode and the workpiece as uniform as possible, and this is usually done by using an anode that is shaped to conform as closely as possible to the shape of the work. If this is not done, the plating will not "throw" into corners and recesses and these portions will be left without protection. The design and the location of the anodes to give proper coverage to work of complicated and irregular contour involves much skill and ingenuity on the part of the plater. Modern electroplating is not only a skilled craft, but also a highly developed science, involving chemistry, electricity, and metallurgy. Close controls are kept of the temperature of the bath, the chemical composition, the current density, and the composition of the metal anodes. All of these factors, and more, contribute to consistent plating to meet present standards.

Barrel Plating. This is a method of finishing small parts such as screws, nuts and small stampings, and screw machine parts. The parts to be plated are placed in a perforated drum or barrel, usually of hexagonal or octagonal shape, and rotated slowly in the plating solution. The cathode connection is made to the work by means of a series of bars within the barrel and the anodes are in the solution, outside of the barrel. They are often curved to fit around the barrel. The continuous motion exposes various parts of the small pieces to the solution to insure a reasonably uniform plating. The parts rolling over each other have a burnishing action which gives a smooth surface. Barrel plating is standard practice for plated screws and other hardware items and is an economical method for finishing any small metal parts that will not be damaged by the tumbling action.

In all plating, thorough cleaning and preparation of the metal surface is essential to a successful job. Where appearance is an important factor, the metal must be buffed to a fine smooth surface before plating. All trace of oil and grease must be removed chemically. Most bright platings require additional buffing after plating. Nickel is the most widely used material for decorative purposes. It is usually plated over copper and gives a dense coating, free from porosity that resists corrosion and takes a fine polish.

Bright chrome plating consists of a very thin coating (a few hundred thousandths of an inch) of chromium over copper and nickel. The nickel is usually buffed to a fine polish, but the chromium as a rule does not require any final buffing; in fact, the chromium is so hard that buffing is very difficult. The so-called "hard" chrome platings that are used for wear resistance are deposited directly on steel and are much thicker, from a few ten thousandths to several thousandths of an inch thick. These coatings not only reduce wear on metal cutting tools, but act as a dry lubricant, giving smoother cutting action. Tool life is often increased from three to five times by hard chrome plating. This process is used not only on tools but also on dies and the wearing parts of machines which are subjected to extra severe service.

Platings of copper, cadmium and zinc are commonly used where corrosion resistance is the primary function. Cadmium and copper are used quite generally for radio and television chassis bases because they solder easily. Many standard screws, nuts, and similar hardware items are cadmium or zinc plated for rust resistance. Brass plating is commonly used on hinges, locks, and other hardware for furniture and luggage, to simulate solid brass. However, the corrosion resistance of brass and copper platings is poor, and a coat of clear lacquer is often used over them to retard oxidation.

Many parts for electronic equipment are silver plated. This is partly because the high-frequency radio waves have the property of traveling largely on the surface of conducting parts, and the silver, being an excellent conductor, offers a low resistance path for them. Unlike copper, the silver oxides that form on the surface are still good electrical conductors, and switch contacts with silver surfaces do not become noisy and erratic. Moreover, silver solders easily. Although the material is expensive, the amount used in most cases is small and does not add too much to the total cost of the piece. For the same reason, even a light gold plating is not unduly expensive.

Platings of alloys of various metals are coming into more general use and offer many possibilities for improving the characteristics of plated coatings to meet specialized conditions.

HOT DIPPING PROCESSES

The coating of iron or steel sheets or fabricated assemblies with zinc by hot-dip galvanizing is one of the oldest methods of rust and corrosion prevention and is still recognized as the most effective for severe conditions of dampness and outdoor exposure. Galvanized pails and garbage cans are familiar to every household. Galvanized culverts are widely used in road construction. Sheet steel and steel window frames protected by galvanizing are common in the construction industry. Towers for electric lines and radio transmission are almost always galvanized, as are many bolts, nails, and wire fencing for outdoor use. In some applications, electrolytic zinc plate is substituted for hot-dip galvanizing. It gives a much thinner coating and costs less, and, for conditions that are not too severe, is quite satisfactory; but, for maximum protection, hot-dip galvanizing is preferred.

Electrolytic tin plate is largely supplanting the hot-dip tinning for cans and tin kitchen utensils. Here, again, the hot tin dipping gives a heavier coating and is preferable for long life and severe service. Any tin coating has the advantage of promoting easy soldering in later fabrication and this property is often used in cans that are to be soldered and in electronic printed circuits (see Chap. 21).

ORGANIC COATINGS

Paint, varnish, enamel, and lacquer are used very widely on metal, wood, and plastics for their decorative value as well as for protection against corrosion or weathering.

Paint is a mixture of pigments in linseed or other oils which have the property of drying by a chemical reaction with the oxygen in the air. Often a combination of oils and other ingredients is used to hasten drying and to give the proper body for easy application and good covering. Special formulations are available for indoor or outdoor use, for wood or metal, and for various degrees of surface gloss. Paints are usually applied by brushing, although they may also be sprayed. The use of cheap paint is very poor economy because the durability is generally low and the labor of application is by far the greatest part of any paint job. Thus a saving of 25 percent in the cost of paint may make only a 5 percent saving on the entire cost and the job may last only half as long. For production purposes, paint has largely been supplanted by the various synthetic resin enamels which give better and more durable finishes and dry more rapidly.

Varnishes are solutions of natural or synthetic resins in solvents and oils. They may dry only by the evaporation of the solvent, as in the case of shellac varnish, or by both evaporation and oxidation. Upon drying, the resins leave a tough film that is more resistant to moisture than paint. Varnishes do not, as a rule, contain pigments, although some varnish stains are sold for one-coat wood finishes for home use. Some of the plastic resins, such as the phenolics and the alkyds, are used to make varnishes with outstanding resistance to water, chemicals, and mechanical damage. Almost all furniture used to be finished with varnishes which required many coats and days of drying time in dustproof rooms. Sprayed lacquers, which dry dust free in a few minutes, have almost completely supplanted the varnishes for furniture work and have made possible modern production schedules. However, varnishes are tougher than lacquer and are used for floors, for marine woodwork, and for other outdoor applications.

Enamels are similar in composition to varnishes but contain a fairly high percentage of pigments. Most enamels are now made with synthetic resins and they may be of the air-drying or the baking type. The baking enamels have greater toughness and durability and adapt themselves better to production schedules because of the shorter drying time. The air-drying time of most enamels is 4 or 5 hr while a baking enamel usually requires only a few minutes to ½ hr in the drying oven. Enamels are very generally used for finishing metal products and are available in an almost unlimited range of colors and textures. Many interesting special effects can be obtained, such as wrinkle enamels, crackle and hammered effects, and speckled or spatter finishes. Some of these two-tone effects require a double coating, but others are done with a double spray gun or even with a single gun using special materials. Enamels may be brushed on, but in production, spraying or dipping is almost always used.

These special-effect finishes, in addition to giving a pleasing surface texture, have the further advantage of concealing many minor defects in the base material. Rough castings, unfinished spot welds and roughly sanded wood surfaces can often be finished attractively in this way without the expensive hand polishing or buffing that would be needed for a smooth enamel finish. They contrast nicely with polished metal trim and are used very widely on office machines, laboratory equipment, and home appliances. A two- or three-tone, single-coat enamel (trade name "Plextone") is being used, not only on metal and wood furniture and cabinets but even on wall panels in homes and offices.

Lacquers. Automobiles which used to be finished, like carriages, with many coats of enamel and varnish, requiring weeks in a dust-free room, are now sprayed with quick-drying lacquers or enamels and dried in a matter of minutes by means of heat. Although lacquers were generally used for this purpose a few years ago, these required hand rubbing or buffing to give a smooth, pleasing surface. Most cars are now finished with synthetic enamels requiring a short bake in ovens or infrared tunnels. These enamels give the necessary smooth luster without any hand finishing.

Lacquers are made of cellulose nitrate dissolved in various solvents and thinners and usually containing plasticizers for increased toughness. They harden simply by the evaporation of the solvents, which takes place at room temperature in a few minutes. They dissolve again if the solvent is applied to them. Lacquers are applied almost exclusively by spraying or dipping since they dry too fast for brush application. Also, if an attempt were made to brush on a second coat, the first coat would be dissolved in the process. Lacquers are used very generally for finishing wood furniture and cabinets for interior use. Certain clear lacquers are used to protect polished brass and copper for either indoor or outdoor exposure but, for most metal parts, enamel is preferred because of better adhesion and resistance to exposure. Lacquers containing pigments are sometimes referred to as "lacquer enamels," and these find considerable use on both metal and wood products. In general, the adhesion of lacquers to metal is not as good as that of the enamels, but with proper preparation of the metal and the right primer, good results can be obtained.

Many of the new finishes are combinations of various resins and solvents and are hard to classify in any of the above general categories. Some of these have outstanding qualities in the particular use for which they are formulated.

Application of organic finishes may be done by several methods. While brushing is the common method of applying paint and varnish to exterior and interior woodwork on buildings, this is hardly to be regarded as a production process. Dipping is sometimes used for a light protective coat of thin lacquer or for applying paint or enamel to such things as parts for farm machinery where the main object is protection, and some unevenness and dripping is not objectionable. Dipping under carefully controlled conditions, sometimes with centrifugal drying or with an electrostatic treatment to prevent the usual drops or "tears" on the bottom, can be used for coating parts with irregular shapes, narrow recesses, or holes that could not be sprayed successfully. Dipping makes for more efficient use of the finishing material than spraying since there is no waste through the overspray.

On parts that are too large for convenient dipping in a tank or vat, flow-coating is sometimes used. The part is suspended over a shallow tank or tray containing the paint or the enamel. The material is pumped through a hose and flowed freely over the part, with the surplus draining back into the tank to be recirculated. The results are similar to those obtained by dipping.

Most production finishing with lacquers or enamels is done by spraying. This is commonly done by hand using a spray gun in a booth with a suction fan to remove the fumes and the "overspray." A curtain or sheet of water is sometimes used to prevent this overspray from being blown out through the exhaust vent. In the case of lacquer, this overspray may be separated from the water and reused by drying and dissolving it again in the solvents. This is economical only in large production installations.

In high production of repetitive parts, automatic spray installations are used which may be simple or quite elaborate according to the application. Where the masking of certain portions of a piece from the spray is required, shields or masks made by electroforming (see Chap. 6), are often used. In the more elaborate automatic machines, a number of these masks are used and they are washed and dried between each use to prevent smearing of the work when the mask is applied.

In some production spraying, an electrostatic charge is used to attract the droplets of finish to the work. This is called "electrostatic spraying" and it greatly reduces the loss of material through overspray and also gives a more uniform coating (see Figs. 577–579). On production spraying of large quantities of metal parts (nonmetallic articles can also be handled by special techniques), this process offers important savings. The reduction in material used is frequently 40 to 60 percent, and sometimes more. The process is completely automatic, so manpower is reduced to a minimum. The quality of work is improved, especially on intricate or irregularly shaped objects that would be difficult to spray uniformly by other methods. The workpiece, which is carried on a conveyor, is at ground potential. A high d-c voltage, of the order of 90,000 v, generated by a special power supply, imparts an electrostatic charge of opposite polarity to the droplets of material in the spray, causing them to be attracted to the work. The charge can be applied by a screen of fine wires on either side of the work, with conventional spray guns directing the material into the charged field. Another method eliminates the spray gun and the screen and both atomizes and charges the material by throwing it centrifugally from the surface of a rapidly whirling disk or cone to which the high voltage is applied. The latter method is the most economical for high production. The electrostatic principle is used on certain dipping and flow-coating applications to draw off the last drops of material that form on the lower edges of the work and so prevent the formation of "tears" that are one serious disadvantage of the dipping process (see Fig. 580).

The baking of enamel finishes may be done either in gas or electrically heated ovens or by infrared bulbs or heating units. The actual heating cost is lower with the gas-fired ovens, but the infrared units are so much more convenient and flexible in their applications that they are in very general use. Induction heating (see Chap. 17) is used in certain specialized applications, such as the coating of tubing or pipe in a continuous process.

VITREOUS OR PORCELAIN ENAMELING

The vitreous enamels are inorganic materials that are fused to sheet or cast metals (usually iron or steel) to form an extremely hard, glasslike coating. They are available in a wide range of colors and have the greatest durability and wear resistance of any metal finish. Because of their great hardness, they are not so flexible as some organic coatings and are more subject to chipping and cracking. Vitreous enamels must be used over the proper grade of sheet steel or aluminum, thoroughly cleaned, and the part must be properly designed to insure an even flow of the enamel. This is composed mostly of silicates with added materials to give proper flow and the desired characteristics to the final coating. Metal oxides are used for coloring. The material is applied in a thin slurry known as the "slip" and, after drying, it is fired at a temperature of approximately 1500 F until it is fused. Porcelain enamels are the preferred finish for kitchen sinks, ranges, and metal bathroom fixtures and for outdoor use on permanent signs and metal store fronts. Prefabricated homes and other buildings are made of sheets of porcelain enameled steel which can be washed clean and never require painting.

A new process for applying inorganic coatings involves the flame spraying of ceramic or ceramet (see Chap. 20) material on metal parts. The material is in powder form or rods of sintered powder and is fed through an intense flame onto the surface, much as in metallizing (see Chap. 7). The process seems to have possibilities for use on jet engine parts and the like which are subjected to extremes of heat and corrosive gases. It is, so far, in laboratory and very limited commercial use.

OXIDE AND PHOSPHATE COATINGS

Anodizing is a process for applying an oxide coating to aluminum. It is done electrolytically in an acid solution with equipment similar to that used for electroplating. Several processes are available, some of which produce a light-colored, porous coating which can be dyed in a wide variety of colors, which become part of the metal surface. Other processes produce a darker and harder coating, without porosity, and these are used very largely in the aircraft and the marine industries for protection against corrosion. The aluminum oxide formed in the anodizing process is about 0.001 in. thick and is very hard. It is a good electrical insulator and, especially in the more porous types, it forms a good base for the organic finishes, such as enamel or lacquer. A variation of the anodizing process, known as "Alzac," produces a highly reflective, mirror-like finish that is very durable.

Other processes are available for producing an oxide coating on magnesium and on iron or steel. On magnesium, the coating is similar to the more porous anodized film on aluminum, and it can be dyed for decorative effects or impregnated with sealers for corrosion resistance. The oxide coatings on iron or steel are usually in the form of various blackening processes which form a very thin, porous surface. By itself, this coating is soft and offers little protection, but, when impregnated with oils, waxes, or lacquers, it gives fair corrosion resistance and is inexpensive.

Phosphate coatings on iron or steel give much better protection, when properly impregnated, than the oxide, but their primary use is to provide a good bond between the metal and the subsequent coats of paint or enamel. "Parkerizing" and "Bonderizing" are examples of these phosphate processes and are very widely used in the automotive industry and in other applications where durability and exposure resistance are required of organic finishes on ferrous metals.

A variation of this process is sometimes used to provide a surface that reduces friction and holds oil on wearing surfaces. This is also used to provide a lubricating and anti-seizing surface on steel blanks that are to be formed by the cold extrusion process (see Chap. 3).

TUMBLING AND SAND BLASTING

These are commonly used as methods for cleaning and preparing metal surfaces for other finishing, but in certain applications, especially on aluminum, no further finishing is required. Both tumbling, in its several variations, and sand blasting, depend on the impact of abrasive particles against the work. The abrasive may vary from coarse sand, granite chips, or metal grit to fine soft abrasives such as pumice or chalk or even sawdust, used with or without fluid lubricants. Sand is not used as much as it used to be in sand blasting because of the hazard of silicosis to the operators. The abrasive may be thrown against the work either by an air blast or by centrifugal force. The blasting operation is used primarily for cleaning castings and other fairly rough work where heavy scale or rust deposits are to be removed. The grit size and the velocity must be adjusted to the type of work being done since excessive impact may cause distortion, or set up strains in the work, or cause excessive rounding off of sharp corners. In cases where only relatively soft dirt is to be removed, plastic pellets, ground fruit pits, or similar materials are used instead of the harder grit.

Quite far removed from the coarse sand blasting used on large rough castings is the liquid abrasive polishing used for light cleaning, deburring, and finishing under closely controlled conditions. In this process, fine abrasives of 40 to 5000 mesh size are suspended in chemical solutions and forced against the work through special nozzles. The finer of these abrasives are used, among other things, for the polishing of die and mold cavities, for preparing irregular parts for plating, for removing the minute burrs of gears and machined parts, and for the frosting of glass surfaces.

Tumbling is an important production method for cleaning, polishing, and removing sharp corners and burrs from small parts, such as screw machine parts, small- or medium-size castings, forgings, and stampings. The parts are placed in a barrel, usually of hexagon or octagon shape, with an abrasive mixture, and the barrel rotated slowly to roll the parts around and give the necessary smoothing action. The size and the shape of the barrel, the speed of rotation, the type of abrasive and lubricant, the proportion of parts and abrasive, and the length of time—all help to determine whether the result is a grinding, deburring, descaling, or polishing effect or honing to a mirror finish such as might be required after plating. Where the parts are fragile or large or of such a shape that they might be damaged by rolling against each other, they may be clamped in fixtures in the barrel and the abrasive rolled around them to give the necessary polishing action. Sometimes the part may be rotated also, to allow the abrasive to flow over all parts of it. Some techniques and materials for abrasive cleaning and finishing are embodied in patented processes or machines and go by such names as Roto-Finish, Liquid Honing, Wheelabrating and Roll Brite.

POWER BRUSHING

Another method of cleaning and deburring that has attained considerable commercial importance is the use of rotating brushes. The brushes may be made of wire of various materials and stiffness or of fiber or bristles. The wire brushes are usually used dry for removing burrs and sharp corners, while the softer brushes are commonly used with abrasives or detergents. For small production, the work may be held manually against the wheel or the wheel may be driven by a flexible shaft and held against the workpiece. For high production items, machines are made that hold the work and automatically bring the work and the brushes together in exactly the proper relation and for the proper time. Used in this way, power brushing is a highly efficient process and has shown large savings on such items as gears, bearing races, and stampings.

ELECTROPOLISHING

This is a method of etching away the high points of a rough surface more rapidly than the lower portion, so that a smooth, polished surface results. It is done by passing an electric current through the work and a chemical electrolyte with equipment similar to that used for electroplating. For parts having knurled surfaces or intricate shapes that would be difficult to handle by other methods, it is quite satisfactory, but its use is limited by cost and by the metal-removing action that makes it hard to hold close dimensional tolerances on the finished parts. Several variations of the process are available for different types of work and most of these are covered by patents which are used under license.

VACUUM METALLIZING

The deposition of metal in a vacuum is a method for applying an extremely thin coating (approximately $2\frac{1}{2}$ to 16 millionths of an inch) of metal to plastics, glass, or metal objects. It is done by placing the parts to be coated on suitable racks in an air-tight chamber and pumping the air out to form a high vacuum. A filament of the metal to be deposited is then heated electrically in the vacuum chamber until the metal evaporates. Since there are no molecules of air to stop them, the molecules of metal travel out from the filament in straight lines until they strike some object and are deposited on it. To get a uniform coating, the parts and the filaments must be located properly, and in some cases the parts must be rotated to insure complete coverage. The resulting coating is extremely bright and attractive in appearance, but it is so thin that it will not stand any abrasion unless it is protected by a coat of clear lacquer or by laminating with a layer of clear plastic.

The process is inexpensive and is used mostly to finish plastic toys such as horns and toy pistols to look like polished metal. It is also used commercially to finish sheet plastic with a bright metallic coating in simulated gold, silver, or brilliant colors for displays and novelties. Attractive textures can be obtained by embossing of the metallized sheets, with or without a protective coating of clear plastic. By using suitable masks and depositing two or more colors, attractive plastic or metal name plates can be formed. For this purpose, the metallizing is usually applied to the back of a flat or molded clear plastic so that the surface is protected in use. Other uses will no doubt be found for this very promising new process.

"ELECTRO-LESS" PLATING

This is a new method of depositing nickel from a solution without the use of electric current. It is more expensive than electroplating but has the decided advantage of forming a uniform thickness of plating, regardless of the shape of the piece (see Figs. 610–612). This is not possible with electroplating in parts having sharp corners or deep recesses. Electro-less plating can be used also for coating the inside of large tanks and other objects that are not practical to plate by other methods. Heavy coatings can be made by this process, but the plating is much less porous than an electrolytic deposit so a thinner deposit gives equivalent protection. The coating is very hard and, because of its uniformity, can be used instead of chromium for hard plating dies and molds without change of critical tolerances.

PREFINISHED METALS

These metals, while not new, are increasing in variety and in adaptability to new uses. While not usually thought of in this category, the galvanized iron and terne plate sheets that have long been used in sheet metal work are actually prefinished metals. Terne plate is given a light coat of lead with a small percentage of tin which makes it easy to solder and gives a small amount of corrosion resistance. It is sometimes used in low-priced stampings such as small radio chassis bases to avoid the need for plating. After shearing and perforating, the edges are unprotected except for the slight coating that is carried over them by the dies. Galvanized sheet has a heavy coat of hot-dipped zinc and has excellent corrosion resistance except where the edges are broken by shearing or punching.

The newer prefinished metals include plated and polished sheets that may include etched, embossed, or burnished designs, and also enameled or lacquered sheets and strip stock in a wide variety of colors. The adhesion and the flexibility of the finish is good enough to allow quite severe forming of the finished material.

A new process, based on the improved synthetic adhesives now available, bonds a sheet of vinyl plastic, approximately 0.020 in. thick, to steel or aluminum sheets (see Figs. 491 and 492, Chap. 14). The vinyl may be embossed to simulate leather or other materials and the material will withstand even sharp 180 deg bends without cracking or separation. It is being used for television cabinets, business machine housings, and similar products.

Metal sheets are available which are not only plated and polished but also embossed in a variety of ornamental patterns (see Fig. 613). These not only add to the appearance but also serve to make the thin sheet metal much more rigid.

All of the prefinished metals are expensive when compared with unfinished sheets, but when all of the costs of cleaning, polishing, and finishing are considered, they are often economical, provided that the complete assembly is such that it does not require an overall finish after it is put together. The use of prefinished metals should be considered in the design stage of a product so that exposed edges can be avoided and the forming done in such a way as to adapt itself to the strong features as well as the limitations of the materials.

A new fluidized bed coating process, known by the trademark "Whirlclad," developed and patented in Germany and available under patent license in the United States, makes it possible to coat many articles with nylon, polyethylene and other thermoplastic materials. These materials have not previously been applied satisfactorily as coatings. No solvents are used. The parts to be coated are heated to a temperature above the melting point of the coating material and immersed in a bed of specially prepared coating powders, agitated to a fluid state by currents of gas or air ascending through it. The first use of the process has been primarily on metal parts with nylon coatings used especially for low-friction and wear-resisting properties. Coatings of 0.008 in. to 0.020 in. are obtained. Coatings of polyethylene 0.010 in. to 0.040 in. have also been used for electrical and corrosion resistance. The process is illustrated in Figs. 616 and 617.

Fig. 565. A typical cleaning setup before a black oxide finishing operation. Close control of the solutions insures quality work. (Courtesy, Oakite Products, Inc.)

Fig. 566. Basket dipping of small parts in a cleaning solution. (Courtesy, American Airlines, Inc.)

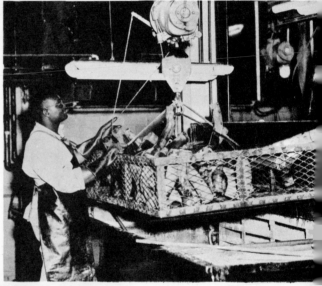

Fig. 567. A convenient setup for an ultrasonic cleaning system and the associated equipment. The tall cabinet contains the ultrasonic generator, the ribbed tank below the table is the cleaning unit, and a rinse tank is at the right. (Courtesy, Pioneer-Central, Div. of Bendix Aviation Corp.)

Fig. 568. A basket of small parts being removed from the ultrasonic cleaner. Even the most minute crevices are thoroughly cleaned by the "cold boiling" action that is created. (Courtesy, Pioneer-Central, Div. of Bendix Aviation Corp.)

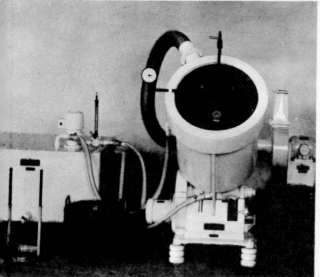

Fig. 569. A barrel chrome-plating unit for hard chrome plating of small parts or tools for wear or corrosion protection or building up of worn or undersize parts. The solution is circulated between the barrel and the storage tank. (Courtesy, The Dawson Corporation.)

Fig. 570. Hot-dip galvanizing of large steel gratings by immersion in molten zinc. (Courtesy, American Hot Dip Galvanizers Association, Inc.)

Fig. 571

Figs. 571–572. For galvanizing small parts, racks or baskets may be used, or, for high-production applications, rotating barrels as shown here, to hold the parts during dipping in the molten zinc. (Courtesy, American Hot Dip Galvanizers Association, Inc.)

Fig. 572

Fig. 573. A typical finishing setup for television cabinets. A hand gun is used for the lacquer and the work is moved into position on dollies. A dry type exhaust booth is used here. (Courtesy, The DeVilbiss Company.)

Fig. 574. An automatic spray machine applies white enamel to refrigerator liners as they are carried through the booth on an overhead conveyor. This booth uses a water curtain to trap overspray and fumes before the air is exhausted outside the building. (Courtesy, The DeVilbiss Company.)

Fig. 575. A rotary machine and an automatic spray gun increased production on this lighting fixture part from 900 to 2700 pieces per day. At the same time, material consumption was reduced from 40 pieces per gal to 160. (Courtesy, The DeVilbiss Company.)

Fig. 576. A heavy rubber-like undercoating is often used on the underside of automobile and trailer fenders and similar parts to resist the abrasion of particles thrown up by the tires, to prevent rusting and to deaden sound. This material is here being sprayed on the underside of a trailer body. (Courtesy, Minnesota Mining & Mfg. Co.)

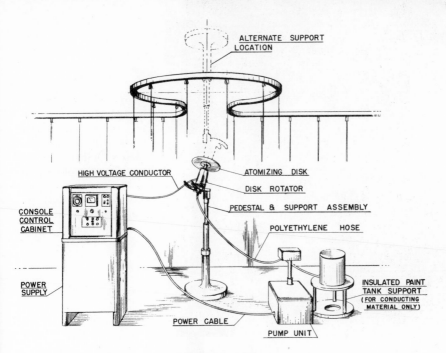

ALTERNATE SUPPORT LOCATION

HIGH VOLTAGE CONDUCTOR

ATOMIZING DISK

DISK ROTATOR

PEDESTAL & SUPPORT ASSEMBLY

CONSOLE CONTROL CABINET

POLYETHYLENE HOSE

POWER SUPPLY

INSULATED PAINT TANK SUPPORT (FOR CONDUCTING MATERIAL ONLY)

POWER CABLE

PUMP UNIT

SCHEMATIC VIEW
TILTING DISK INSTALLATION
WITH
CONSOLE TYPE CONTROLS

Fig. 577. A typical installation of electrostatic spraying equipment. (Courtesy, Ransburg Electro-Coating Corp.)

Fig. 578. Speedometer housings are electrostatically sprayed by the atomizing disk method. On intricate parts like this, electrostatic spraying gives a more uniform coating and shows a large saving in material over other spray methods. (Courtesy, Ransburg Electro-Coating Corp.)

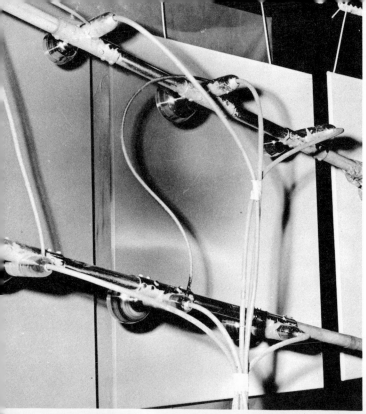

Fig. 579. Electrostatic atomizing cones spray toilet partitions as they move past two stations to receive primer and finishing coat. (Courtesy, Ransburg Electro-Coating Corp.)

Fig. 580. Three views showing the action of electrostatic detearing on a wire bracket. (Left) The bracket as it comes from the dipping tank. (Center) The electrostatic field is turned on, drawing the surplus paint to the screen below. (Right) The smoothly coated bracket after detearing. (Courtesy, Ransburg Electro-Coating Corp.)

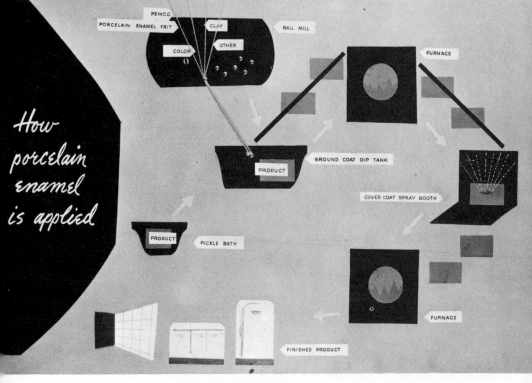

How porcelain enamel is applied

Fig. 581. The various steps in the porcelain enameling process. (Courtesy, Pemco Corporation.)

Fig. 582. An over-all view of a production porcelain enameling setup. (Courtesy, Ferro Corporation.)

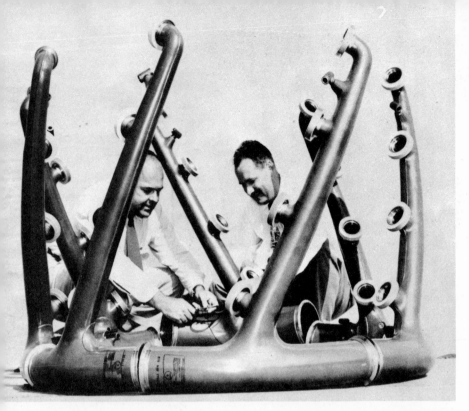

Fig. 583. Porcelain enamel finish is used not only for the familiar household appliance and architectural uses, but also for heat-resistant coatings such as these jet engine parts. (Courtesy, Ferro Corporation.)

Fig. 584. A hand spray gun is here used to apply porcelain enamel to the top of a gas range as it travels through the spray booth on a cable type conveyor. (Courtesy, The DeVilbiss Company.)

Fig. 585

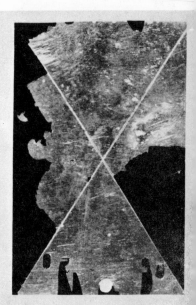

Figs. 585–586. A steel panel (Fig. 585) and an aluminum panel (Fig. 586) given an enamel finish. Upper panel in each figure was on the plain metal, lower panel treated first with Bonderite phosphate coating. Both panels were scratched and exposed to salt spray. The phosphate prevents the corrosion from spreading under the enamel and destroying the finish. (Courtesy, Parker Rust Proof Company.)

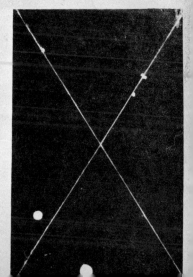

Fig. 586

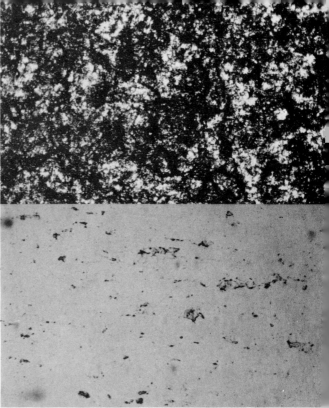

Fig. 587. Photomicrograph (magnification 100 times) of bright steel surface before (*below*) and after (*above*) treatment with Bonderite phosphate coating. The treated surface gives a good base for paint, enamel, or lacquer. (Courtesy, Parker Rust Proof Company.)

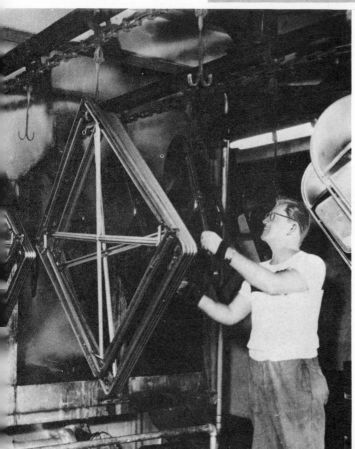

Fig. 588. Metal chairs and tables being phosphated in an automatic washer. (Courtesy, Oakite Products, Inc.)

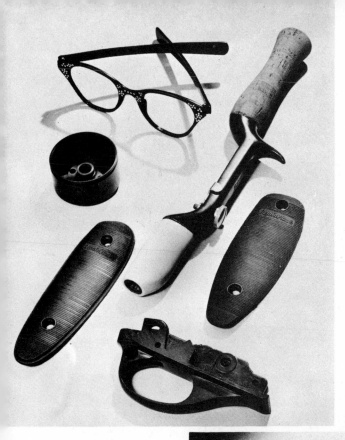

Fig. 589. A wide variety of colors is available in durable anodized finishes on aluminum. These parts are anodized in Aluminite black for the gun parts, Aluminite red for the fishing rod handle and spectacle frames. (Courtesy, Aluminum Company of America.)

Fig. 590. A cut-away view of a blast-cleaning room. The operator wears protective clothing and directs the air-driven abrasive to all parts of the work. The abrasive drops through the floor grating where it is cleaned and reused. The work is moved in and out on a car. (Courtesy, Pangborn Corporation.)

Fig. 591. Each work-carrying table revolves on its own axis as it passes under the abrasive stream in this "Rotoblast" centrifugal blast-cleaning machine, thus exposing all surfaces to the abrasive. (Courtesy, Pangborn Corporation.)

Fig. 592. A "Rotoblast" centrifugal force-blast cleaning machine cleans 10 tons of lawn mower castings in 4 hr. (Courtesy, Pangborn Corporation.)

Fig. 593. Scale is removed from these cast brake drums as they pass through the abrasive blast cleaner on the conveyor. (Courtesy, Wheelabrator Corporation.)

Fig. 594. A variety of castings come down the conveyor from the continuous blast-cleaning machine in this large foundry. (Courtesy, Wheelabrator Corporation.)

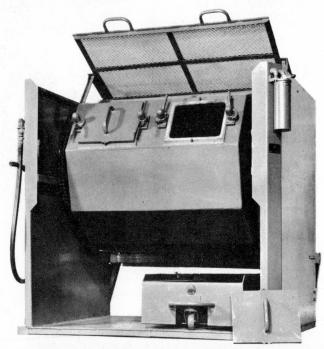

Fig. 595

Figs. 595–596. A production machine for polishing and deburring by a highly developed wet tumbling process. The choice of abrasive and chemical compounds permits a wide variety of work. Fig. 596 shows a group of parts polished by this process and the very fine lustrous surface that can be obtained without hand buffing. (Courtesy, Roto-Finish Company.)

Fig. 596

Fig. 597

Figs. 597–598. This centrifugal abrasive blast machine is designed especially for deflashing plastic moldings. A load of 100 to 6000 moldings is deflashed and left ready for use in from 2 to 12 min. Fig. 598 shows typical moldings before and after treatment. (Courtesy, Wheelabrator Corporation.)

Fig. 598

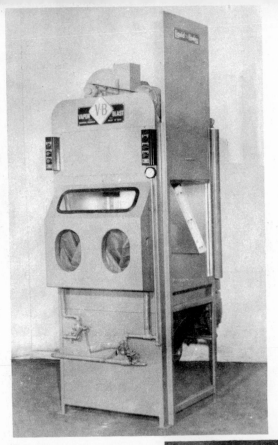

Fig. 599. A Liquid Honing machine for cleaning, polishing, and deburring operations. (Courtesy, Vapor Blast Manufacturing Company.)

Fig. 600. A drop-forging die before and after a Liquid Honing operation to smooth the surface and blend machining marks. (Courtesy, Vapor Blast Manufacturing Company.)

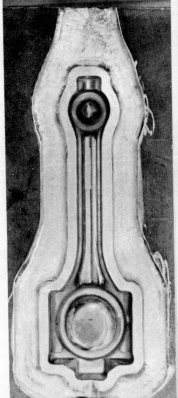
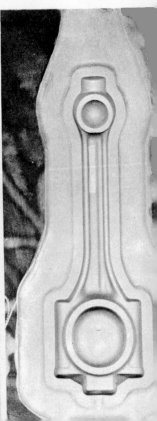

Fig. 601. An enlarged view of a ⅜-in. tap before and after deburring by Liquid
Honing. (Courtesy, Vapor Blast Manufacturing Company.)

Fig. 602. Shot peening throws round metallic shot at high velocity against the
surface of parts like these connecting-rod forgings, it increases fatigue resistance and
strength by cold working the surface of the metal. It is done in special machines
similar to those used for abrasive blast cleaning. (Courtesy, Wheelabrator Corporation.)

Fig. 603

Fig. 604

Figs. 603–604. An automatic wire-brushing machine removes scale and preservative oil from the ends of boiler tubes at The Babcock-Wilcox Company's plant at Barberton, Ohio, prior to welding. Fig. 604 shows the tube end after brushing. (Courtesy, The Osborn Manufacturing Company.)

Fig. 605

Figs. 605–607. An automatic brushing machine removes the burrs and sharp corners that can cause stress concentration, quickly and economically. Figs. 606-A and B show a closeup of the gear teeth before and after brushing. Fig. 607 shows a group of precision aircraft gears finished on the "Brushamatic." (Courtesy, The Osborn Manufacturing Company.)

Fig. 606-A

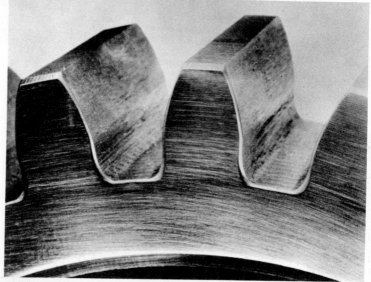

Fig. 606-B

Fig. 607

Fig. 608

Figs. 608–609. Plastic trumpets being removed from a vacuum metallizing machine. Fig. 609 shows a plastic saxophone before (*left*) and after (*right*) vacuum metallizing. (Courtesy, F. J. Stokes Machine Company.)

Fig. 609

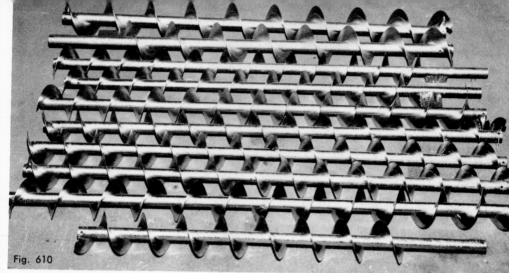

Fig. 610

Figs. 610–612. A group of parts nickel plated by the Kanigen ® chemical or electro-less plating method. This gives a uniform plating to complex shapes like the conveyor screws in Fig. 610, to the entire surface of the teeth on the gears in Fig. 611, and to internal cavities on parts like Fig. 612, which would be difficult or impossible with conventional electroplating methods. (Courtesy, General American Transportation Corporation.)

Fig. 611

Fig. 612

Fig. 613. A few of the many patterns available in preplated Rigid-Tex Metal sheets. The Rigidizing not only gives a pleasing texture that resists marking and scuffing, but also stiffens the material so that thinner gages can be used with substantial weight reductions. (Courtesy, Rigidized Metals Corporation.)

Fig. 614. All the qualities of design-strengthened patterns embossed in metal sheet mentioned in Fig. 613 are advantageous in this application as wainscoting in a railroad car. (Courtesy, Rigidized Metals Corporation.)

Fig. 615. Stiffness and light weight are the reasons for the use of Rigidized Metal for the aircraft heater jacket. (Courtesy, Rigidized Metals Corporation.)

ig. 616

Fig. 617

Figs. 616–617. A metal part (*left*) coated with nylon by the "Whirlclad" process (*right*). The coating is here used on a sliding part to impart smooth, quiet operation without lubrication. Fig. 617 shows the heated parts being immersed in the bed of nylon powder, fluidized by air agitation. (Courtesy, Polymer Processes, Inc., Reading, Pa.)

17

Induction and Dielectric Heating

These are methods of creating heat within a material by means of the losses set up by placing the piece in the field of a strong alternating electric current. Induction heating uses the magnetic field and is used only with metal objects. Dielectric heating uses the electrostatic field and is suitable for insulating materials, such as rubber, ceramics, wood, and plastics, and for baking sand cores for use in sand casting (see Chap. 1). Both methods are widely used in production processes and often reduce the time schedule to a small fraction of that required for other heating methods.

Low-frequency induction heating, using standard 60-cycle current, either single-phase or three-phase, is very useful for the heating of large cross sections of ferrous or nonferrous metals from 3 in. or 4 in. in diameter up. It heats completely through the piece and cannot be used for small pieces or surface heating as the higher frequency currents can. However, for work adapted to low-frequency heating it is very economical, and the equipment costs much less than the more elaborate generators needed for the higher frequencies.

For high-frequency induction heating, alternating currents with a frequency of 960 to 500,000 cycles per sec are used. Frequencies between 1000 and 1 million cycles are usually given in kilocycles (kc), 1 kc being 1000 cycles. Over 1000 kc, they are usually measured in megacycles (mc), (1 million cycles or 1000 kc). This high-frequency current is generated by a power supply using either electronic tubes, a spark-gap oscillator, or a rotary generator. Rotary generators are used for frequencies up to about 10 kc, and in power up to 10,000 kw. For higher frequencies, tube generators or spark-gap circuits are used with power up to 200 kw, but usually lower. The current flows through a heavy copper coil and the piece to be heated is placed within the coil or immediately adjacent to it.

The magnetic field causes eddy currents to be set up in the work-piece and these cause the piece to heat up. Since the heat is created within the piece, instead of having to soak through from the outside, the action is very rapid. Temperatures up to 2000 F or 2500 F can often be obtained in a matter of seconds under favorable conditions. The efficiency of the process depends on the design of the coil to concentrate the magnetic field in the desired place, the frequency of the current, and the material and the shape of the work.

In general, the higher frequencies do not penetrate as deeply into the work and therefore tend to concentrate the heat near the surface. This is a very useful property in selectively hardening the outer portions of gears, splines, and shafts, leaving the interior relatively soft and ductile (see Chap. 13). The lower frequencies are used for heavy-duty heating for forging, hardening, annealing, and brazing. The same principle is used in induction furnaces for melting metal.

One of the chief difficulties in the use of induction heating is the design of properly shaped induction coils to concentrate the heat in the desired sections of the work without undue losses. These coils are usually made of copper tubing with cooling water circulated through them, although bronze castings in the form of a single-turn coil with water passages in them are used for certain applications. For heating straight cylindrical pieces like shafts and tubes, a plain helical coil is all that is required, but, as the work becomes more complex, the design of the coil and the proper coupling between the generator and the coil become very important.

The equipment for induction heating is, of course, much more expensive than gas-fired furnaces, and the operating cost is more, but there are several advantages that make it highly desirable in many applications. The equipment is clean, and, since there is very little heat lost to the surrounding air, it is practical to locate the heating process at its proper place on the production line, rather than in a separate room or building requiring extra handling of material. The heating action is much faster than in a gas or electric furnace, so less space is usually required and production rates can be increased. Because of the rapid heating, the formation of oxides and scale is minimized and often savings can be made in subsequent cleaning and machining operations. The ability to concentrate the heating action in the surface of a part or in a small area may reduce distortion and stresses and also make possible the surface hardening of gear teeth, splines, and similar parts that could not be done in conventional furnaces. In this respect, it competes with flame hardening (see Chap. 13) and the choice will depend on the particular work to be done and the possible adaptability of the equipment to other operations. Induction heating is well adapted to automatic setups for production brazing or soldering of small assemblies on a large-quantity basis.

Dielectric heating uses currents of higher frequency, from 2 mc to 100 mc. These are generated by electronic tubes in special power supplies which may range in capacity from 1 to 100 or more kilowatts. The high-frequency voltage, usually at 8,000 to 12,000 v, is applied to a pair of metal plates and the work is placed between them. The plates or electrodes form a condenser with the material to be heated as the dielectric. Since most dielectric materials are quite imperfect at these frequencies, losses are set up which cause the material to heat up. As in induction heating, the heat is created within the work and very little time is required to reach the working temperature. In bonding plywood with synthetic resin glues which require heat for curing, the time required is often only a matter of minutes, against hours for the same operation by other methods. For gluing of furniture, the time required in the clamping fixtures is often reduced to a matter of seconds, with a tremendous increase in production and saving in space requirements. Dielectric heating is also used commonly to heat plastic preforms used in compression and transfer molding, resulting in a greatly reduced molding cycle and increased production from the press. Almost any electrically nonconductive material may be heated by this process with the efficiency determined by the nature of the material, the frequency and the voltage used, and the design of the electrodes.

The electrodes for flat work are simply flat plates of copper or aluminum connected to the output of the generator. For the bonding of multiple sheets of plywood in a hydraulic press, a center electrode is often used with the grounded side of the high-frequency output connected to the upper and the lower platens of the press. Flat electrodes are also used where small parts, such as plastic preforms or foundry cores, are heated in a continuous process with the parts passing on a conveyor through the heating zone. Other shapes of electrodes are used to concentrate the heat in the various types of joints used for assembling furniture and cabinets and for special types of work. In some cases, it is possible to use both electrodes on one side of the work and to utilize the stray field between the ends of the electrodes for heating the workpiece.

The use of high-frequency dielectric heating is finding applications in fields outside of industry. It has been used experimentally for several years for cooking purposes and commercial installations have been made in such places as railroad dining cars, where the saving in time offsets the high cost of the equipment. A complete frozen meal can be thawed and heated in a matter of seconds. Roasts and other foods are cooked uniformly all the way through in a few minutes. In some cases, this uniform cooking may be a disadvantage since the outside of the food is not browned as we are used to having it, and auxiliary heaters of the conventional type may be needed to correct this. A range for home use has been introduced to sell in the neighborhood of $1000, using a vacuum-tube high-frequency generator with a frequency of 2450 mc. As with all units of this type, the oven remains cool and all the heat is concentrated within the food itself. A conventional electric heating element is provided in case surface browning of the food is required.

An interesting suggestion has been made that homes might some day be heated by a high-frequency generator with electrodes on the floor and the ceiling. Although the room itself would be cold, the people in the room would be warmed by the dielectric heating effect within their bodies. The future thus looks bleak for those of us who like charcoal-broiled steaks and open fireplaces!

All high-frequency equipment for induction and dielectric heating must be well designed and carefully shielded to prevent radio interference above the limits set by the Federal Communications Commission. Precautions must also be taken to guard the operating personnel from the high voltages used.

Fig. 618

Fig. 619

Figs. 618–619. This induction hardening unit at The Cooper-Bessemer Corporation handles a wide variety of engine and compressor parts as shown in Fig. 619. These range from ½-oz set screws to 186-lb cross-head pins. (Courtesy, The Ohio Crankshaft Co.)

Fig. 620. A four-place induction heating coil for forming the areas shown on the sample piece in the foreground. Production rate is 3½ sec per piece with a 25-kw generator. (Courtesy, Induction Heating Corporation.)

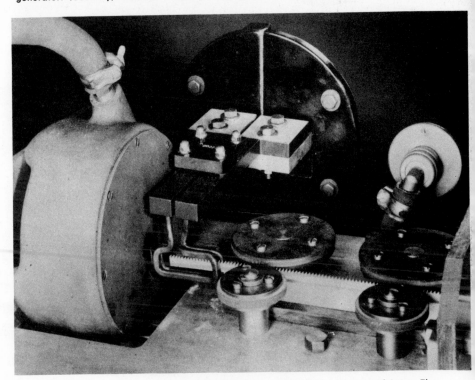

Fig. 621. Rack gear teeth being hardened automatically at the rate of 1 ips. The quenching unit is at the left just beyond the induction heating coil. (Courtesy, Induction Heating Corporation.)

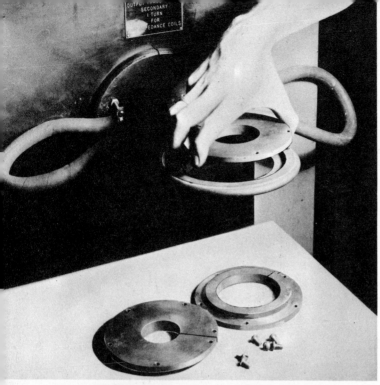

Fig. 622. A master coil for induction heating with different inserts for various size work. (Courtesy, Induction Heating Corporation.)

Fig. 623. An automatic induction hardening machine for camshafts which hardens all cams, bearings, and eccentrics simultaneously. Production can run as high as 600 shafts per hour. (Courtesy, The Ohio Crankshaft Co.)

Fig. 624. Induction hardening of the surface of automotive rear axle shafts is used almost universally since it permits the use of less expensive, easier machining steels and gives superior torsional fatigue characteristics. The hardening operation itself is also much faster and less expensive than furnace hardening of alloy steel shafts. The unit shown automatically hardens six axle shafts at a time. (Courtesy, The Ohio Crankshaft Co.)

Fig. 625. The teeth on this final drive for an Army tank are induction hardened in 50 sec per tooth with a 100-kw generator. (Courtesy, Induction Heating Corporation.)

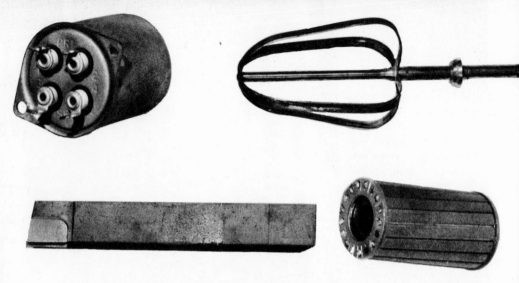

Fig. 626. A group of induction brazing and soldering jobs, showing a carbide cutting tool tip, an electronic relay can (soldered), an egg beater, and an electric motor armature. (Courtesy, Induction Heating Corporation.)

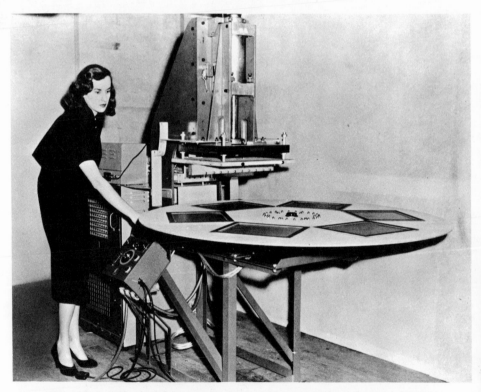

Fig. 627. A 6.2-kw high-frequency generator with a turntable and a press for heat sealing of plastic sheeting. An arc suppressor unit is mounted under the turntable which cuts off the power just before an arc occurs, which could damage the electrodes. (Courtesy, Radio Receptor Company, Inc.)

Fig. 628. A hydraulic press equipped with a 15-kw "Thermatron" high-frequency generator for the dielectric bonding of plywood panels. Other examples of this operation are shown in Chap. 19. (Courtesy, Radio Receptor Company, Inc.)

Fig. 629. A 2-kw high-frequency dielectric heating unit with integral oven for preheating plastic and rubber preforms prior to molding. (Courtesy, Radio Receptor Company, Inc.)

Fig. 630. A high-frequency oven for baking foundry cores by dielectric heating with a conveyor for handling the work. (Courtesy, Induction Heating Corporation.)

Fig. 631. Bacon broils on a paper napkin and a paper plate in this high-frequency dielectric oven, but the oven itself remains cool. A potato bakes in 5 min, a 5-lb roast cooks in 30 min. A conventional heating unit in the top of the oven is used for only a short period where surface browning is desired, as on a steak or roast. (Courtesy, The Tappan Stove Company.)

18

Inspection and Gaging

Modern mass production is based on the interchangeability of parts, and this, in turn, is based on the maintenance of specified dimensional tolerances on these parts. For this reason, the inspection department has become a very important part of the modern manufacturing organization. Its function is to see that the quality standards set up by engineering are maintained and dimensional tolerances held so that all parts of an assembly will fit together properly to avoid delays on the assembly line. If cases arise where the tolerances seem unnecessarily severe, or not close enough, the inspectors should work closely with engineering and production to get the matter straightened out. On questions of appearance, inspectors and engineers should collaborate with the sales department to determine just what will be acceptable to the customers without adding unduly to the cost. On work for governmental agencies, the inspectors must also see that the applicable specifications are complied with and demonstrate this to the satisfaction of the government inspectors.

Most inspection consists of checking parts for dimensions, finish, and physical characteristics, and checking finished equipment for performance and appearance. This sounds simple, but the practical application of inspection techniques requires judgment, ingenuity, and a thorough understanding of the manufacture and the function of the equipment.

It is obviously impractical to make all measurements and tests on each piece of material passing through the inspection department. It is therefore necessary to decide what proportion of each piece to subject to each test and to modify this decision on the basis of day-to-day experience. Statistical quality control is now a standard basis for many of these decisions, and volumes have been written on this phase of inspection alone. Formulas and tables have been worked out, based on the size of a production lot, the size of a random sampling, and the proportion of rejects in the sample lot. If these formulas are applied properly, much of the guesswork is taken out of the partial inspection that has to be relied on in much production work. A 100 percent inspection should be made of the important dimensions and characteristics of large or important parts, especially where much labor is going to be involved in further operations or assembly that would be lost if defects were discovered later.

MEASUREMENT OF DIMENSIONS

Size is the factor most commonly measured in inspection work and the size on drawings is specified with a tolerance or a variation that may be allowed from the standard dimension. Often this is given as a decimal or fraction after the standard dimension. Thus, 1 in. ±0.002 (two thousandths) means that the size may vary from 1.002 in. to 0.998 in. and still be within the acceptable limits. 10 in. ± $\frac{1}{64}$ could vary from 10$\frac{1}{64}$ in. to 9$\frac{63}{64}$ in.

It is extremely important that tolerances be established properly by engineering and clearly marked on all drawings. Too wide a tolerance makes for poor workmanship and also causes delays in production, due to improper fit of the parts. Too close a tolerance adds considerably to the cost without any real advantage in the final result. Usually a footnote on a drawing indicates the tolerance that applies to dimensions not otherwise marked. A common figure for this is ± $\frac{1}{64}$ in. on dimensions given in fractions and ±0.005 in. on dimensions given in decimals. These are not close enough for many fitted and machined parts and are too close for other parts, such as castings or welded assemblies. Standard tolerances on such parts as these are often given as the variation allowed per inch of dimension, as ±0.005 in. per inch. Where wider tolerances than the standard ones can be allowed, or where closer ones must be held, they should be so indicated on the drawings. The production people should be consulted before extremely close tolerances are specified to determine how these are going to affect the cost of the parts. Often dimensions of parts that must fit together are specified with a tolerance in only one direction. For instance, a shaft diameter might be 1 in. − 0.001 in. + 0.000 in. while the bearing in which it runs might be

1.001 in. + 0.001 in. − 0.000 in. When the two parts are assembled together, the clearance could vary from 0.001 in. to 0.003 in.

If only a few of the above pieces were to be measured, this would be done by means of micrometers (Fig. 632), or on larger pieces by vernier calipers (Fig. 634), but these are slow to use and require some skill to obtain accurate readings. If the number of pieces were larger, a simple way of measuring the shaft in the above example would be a "go and no-go" snap gage, as shown in Fig. 638, with the front anvil set for the maximum size (1 in.) and the rear anvil for the minimum size (0.999 in.). The setting of the gage would be done by means of gage blocks, which are the basic standard of measurement and are accurate to a millionth or a few millionths of an inch. The front section of the gage should now slip over the shaft and the rear section should not, if the shaft is within tolerance. Checks should be made at several points and in several directions to be sure that the shaft is not out of round or tapered. There would still be a possibility that high spots or ridges might exist that would interfere with a proper fit in the bearing and a still better check could be made with a pair of ring gages (Fig. 639), ground accurately to the maximum and the minimum sizes of the shaft. These simulate more closely the actual operating conditions, but, since they would have to be made especially for each size and tolerance required, they might not be practical unless a considerable number of parts were to be measured.

The bore of the bearing might best be measured with "go and no-go" plug gages (Fig. 639) but an inside micrometer (Fig. 636), a dial bore gage (Fig. 640), or a pair of simple adjustable rod gages also could be used.

This shows that considerable discretion must be used in making even the simplest measurements. As the pieces become more complex and the dimensions more exact, and more difficult to measure, great ingenuity is needed and often special gaging setups and fixtures may be required.

Dial indicators are often used, either in standard gages or as parts of special gaging devices. They are really comparison devices since they must be set to zero by means of gage blocks (Figs. 641 and 642) or other standards. They are available with graduations of 0.001 in. (one thousandth), 0.0005 in. (one half thousandth or five "tenths"), or 0.0001 in. (one ten thousandth—more commonly referred to as a "tenth"). Dial gages using these indicators are easy and rapid to use and give quite accurate indications provided that the supporting members that form the rest of the gage are sufficiently rigid.

Surface plates, which are plates of iron or granite, ground and sometimes lapped to a smooth, flat surface, are often used to give a base for measurements on castings and other complex pieces. Height gages (Fig. 643) are often used in connection with a surface plate to take measurements or to scribe lines at fixed levels above the flat surface. These are usually calibrated in thousandths of an inch. Dial surface gages are also used with a surface plate to measure variations in flatness of surfaces parallel with or at an angle to the reference surface, which is flat on the surface plate. Sine bars or plates (Figs. 646–648) are used to give accurately controlled angles with relation to the surface plates.

Another method of measuring and laying out angles is by means of a vernier protractor (Fig. 649). This is calibrated in degrees and minutes of arc and is graduated to an accuracy of ±5 min.

With tolerances of $\frac{1}{64}$ in. or more, measurement with a steel scale or calipers is quite adequate. With tolerances of 0.001 in. or more, standard micrometers and snap, ring, and plug gages are satisfactory. When tolerances get down to 0.0001 in., new problems are encountered. Vernier micrometers and carefully made snap, plug, and ring gages can be used, but they require considerable skill for accurate results and the operation is not rapid.

For production measurements of high accuracy, several methods are used. The simplest is the mechanical magnification of small movements of a measuring point so that they show up as much larger movements on a calibrated dial or scale. This principle is used in sensitive dial gages which are calibrated in 0.0001-in. graduations.

Another method that is especially useful on deep internal bores, such as gun barrels and long cylinders, is the air gage. This requires no actual contact between the measuring plug and the walls of the hole, but depends on the leakage of compressed air between the plug and the inside of the hole. Back pressure is built up in this process and the measurement of this back pressure gives an accurate indication of the hole size. The change in back pressure may be measured by a gage with a dial and pointer, by a Venturi tube with a small cork floating on the air stream, or by a manometer type of

U-tube in which the height of the liquid in the tube indicates the pressure. This latter type is the most sensitive and a variation of 0.0001 in. in the dimension being measured shows up as about ¼ in. on the tube. Thus it can be read easily down to 0.00005 in. (one half tenth). The parts to be measured with the air gage must be thoroughly clean and free from oil since any foreign matter will affect the reading. The surface roughness also affects the accuracy of the reading, so it is best to calibrate the air gage with a master ring gage having a surface somewhere nearly comparable with the pieces to be measured. However, the air gage is not suitable for use on rough surfaces. Special gaging elements adapt the air gage to the measurement of outside diameters and the thickness of flat or rectangular pieces.

The electronic gage is another method of making extremely close measurements. This, like the air gage, is a comparison gage, and must be calibrated by means of gage blocks or master gages. The variations in dimension from this standard are then converted by the gaging head into changes in inductance, resistance, or capacity in an electronic circuit, and these changes may be amplified by means of vacuum tubes to give almost any sensitivity required. Measurements to 0.00001 in. (one hundred thousandth) or even 0.000005 in. (five millionths) can be made, but at these tolerances the mechanical limitations of the measuring fixture and the human limitations of the inspector make the readings of questionable value. With such extreme accuracies, the temperature of both the workpiece and the gaging members must be controlled carefully to prevent the expansion or the contraction of the metal from affecting the readings. Electronic gages are well adapted to automatic gaging processes, since the amplified electric impulse can be used to operate sorting mechanisms or to warn an operator if rejections are running too high.

Various optical methods are also used to make accurate measurements. The toolmaker's microscope is used mostly for tool and die work for measuring hole spacings and irregular contours on flat work. By combining this microscope with a very heavy and rigid micrometer, we have the "measuring machine" which is often kept in a temperature-controlled room and used only as a standard for checking other gages. This makes direct measurements to 0.00001 in.

An optical method much more commonly used for production inspection is the optical comparator. This projects an enlarged image of a part on a screen where it is superimposed on an accurate pattern or template of the correct size and shape. The comparison is made visually. It is not adapted to extremely high accuracies, but is very useful for checking gear tooth shape and irregular outlines that would be very difficult by other methods. Variations of 0.001 in. or even 0.0005 in. are detectable by a careful operator.

Optical flats are disks of glass or fused quartz ground to almost perfect flatness on one side. By placing one of these on a flat surface and viewing it by monochromatic light, a series of dark bands will be seen. If the surface is perfectly flat, these bands will be straight and evenly spaced. If any unevenness or curvature is present, even though it may be only a few millionths of an inch, the bands become distorted or irregular. Various patterns are characteristic of each type of irregularity, so a skilled operator can interpret them with great accuracy. Obviously, such extreme precision is very seldom required in production, nor is it economically practical to specify tolerances of this kind unless they are really needed.

The measurement of gear teeth presents some special problems. An accurate measurement of the pitch diameter (see Chap. 5) is usually required. This is often made by the use of wires or rolls of the proper diameter to make contact with the teeth at the pitch circle. These are placed opposite each other (or as nearly opposite as possible if the gear has an odd number of teeth) and a measurement taken over them with micrometer or vernier caliper. The correct diameter of roll for each pitch of gear and the correct measurement for each number of teeth are given in tables in most handbooks. Tooth spacing can be measured also by means of the rolls, and a dial gage based on this principle (Fig. 669) makes the measurement of tooth spacing and, indirectly, several other gear characteristics, rapid and easy. Tables give the correct reading for each size and pitch of gear.

Gears may also be checked for many characteristics by running them against a master gear in a special machine. The tooth shape of small gears can be checked accurately by means of the optical comparator described earlier in this chapter. Internal gears, bevel gears, helical and worm gears present special problems, but the same basic principles apply to measurements on these that apply to the simple spur gears just described.

The measurement of screw threads involves many of the same principles as gear teeth. Wires of the proper size can be used and measurements taken over them to get the pitch diameter of the screw. Special micrometers with V-shaped anvils to fit the thread contour are calibrated to read the pitch diameter directly. The commonest measurement of screws is made by means of "go and no-go" plug and ring thread gages. These are made with the proper tolerance for the class of fit specified in the drawings, class 2 being the standard for commercial machine screws and bolts, class 3 being used for closer tolerance fits and class 1 for wider tolerances.

The measurement of internal and external splines presents many of the same problems as that of gears, and similar methods of measurement can be used. However, most splined parts are of such a size and shape that special plug and ring gages can be used conveniently, and this is the usual method of checking them (see Fig. 651).

MEASUREMENT OF SURFACE ROUGHNESS

In addition to dimensions and tolerances, many drawings are marked with a symbol indicating the surface finish or the smoothness required. This is usually in the form of a small check mark or radical sign, with a number directly above it like this: $\sqrt[63]{}$. This means that a finish of 63 μin. is required on the surface indicated. It is necessary for the inspector to have some means of determining whether this requirement has been complied with.

It is first necessary to have some idea of just what is meant by a 63-μin. finish, and this is not as simple as it sounds. It is only recently that standards have been set up for the measurement of surface roughness, and these were agreed to only after considerable compromise among the experts in the field. Basically, the roughness is defined as the average variation, from a mean or nominal surface line, of the peaks and valleys in the minute irregularities of the surface. This average may be the arithmetical average or the root mean square (rms) value. These two figures differ by about 10 percent (the arithmetical average being less), but this is not too important since accurate measurements are very hard to make.

Several instruments are available for surface-finish measurements and all of them depend on moving a fine stylus over the surface and amplifying its motion electronically so that it can be indicated on a chart or an electric meter. The accuracy of these measurements depends on the shape of the stylus (no practical stylus is fine enough to reach the extreme bottom of the finest irregularities), the shape of the supporting skids that guide its movement, and the direction and the speed with which it is moved over the surface. Much work is still to be done on standardizing all of these conditions, but progress is being made and present standards are a very useful guide. Table 2 shows the range of microinch surfaces obtainable by dif-

TABLE 2. SURFACE FINISHES NORMALLY EXPECTED

Process	Microinches
Cutting torch, saw.........	500–1000
Sand castings..............	250–1000
Shell mold castings........	90–250
Disk grind, file............	63–500
Lathe, shaper, mill.........	32–500
Forgings..................	63–250
Investment castings.......	63–125
Permanent mold castings....	32–125
Die castings..............	32–125
Rolled surfaces...........	16–250
Extrusions...............	32–250
Bore.....................	16–250
Drill.....................	63–250
Ream.....................	16–125
Surface grind.............	16–250
Cylindrical grind..........	8–63
Hone or lap...............	2–16
Polish or buff.............	2–16
Superfinish...............	1–8

ferent machining methods. A very convenient method of comparison is available in metal or plastic standard surfaces which reproduce accurately measured specimens of various surface finishes obtained by various machining methods. A fingernail drawn first over the piece being inspected and then over these specimens gives a quite accurate comparison. These samples are inexpensive enough so that they can be used freely in engineering, inspection, and production departments.

The cost of parts with very fine surface finishes is much greater than those produced by normal good machining practice. It is therefore important that engineers have a thorough understanding of this subject and that the finish specified is no better than is actually required for a given application.

DETECTION OF STRUCTURAL FLAWS

Cracks, holes, and other defects can occur in even the most carefully made castings, forgings, and rolled metal parts. These may be due to defects in the original ingot or to gas bubbles or strains set up in the heating or the cooling of the piece. They may have a serious effect on the strength of the piece, and in critical parts of aircraft and other important applications it is vital that these defects be discovered in the inspection process. Several methods have been developed for detecting these flaws, whether they appear on the surface or not. Some of these require elaborate and expensive equipment that is beyond the scope of the average inspection department. For this reason, some such inspection is often specified when ordering castings, forgings, etc., from the supplier. The proper certification is then furnished with the parts (at additional cost, of course).

The x-ray machine is the most commonly used method of detecting internal flaws. The thickness of the section to be inspected determines the voltage required in the x-ray machine. Machines of 50 kv to 2000 kv (kilovolts or thousands of volts) are in common use. The 150-kv equipment measures steel or iron sections up to about 1¼ in. thick, or aluminum up to 6½ in. Large x-ray machines, rated at 2000 kv, can look through 12 in. of steel.

A more recently developed device for detecting internal flaws makes use of ultrasonic vibrations (see Chaps. 8 and 11). These vibrations or waves are introduced into one surface of the workpiece by simply holding the measuring head of the apparatus against it. A coating of oil may be used to obtain better coupling of the waves to the work. The original wave and a reflection from the opposite side then shows up on the screen of a cathode ray tube similar to those used in television sets. If the piece is sound, the reflection from the back of the piece is the only one seen, but if there is a flaw in the structure it shows up as an additional reflection. Ultrasonic inspection units can be used on metal sections up to 10 ft thick, far beyond the range of x-ray inspection. They can also be taken easily into the field or the shop for the inspection of shafts or other parts already installed in large machines. This is useful for locating defects that may develop after a part has been in use.

The spacing on the cathode-ray screen between the original pulse of ultrasonic waves and the reflected pulse is proportional to the thickness of the material under test, so it is also possible to tell the depth below the surface of any defect indicated. This same principle is used also to measure the thickness of metal sections such as pipe and tank walls where it is not practical to reach both sides of the piece. This is very useful in determining the extent of corrosion on pipes, tanks, and ship hulls. These measurements do not require the emptying of tanks or taking the equipment out of service.

For the detection of minute cracks and other flaws, at or near the surface, which are normally not visible to the eye, several methods may be used. One of these is the Magnaflux method, which may be used only on materials such as iron or steel that can be magnetized. A source of high amperage d-c current is required and the piece is magnetized, by passing a current either through it or through an external conductor with the piece in its magnetic field. The part under inspection is then coated with fine magnetic powder, either dry or in suspension in a liquid vehicle. Any flaw at or near the surface interrupts the magnetic field and changes the configuration of the magnetic particles to make the defect readily visible. After inspection, the piece is demagnetized by placing it in an a-c magnetic field, and the magnetic powder is cleaned off the surface. Magnaglo inspection is very similar to the Magnaflux, except that the magnetic coating material is made fluorescent and the resulting pattern, when viewed by ultraviolet light, shows up the defects more clearly, especially on rough surfaces.

The Zyglo method makes surface defects readily visible by saturating the piece with a fluorescent penetrating oil. The surplus oil is washed from the surface with water and the piece is dried. A small amount of the oil remains in any minute cracks or flaws, and, when the part is coated with a light-colored powder, this oil is drawn up to the surface and the defects are clearly visible when the piece is viewed by ultraviolet light.

Another method uses a red-dyed penetrating oil. After the piece is saturated in this oil, the surface is wiped clean and a light-colored, absorbent powder is dusted on. This draws the dyed oil out from any flaws and makes them visible by natural light. While this method is not quite so sensitive as the Zyglo, it has the advantage that no source of ultraviolet light is required and the test therefore can be made outdoors or in the factory with natural light.

TESTS FOR PHYSICAL CHARACTERISTICS

These tests, for such factors as hardness and tensile strength, have been discussed in Chap. 13. They are sometimes functions of the inspection department, but, in most cases, they are performed by the supplier of the steel parts or by the heat treater or by an outside laboratory. The same thing is true for the chemical analysis of metals. Here, a certification from the original supplier of the metal is usually sufficient, even to satisfy government inspectors that the specifications are being complied with. In the case of castings, it is often specified that the foundry furnish test bars from each heat of metal, and these are checked for hardness and tensile strength to be sure that the materials are running uniform.

TESTS FOR COLOR

With color playing an increasing role in the sale of all consumer products, and even in industrial equipment, it is part of the inspector's job to see that specified colors are held true within reasonable limits. Often this can be done with sufficient accuracy by making reference samples of the desired color and of the maximum deviation that is acceptable in either direction from the standard. These limits should be decided on by all departments concerned—usually engineering, sales, production, and inspection—and the approved samples will then settle many arguments that might otherwise arise should some customer complain about the color being "off." The source of light under which color is inspected is important. Open daylight, away from colored reflecting objects, is good. The color of sunlight in the early morning or the late evening is quite different and does not give a true indication. For articles that are to be used indoors and usually seen by artificial light, standard incandescent bulbs may furnish a suitable source of light for color comparison. The reflectors should be pure white or silvered and the bulbs should be replaced often since their color spectrum changes as they age. Fluorescent lights are totally unsuited for color matching. In all cases, the light intensity for color inspection should be kept as uniform as possible since the eye interprets colors differently under different light intensities. Since most colors fade or lose brightness by aging, color sample specimens should be protected from light and air as much as possible when not in use, and should be replaced by new samples rather frequently.

Where extremely accurate matching of color is necessary, electronic instruments known as color analyzers or spectrophotometers are available. These examine a color specimen under closely controlled light and break the reflected light down into its separate wavelengths, measuring each with great accuracy so that the color can be reproduced exactly at any time.

The same general principles mentioned for color also apply to the brightness or sheen of polished or plated surfaces. Samples of the desired standard and the worst acceptable finish should be agreed upon, and these samples used for reference in any doubtful cases.

MEASUREMENT OF PLATING THICKNESS

It is not possible for the electroplater to control accurately the thickness of plating deposited on each section of an irregularly shaped piece, so when a figure such as 0.0003 in. is specified for the plating thickness, this is taken to be the minimum acceptable, and it is to be expected that thicker deposits will build up in some spots. It is also extremely difficult to measure plating thickness accurately without removing the plating chemically from a portion of the piece and measuring the plated and the unplated parts. This, of course, makes it necessary to replate the piece.

For these reasons, a certification from the plater with a visual inspection for cleanness and brightness is usually all that is made. There are magnetic and electronic instruments made that measure the thickness of a nonmagnetic coating on a magnetic base material. These will measure a plating of nickel, copper, zinc, or cadmium on iron or steel, and also the thickness of lacquer, paint, or vitreous enamels on magnetic materials.

THICKNESS MEASUREMENTS BY RADIOACTIVITY

When radium was the only source of radioactivity, it was too scarce and too expensive for any wide application. Now that large quantities of low-cost by-products of nuclear reactors are available, industry has been finding many new uses for them. One of these uses is for measurements of the thickness of sheet materials, usually in the process of manufacture. These measurements can be made continuously without any actual contact with the material, and the readings obtained are instantaneous. The radioactive material is placed on one side of the work and the electronic measuring instrument on the opposite side. Some of the radiation penetrates the sheet material, and the exact amount depends on the thickness of the sheet. This can be measured with great accuracy. Thus, in a steel rolling mill, a continuous and instantaneous reading can be obtained of the thickness of a steel sheet. This reading can be amplified electronically and used to control the setting of the rolls so that great uniformity can be obtained without the errors and the delays that would be inherent if a human operator had to interpret the readings and make the adjustments.

So far, these radioactive materials have found only very limited applications in the usual inspection procedures, but new uses are being discovered for them daily.

STATISTICAL QUALITY CONTROL

While this is not the answer to all inspection and quality control problems, statistical quality control is a very useful tool, and its proper application can save time and greatly reduce the errors of a partial inspection or sampling procedure. Only a brief outline of the method can be given here, but inspection personnel should study some of the specialized books written on statistical quality control for a thorough understanding of the subject. It is not necessary to go into the involved mathematics of probabilities, since the results of these calculations have been reduced to simple and easily used tables.

Statistical quality control is based on sampling procedures, and it should be recognized that no sampling will be as accurate as a 100 percent inspection. It should also be recognized that a 100 percent inspection made by even a careful and skilled inspector will not necessarily be 100 percent accurate. Due to fatigue, monotony, or just human fallibility, a score of 95 percent is exceptionally good and the average is probably nearer to 90 percent or even 80 percent, and the balance of the defective pieces just "slip by." This human error is reduced somewhat by a sampling procedure since the lots are smaller and the factors of monotony and boredom are less pronounced. It is important that samples be selected truly at random throughout the lot and not just picked off the top.

To decide the size of sample required, it is first necessary to decide on the percentage of defective pieces allowable, referred to as the Acceptable Quality Level or AQL. This decision is based on the cost in lost production time, or otherwise, if a defective part gets through and also on the cost of the inspection itself. Experience with a particular type of part will show just about what the percentage should be. The size of the sample required is then determined from tables such as the following:

TABLE 3. 1 PERCENT ACCEPTABLE QUALITY LEVEL—
NORMAL INSPECTION

Lot Size	Sample Size	No. Defective to	
		Accept	Reject
2–8	2	0	1
9–15	3	0	1
16–25	5	0	1
26–40	7	0	1
41–65	10	0	1
66–110	15	0	1
111–180	25	1	2
181–300	35	1	2
301–500	50	1	2
501–800	75	2	3
801–1300	110	3	4
1301–3200	150	4	5
3201–8000	225	5	6
8,001–22,000	300	7	8
22,001–110,000	450	10	11
110,001–550,000	750	15	16
550,001 and over	1500	25	26

It will be seen that the method becomes much more accurate for large lots and the required sample becomes a much smaller percentage of the total lot.

The decision made on the basis of this sampling is simply whether to accept or reject the entire lot of parts. A more accurate decision can be made by the use of double or sequential sampling plans. These use other tables such as the following:

TABLE 4. 1 PERCENT ACCEPTABLE QUALITY LEVEL, NORMAL INSPECTION
FIRST THREE STAGES OF MULTIPLE SAMPLING TABLE, LARGER LOTS

Lot Size	Sample	Sample Size	Cumu- lative Sample Size	No. Defective to		
				Accept	Take Next Sample	Reject
3,201–8,000	1st	50	50	0	1–2	3
	2nd	50	100	1	2–3	4
	3rd	50	150	2	3–5	6
8,001–22,000	1st	75	75	0	1–3	4
	2nd	75	150	2	3–4	5
	3rd	75	225	3	4–6	7
22,001–110,000	1st	100	100	0	1–4	5
	2nd	100	200	2	3–6	7
	3rd	100	300	5	4–8	9
110,001–550,000	1st	150	150	0	1–5	6
	2nd	150	300	4	5–8	9
	3rd	150	450	7	8–11	12
550,001 and over (extended to illustrate fur- ther stages)	1st	300	300	2	3–8	9
	2nd	300	600	7	8–13	14
	3rd	300	900	12	13–17	18
	4th	300	1200	18	19–22	23
	5th	300	1500	23	24–27	28
	6th	300	1800	28	27–33	34
	7th	300	2100	33	34–38	39
	8th	300	2400	38	39–43	44
	9th	300	2700	46	..	47

It will be seen from this that, if the rejects in the first sample are low enough, the entire lot is accepted. If the rejects are definitely too high, the entire lot is rejected. It is only in doubtful cases where the rejects are between these two figures that further samples are taken to assist in the final decision.

The tables for sequential sampling extend this to as many as 9 samplings in border-line cases where no definite decision can be made from the earlier samplings.

The decision on what happens to a rejected lot of parts is beyond the responsibility of the inspection department. If it was bought from a supplier, it probably will be returned to him. If it was made in the same plant, it will be returned to the production department. In either case, it will have to be sorted, on the basis of a 100 percent check, into good and bad pieces and the good ones submitted again to inspection.

Where samples are checked during the production of a part, it is very helpful to have them classified according to size even if they are within the tolerance range. If a large majority of parts are near the center of the range with the others running about evenly above and below this, as shown in Fig. 684, the work is running normally. If the center of the curve starts to run decidedly to the plus or minus side of the range, a correction in the machine should be made at once to prevent a large number of rejects if the trend continues too far. Charts like these are very helpful in visualizing conditions of this kind and in analyzing the remedial action that should be taken.

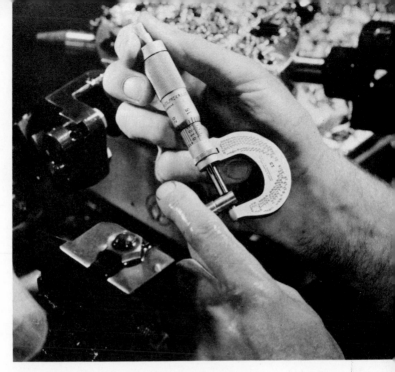

Fig. 632. The hand micrometer is the basic measuring tool in the machine shop. This one has a vernier scale to read to 0.0001 in. (Courtesy, Brown & Sharpe Mfg. Co.)

Fig. 633. A larger micrometer measuring a crankshaft bearing. (Courtesy, The Lufkin Rule Co.)

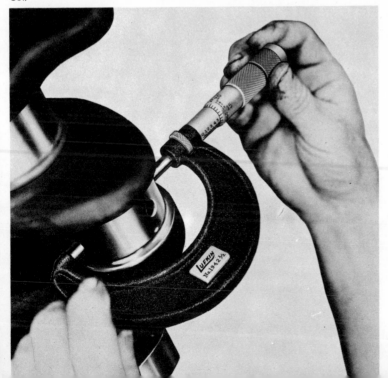

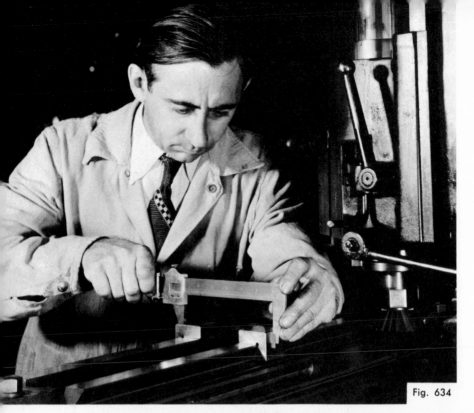

Fig. 634

Figs. 634–635. The vernier caliper supplements the micrometer on larger work. Fig. 635 shows a closeup of the tool in use. (Courtesy, Brown & Sharpe Mfg. Co.)

Fig.

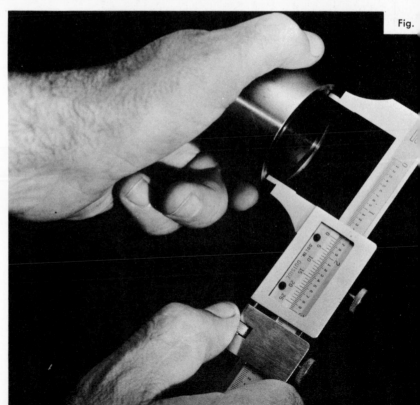

Fig. 636. An inside micrometer measuring the inside diameter of work in a lathe. (Courtesy, The Lufkin Rule Co.)

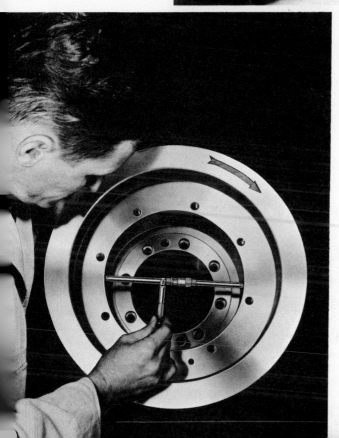

Fig. 637. The inside micrometer can be fitted with extensions for larger work. (Courtesy, The L. S. Starrett Company.)

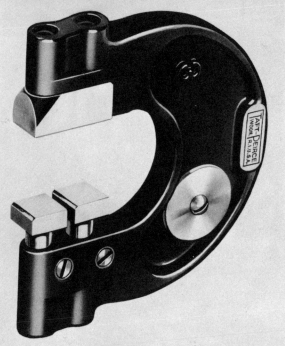

Fig. 638. An adjustable "go and no-go" snap gage which is one of the most universally used of all gages. (Courtesy, The Taft-Peirce Manufacturing Company.)

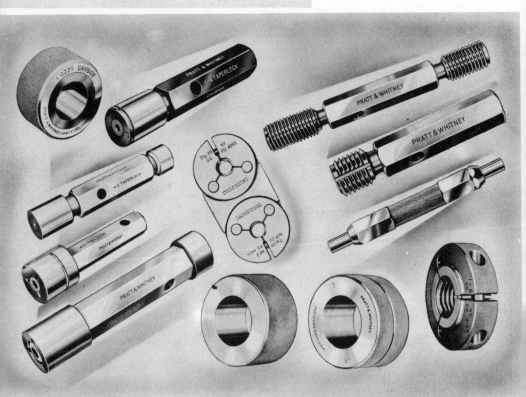

Fig. 639. A group of typical thread, plug, and ring gages that are widely used for production gaging. (Courtesy, Pratt & Whitney Company.)

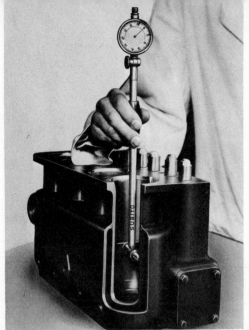

Fig. 640. The dial bore gage is one of the most useful of inspection tools. Furnished in sets with extension measuring rods, each gage may cover a range of several inches. The indicators may be calibrated in 0.001 in. or 0.0001 in. according to the accuracy required. This cut-away view shows the measurement of an automobile cylinder. (Courtesy, L. G. Rose Associates.)

Fig. 641. Gage blocks are used for standards in checking and setting most gages. They usually come in sets like this with the sizes so assorted that any combination, within the range of the set, can be formed. (Courtesy, C. E. Johansson Gage Co.)

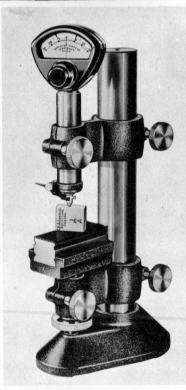

Fig. 642. A 1-in. gage block is used to set a dial comparator. (Courtesy, C. E. Johansson Gage Co.)

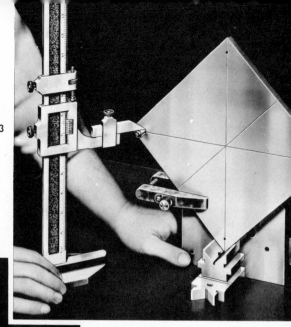

Fig. 643

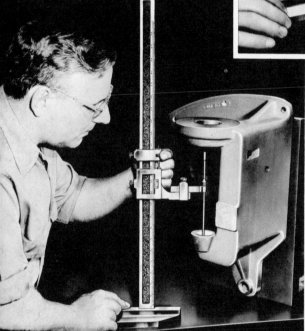

Figs. 643–645. The vernier height gage is a versatile tool for precision layout or measurement from a flat surface. In Fig. 643 it is used for layout work on a surface plate. Figures 644 and 645 show two difficult measuring jobs handled with special attachments. (Courtesy, The L. S. Starrett Company.)

Fig. 644

Fig. 645

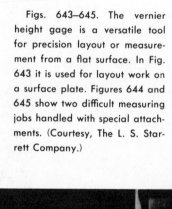

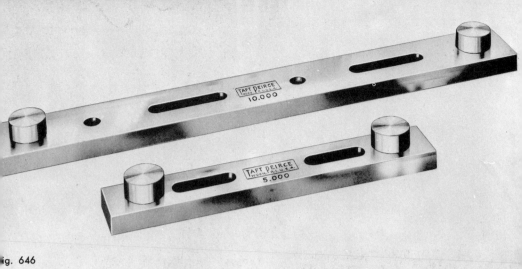

Figs. 646–647. A 10-in and a 5-in. sine bar used for accurate setups for measuring and forming angles. Figure 647 shows a sine bar used on a surface grinder for an angular cut. (Courtesy, The Taft-Peirce Manufacturing Company.)

Fig. 647

Fig. 648. A sine block working on the same principle as Fig. 64[7] used with a surface grinder set up. (Courtesy, The Taft-Peirce Manufacturing Company.)

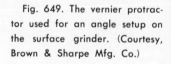

Fig. 649. The vernier protractor used for an angle setup on the surface grinder. (Courtesy, Brown & Sharpe Mfg. Co.)

Fig. 650. A comparator setup for production checking with an indicator at the left that flashes "OK," "+" or "—" as each piece is measured. (Courtesy, George Scherr Co., Inc.)

Fig. 651. Plug and ring gages for internal and external splines and two master gears for use in a gear checking machine. (Courtesy, Michigan Spline Gage Co.)

Fig. 652. A special gage with helical flutes for use with 105-mm shells. (Courtesy, Michigan Spline Gage Co.)

Fig. 653. Spline gages are made in all sizes down to these tiny units. (Courtesy, Michigan Spline Gage Co.)

Fig. 654

Figs. 654–655. A versatile dial gage with interchangeable tips for internal and external grooves and diameters from $\frac{3}{16}$ in to 6 in. In Fig. 654, two of these gages are set up for internal and external grooves. In Fig. 655, one of them is used in a stand as a bench comparator. (Courtesy, Mueller Laboratory.)

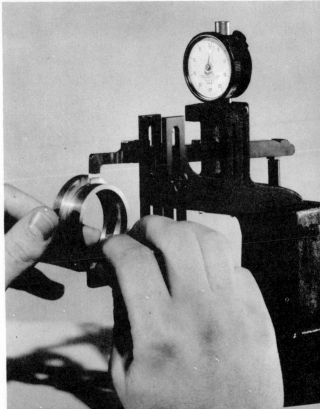

Fig. 655

Fig. 656

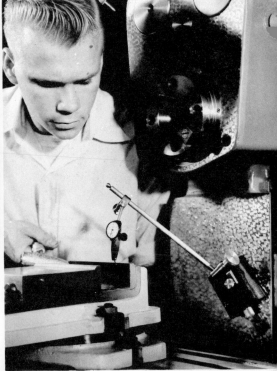

Fig. 657

Fig. 658

Figs. 656–658. The dial indicator with various supporting fixtures does a variety of work. In Fig. 656 it is used to center the work in a lathe chuck. In Fig. 657 it tells when the vise is set properly on a milling machine. In Fig. 658 it centers the work for a boring operation. (Courtesy, Brown & Sharpe Mfg. Co.)

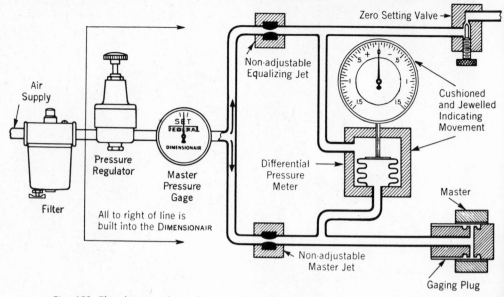

Fig. 659. This drawing shows the principle of operation of the air gage. (Courtesy, Federal Products Corporation.)

Fig. 660. An air gage with a plug and setting ring. Note that each graduation on this dial is 0.00005 in. (½ a ten thousandth) and ±.001 in. is spread out over 180 deg of the dial. (Courtesy, Federal Products Corporation.)

Fig. 661

Figs. 661–662. The air gage is ideal for production checking of precision parts. In Fig. 662 it has been moved to the shop to check work as it comes from the machine. (Courtesy, Pratt & Whitney Company.)

Fig. 662

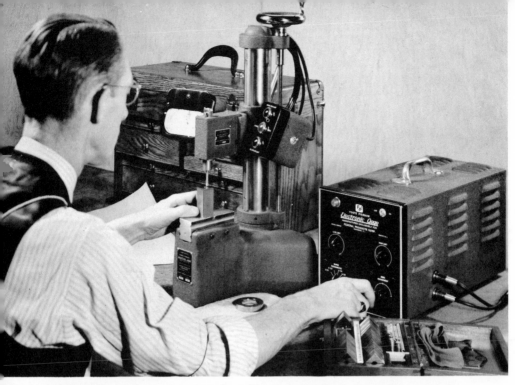

Fig. 663. An electronic gage such as this can be made to give almost any sensitivity required by simply changing the degree of amplification. (Courtesy, Federal Products Corporation.)

Fig. 664. An optical comparator checking the profile of a small gear. (Courtesy, Eastman Kodak Company.)

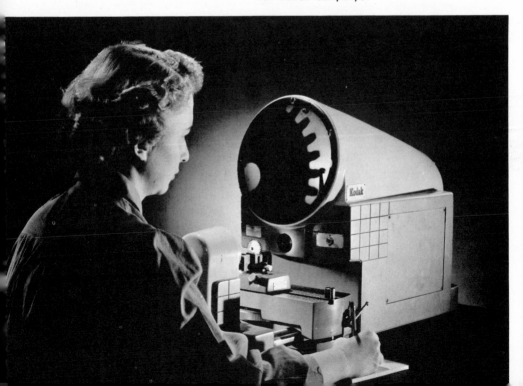

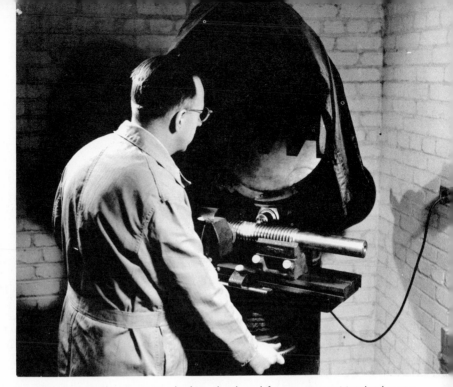

Fig. 665. An optical comparator checking the thread form on a precision lead screw for a grinding machine. (Courtesy, Norton Company.)

Fig. 666. A measuring machine for direct measurements of very high precision. Here it is checking a thread plug gage. (Courtesy, Pratt & Whitney Company.)

Fig. 667. A light wave micrometer for making direct measurements to an accuracy of 0.00001 in. It is here measuring the pitch diameter of a precision screw by means of wires. (Courtesy, The Van Keuren Co.)

Fig. 668. The toolmaker's microscope is an instrument of high precision, especially for toolroom work. (Courtesy, George Scherr Co., Inc.)

Fig. 669

Fig. 670

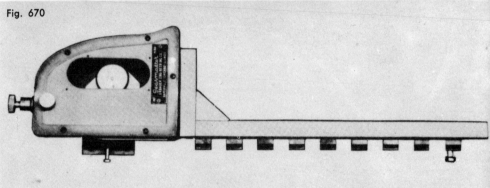

Figs. 669–670. A dial type of gear gage that is adaptable to a wide range of work. Used with charts that give the correct reading over a group of teeth in gears of any size, this accurately checks tooth spacing, cumulative error, and eccentricity in all types of gear. Figure 670 shows a setup for internal gears. (Courtesy, Urbauer Engineering Co.)

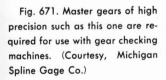

Fig. 671. Master gears of high precision such as this one are required for use with gear checking machines. (Courtesy, Michigan Spline Gage Co.)

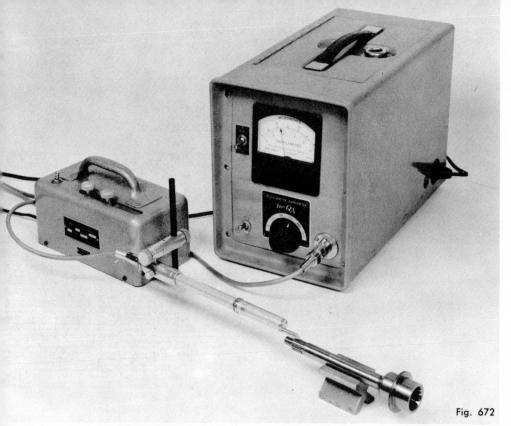

Fig. 672

Figs. 672–673. Accurate measurement of surface roughness is made by electronic instruments such as this Profilometer ® shown measuring a piston ring groove (Fig. 673) and a splined shaft (Fig. 672). (Courtesy, Micrometrical Manufacturing Co.)

Fig. 673

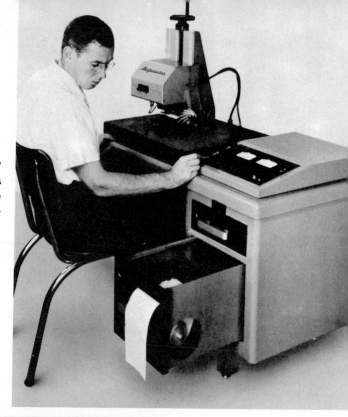

Fig. 674. The "Proficorder" provides a record of the waviness profile of the surface of the piece under test. (Courtesy, Micrometrical Manufacturing Co.)

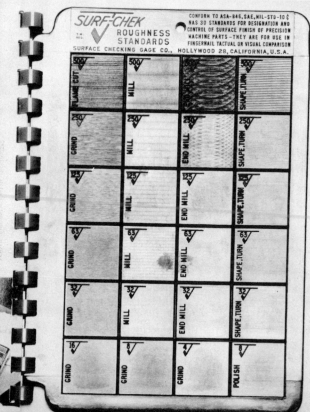

Fig. 675. Surface roughness comparison standards of plastic or metal furnish a convenient guide to surface finish and are often used in the engineering and drafting departments to help in drawing up specifications. (Courtesy, Quality Control Company.)

Fig. 676

Figs. 676–677. The control panel and the interior view of an industrial x-ray unit for both radiographic and fluoroscopic inspection. (Courtesy, X-Ray Division, Westinghouse Electric Corporation.)

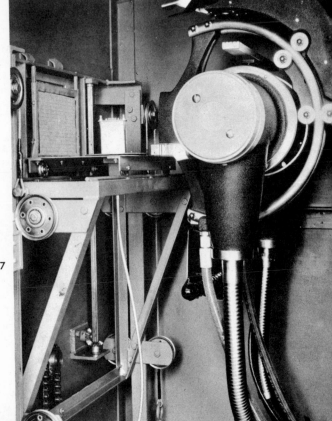

Fig. 677

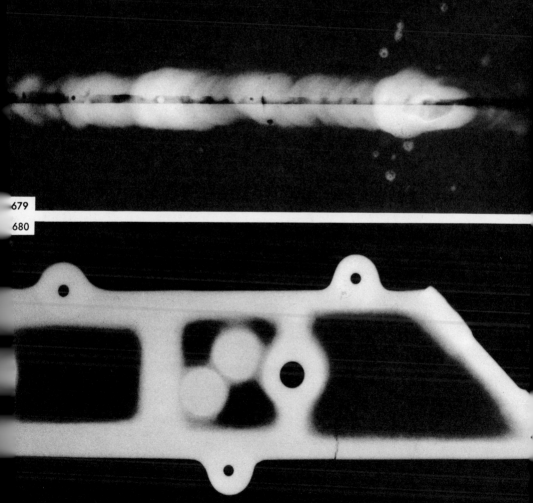

Figs. 678–680. Defects as revealed by the x-ray; porosity in an aluminum casting (Fig. 678); porosity and incomplete fusion in a weld (Fig. 679); a crack in a casting (Fig. 680). (Courtesy, X-ray Division, Westinghouse Electric Corporation.)

Fig. 678

679

680

Fig. 681. A machine for making tests of tensile strength and elongation. The sample under test is clamped between the two heavy members at the left and stretched to the breaking point. (Courtesy, Baldwin-Lima-Hamilton Corp.)

Fig. 682. A Rockwell hardness tester in use. (Courtesy, Wilson Mechanical Instrument Div., American Chain & Cable Company, Inc.)

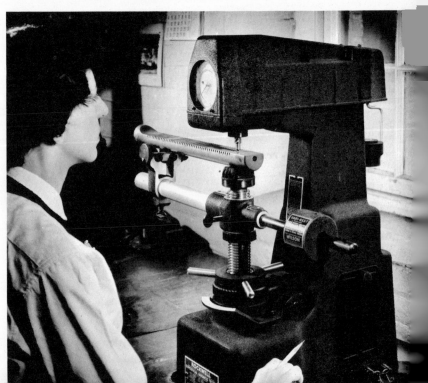

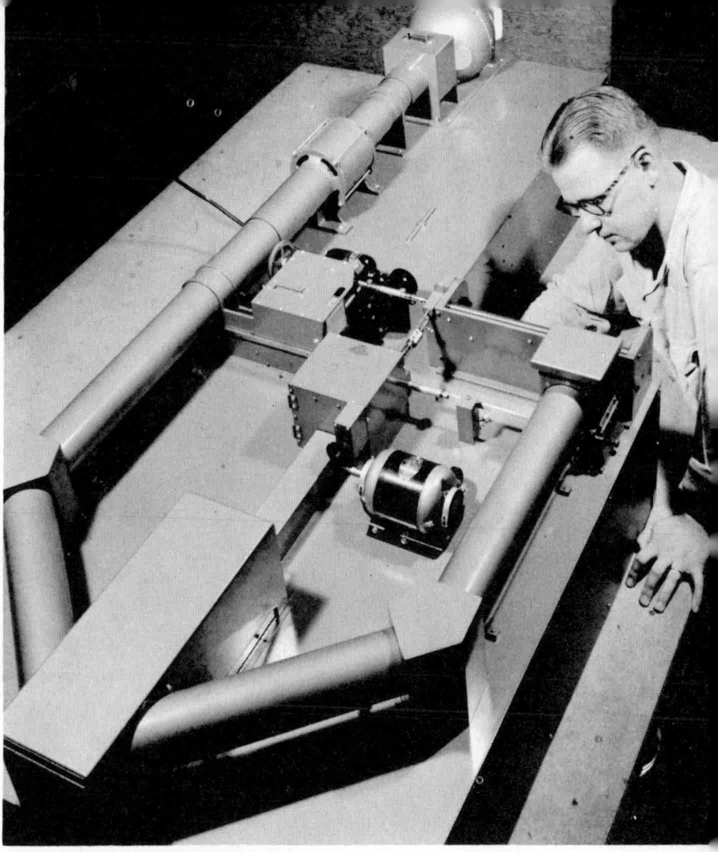

Fig. 683. The spectrophotometer makes accurate color matching possible. It records a curve showing the reflectance for each wavelength of the visible spectrum. This one is used for porcelain enamels. (Courtesy, Ferro Corporation.)

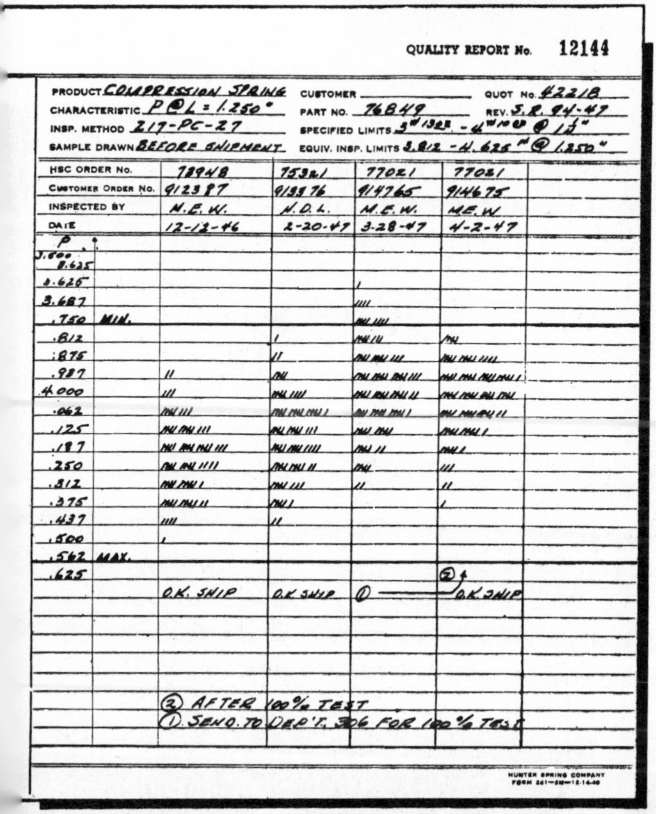

QUALITY REPORT No. 12144

PRODUCT *COMPRESSION SPRING*   CUSTOMER _____   QUOT No. *42218*
CHARACTERISTIC *P @ L = 1.250°*   PART NO. *76849*   REV. *S.R. 94-47*
INSP. METHOD *217-PC-27*   SPECIFIED LIMITS *3#/32R - 4#/10# @ 1¼"*
SAMPLE DRAWN *BEFORE SHIPMENT*   EQUIV. INSP. LIMITS *3.812 - 4.625# @ 1.250"*

HSC ORDER No.	78948	75321	77021	77021
CUSTOMER ORDER No.	912387	913976	914765	914675
INSPECTED BY	N.E.W.	N.D.L.	M.E.W.	M.E.W.
DATE	12-12-46	2-20-47	3-28-47	4-2-47

P				
3.800				
3.625				
0.625			I	
3.687			IIII	
.750 MIN.			PHI IIII	
.812		I	PHI III	PHI
.875		II	PHI PHI III	PHI PHI IIII
.937	II	PHI	PHI PHI PHI III	PHI PHI PHI I
4.000	III	PHI IIII	PHI PHI PHI II	PHI PHI PHI PHI
.062	PHI III	PHI PHI PHI	PHI PHI PHI I	PHI PHI PHI II
.125	PHI PHI III	PHI PHI III	PHI PHI	PHI PHI PHI II
.187	PHI PHI PHI IIII	PHI PHI IIII	PHI II	PHI I
.250	PHI PHI IIII	PHI PHI II	PHI	III
.312	PHI PHI I	PHI III	II	
.375	PHI PHI II	PHI I	I	I
.437	IIII	II		
.500	I			
.562 MAX.				
.625	O.K. SHIP	O.K. SHIP	① ——	② O.K. SHIP

③ AFTER 100% TEST
① SEND TO DEP'T. 306 FOR 100% TEST

Fig. 684. A quality report made out as the parts are inspected. The first two columns show normal distribution near the center of the tolerance range. The last two columns show parts running near one end of the range and requiring further check. (Courtesy, Hunter Spring Company.)

19

Woodworking Processes

When we think of modern manufacturing, we are inclined to think only of the metal-working industries. However, woodworking is a very important part of our national production picture, with its products ranging from mass-produced items such as furniture and television cabinets to precision craftsmanship such as is found in patterns for metal castings. Other important products are mill-work items such as window sash and doors, prefabricated houses, kitchen cabinets, boats, and plywood. Improvements in woodworking machinery and processes have kept pace with those in the metal-working industry, although woodworking machinery is usually more versatile and less automatic because most wood products are not so highly standardized for mass production as are some metal products.

WOOD VARIETIES

Many species of trees are important sources of wood for industry; only a few of the most commonly used varieties will be described here. Trees are divided commonly into hardwood and softwood. This is an arbitrary distinction based not on the relative hardness, but rather on the nature of the tree. All deciduous trees (those that shed their leaves) are referred to as hardwoods and all evergreen trees are softwoods. Actually, some of the "hardwoods" (such as basswood and poplar) may be much softer than some of the "softwoods" (such as yellow and Norway pine).

PLYWOOD MANUFACTURING

Much wood that is used in production processes is in the form of plywood or veneer. The first step in the manufacture of plywood is the cutting of the veneer. Logs that are to be made into veneer may

TABLE 5. AVERAGE CHARACTERISTICS OF COMMONLY USED WOODS *

Variety	Weight per cu ft (12% moisture)	Strength (Bending)	Hardness	Shrinkage (Low Rating Desirable)	Common Uses
Ash	41	good	good	low	Tool handles, agricultural implements
Avodire	36	fair	fair	low	Furniture (light color good for blond finishes)
Basswood	26	low	very low	medium	Boxes, baskets, woodenware, luggage (covered with leather or plastic)
Beech	45	good	good	medium	Flooring, chairs, woodenware (fine uniform grain)
Birch	43	good	good	medium	Furniture, interior trim (takes good maple finish or good base for enamel)
Cherry	35	fair	fair	low	Furniture, paneling, engraver's blocks (fine grain, excellent furniture wood)
Chestnut	30	low	low	low	Lumber cores for veneer panels, caskets, boxes, and crates
Cypress	32	low	very low	low	Doors, sash, exterior woodwork, tanks (decay resistant, holds paint well)
Douglas fir	31	fair	low	medium	Plywood, structural lumber, doors, trim, poles, ties (very important commercial wood)
Ebony	63	very good	very good	low	Brush backs, ornamental wood novelties, cutlery handles, inlay (dense grain, dark color)
Elm	36	good	good	medium	Barrels, kegs, vehicle parts, boxes and crates (very tough, resists splitting)
Gum	34	fair	fair	high	Furniture, plywood (fine grain, warps badly, takes good finish, often finished to imitate mahogany)
Hickory	51	very good	good	high	Tool handles, poles, spokes, ladder rungs, golf club handles (tough, high shock resistance)
Lignum vitae	80	very good	very good	low	Mallet heads, bearings, rulers (extremely hard, dense wood, valuable mechanically)
Mahogany	31	fair	good	very low	Furniture, paneling, cabinets, patterns for castings (beautifully figured veneers available)
Maple, hard	44	good	good	medium	Furniture, flooring, interior trim, bearings, and mechanical parts (fine uniform grain)

TABLE 5. AVERAGE CHARACTERISTICS OF COMMONLY USED WOODS * (Continued)

Variety	Weight per cu ft (12% moisture)	Strength (Bending)	Hardness	Shrinkage (Low Rating Desirable)	Common Uses
Maple, soft	33	fair	fair	medium	Furniture, lumber cores for plywood, interior trim (grain similar to hard maple but much softer wood)
Oak	47	good	good	medium	Flooring, interior trim, furniture, cooperage, timbers (open grain, an important commercial wood)
Philippine Lauan	36	low	low	medium	Furniture, doors, interior paneling and trim (often called Philippine mahogany, open grain, stringy)
Pine, white	27	low	very low	very low	Millwork, interior trim, patterns for castings (fine, uniform grain, easily worked, holds paint well)
Pine, yellow	36	fair	fair	medium	Timbers, framing, general structural use (splits easily, poor paint retention)
Poplar	28	low	low	medium	Interior trim, furniture, lumber cores for plywood, boxes and crates (takes glue and paint well)
Primavera	30	fair	fair	low	Furniture, cabinets, plywood (sometimes called "white mahogany," used for blond finishes)
Redwood	28	fair	low	low	Sash and doors, siding, interior and exterior trim, tanks, timbers (very durable, holds paint well)
Spruce	28	fair	fair	medium	Sash and doors, general construction, ladders, boxes and crates (very high strength to weight ratio)
Sycamore	34	fair	fair	medium	Furniture (especially drawer slides), interior trim, baskets, boxes and crates (fine uniform grain)
Teak	43	good	good	high	Ship decks, floors, furniture (tough oily wood)
Walnut, black	39	good	good	medium	Furniture, interior trim, paneling, gunstocks, novelties (dense, dark color, beautifully figured veneers available)

* Data from Forest Products Laboratory and Fine Hardwoods Association.

be rotary cut or sliced in any one of several ways according to the type of grain desired and the use that is to be made of the veneer. The rotary-cut veneer is the least expensive and is used for the cores of plywood and for face veneer when the figure is not important. Fir plywood is usually rotary cut, as are panels for crating and structural purposes. In most woods, rotary-cut veneer is characterized by a "wild" grain pattern which is sometimes suitable for ornamental paneling if selected carefully.

To obtain the rotary cut, the logs are stripped of bark and soaked in water or steamed for a long period to soften the wood fibers. Then the log is mounted in a heavy veneer lathe and is rotated slowly while a heavy knife, the entire length of the log, is pressed against it. The knife cuts a shaving of the desired thickness as the log revolves, and this is carried away on a conveyor in the form of a continuous sheet of veneer. The sheet is then sheared to the desired sizes.

For most ornamental and furniture purposes, a sliced veneer is preferred to the rotary cut. The slicing may be done in any one of several ways, as shown in Fig. 685, and each of these cuts produces a characteristic type of grain figure in a given wood. Some typical grain figures are shown in Fig. 687. To facilitate the matching of the grain, the strips of veneer are kept in order as they are sliced from the log and all of the strips that are cut from the log, or section of log, are bound up together in a bundle known as a "flitch."

After drying, the sheets of veneer are ready to be formed into plywood. The rotary-cut veneer is usually in large enough sheets so that it does not require much splicing to make up the size of panel desired, but the sliced veneers are in strips of varying widths according to the size of the original log and the method of cutting. These strips must be trimmed to a straight edge and spliced together at their edges to make up a sheet the width of the desired panel. This splicing is done in a special taping machine which glues the edges together and applies gummed paper tape to hold them and reinforce the joint until the panel is completed. Synthetic resin glues are usually used and electronic heating often speeds up the curing cycle for more rapid production. If well-matched grain patterns are desired on the panel, the edge gluing is an important operation requiring skill and judgment on the part of the operator. If rotary-cut face veneers are to be used, and the grain is not important, the process can be very rapid and almost automatic.

The core of most plywood is made up of rotary-cut veneer sheets from $\frac{1}{16}$ in. to $\frac{1}{8}$ in. thick, with the grain running alternately lengthwise and crosswise of the panel. An odd number of layers is always used to make a balanced construction and to minimize warping of the panel. The face veneers, especially if they are made of expensive woods and selected grain patterns, are much thinner—usually $\frac{1}{28}$ in. or $\frac{1}{32}$ in.

Adhesive is applied to the veneer sheets, they are assembled together to make up a panel of the desired thickness, and heat and pressure are applied to complete the bonding process. The type of adhesive (see Chap. 15) and the method of application and curing will vary according to the end use of the panel. Most of the better panels are now made with synthetic resin adhesives, and many of them are cured by dielectric heating units (see Chap. 17). These newer adhesives cost more than the older vegetable and animal glues, but the reduced curing time of the synthetics may make the over-all cost no higher if modern presses and heating methods are used.

For certain purposes, such as furniture tops and doors, where warpage must be kept to a minimum, or the edges must be finished, panels with a core of solid lumber are preferred. Usually the lumber core is made of some close-grained wood such as poplar or soft maple with low warpage. It is preferably made of narrow strips glued together. After gluing, the core is sanded or planed to a smooth surface and uniform thickness, a cross-banding of veneer, with the grain running at right angles to the core, is applied, and then the face veneer with the grain running in the same direction as the lumber core. This construction costs much more than the rotary veneer core, and more than solid lumber, but it forms the best construction for many applications, and is widely used in the better grades of furniture.

Veneer core plywood may be made into curved shapes by forming it over suitable molds and holding it in shape and under pressure until the glue is hard. For small quantities, inexpensive wood molds can be used, but for larger runs and greater accuracy, they are made of iron or steel.

Plywood made with waterproof glue is widely used for boats, trailers, and truck bodies. It has greater stiffness than metal of equivalent weight and the cost is less than that of polyester–glass fiber panels which are now coming into use for some of these applications. Plywood panels are also used for sheathing in homes, and for other building and structural purposes.

Where still greater stiffness to weight ratio is required than in conventional plywood, panels are made up with cores of cellular or honeycomb construction made of strong paper, fiber or wood strips with two layers of thin veneer on each side of it, as shown in Fig. 556, Chap. 15. When these panels are properly bonded with suitable adhesives, they are extremely light and rigid and are suitable for doors and for certain marine and aircraft applications such as floors and partitions.

LUMBER PREPARATION AND GRADING

The first operation, when the logs reach the mill, is to saw them into boards or timbers. The sawing may be done with either a large circular saw or a very heavy bandsaw. Often the logs are cut into thick planks or timbers which are later resawed at the lumberyard or the factory to the desired thickness. This makes for a more flexible inventory where many sizes may be required. The resawing is usually done by means of bandsaws especially designed for this purpose.

Newly sawed lumber has a high moisture content (30 percent to 250 percent of the weight of the dry wood) and for most purposes must be dried before it is used, to prevent excessive shrinkage and warping. The drying can be done in the open air, in piles with air spaces between the layers, or it can be done more quickly and under better control in drying kilns. While much lumber for building purposes is air dried, kiln drying is preferred for most of the material used in production processes. For kiln drying, the lumber is piled on cars or pallets with air space between the layers and is placed in the kilns where it is subjected to a temperature of about 120 F to 170 F for a period of several days. Air is circulated through the kiln to remove the moisture as it is evaporated from the wood. The moisture content of the kiln-dried lumber should be from 4 percent to 15 percent.

Lumber is sold by the "board foot," this being 1 sq ft of surface area, 1 in. thick. A square foot of plank 2 in. thick would be 2 board feet. The thickness of the rough-sawed lumber is usually given in quarters of an inch; 1 in. being ¼, 1½ in. ⁶⁄₄, 2 in. ⁸⁄₄, and so on. Widths are usually random, from 6 in. to 12 in. or more, and lengths are random in 2-ft multiples from 10 ft to 16 ft. Specified widths and lengths can be ordered by paying a premium.

Standard grades of hardwood are as follows:

Firsts	#2 Common
Seconds	Sound Wormy
Selects	#3A Common
#1 Common	#3B Common

CUTTING AND SHAPING PROCESSES

Planing. For most purposes, lumber is planed or dressed before other work is done on it. This removes the rough surface left by the sawmill and reduces the thickness to a more uniform measurement. From $\frac{1}{16}$ in. to $\frac{1}{8}$ in. is removed by the planer from each surface, $\frac{4}{4}$ boards usually being dressed to $1\frac{3}{16}$ or $\frac{3}{4}$ in thickness. The edges may be dressed or not according to the operations to follow. Planers may surface one or both sides of a board in one operation and they are made to take from 12 in. to 52 in. in width. In the wider machines, several boards may be fed in, side by side, at one time. The cutting is done by rapidly rotating heads carrying two or four knives and the boards are fed against them by power-feed rollers.

Jointing. The jointer is quite similar to the planer and is used for smoothing and truing up the edges of boards. It has the same type of rotating cutting head, but this is not so long as in the planer, sizes from 6 in. to 24 in. being commonly used. The cutter is located below the table or bed, and a "fence" or guide at right angles to the table is used to support and guide the board, which is usually fed by hand across the cutting knives. The fence may be adjusted to cut bevels or angles and the front section of the table, ahead of the cutter, is raised or lowered to regulate the depth of cut.

Circular Sawing. Most straight cutting of lumber or plywood, either with or against the grain of the wood, is done with circular saws. They are made with a wide variety of teeth for different purposes and in diameters from 6 in. to 6 ft. The largest sizes are used only in sawmills for cutting logs into lumber. Sizes from 8 in. to 24 in. are most commonly used for production work. The principal types of machines for using circular saw blades are as follows:

1. The swinging or sliding cut-off saw, where the blade and its supporting shaft or "arbor" swing or slide across the work. The work is supported on a stationary table with the saw mounted above it. These are used principally for cutting lumber to lengths.

2. The tilting arbor saw table, which is the most versatile of all circular saws and is widely used for ripping, cross-cutting, grooving (with a special wide cutter called a "dado head") and forming shaped edges (with a special "molding head"). The saw and arbor may be set at any angle up to 45 deg with the table for cutting bevels, and the cut-off gage may be set at an angle for cutting miters like the corners of picture frames.

3. The radial saw, which rivals the versatility of the tilting arbor saw, but which carries the saw and its driving motor above the work table instead of below. For most operations on the radial saw, except ripping long boards, the saw is moved across the work, which remains stationary. The saw may be tilted and moved at various angles to do the operations described for the tilting arbor saw.

4. The tilting table saw, which is similar to the tilting arbor type except that the table tilts, and the saw and arbor remain stationary, for bevel cuts.

5. Specialized rip saws, often with power feed for ripping boards to width. These may be used in gangs of two or more blades, side by side, for multiple ripping of narrow strips.

6. Electric hand saws, which are convenient for use on construction work and for rough cutting of large panels which are awkward to handle on a saw table.

Band Sawing. In the band saw, the blade, instead of being circular, is in the form of an endless band or belt of flexible steel with the teeth formed in one edge. This band runs around two large-diameter rubber-surfaced wheels, one of which is driven by a motor and one is an idler (see Fig. 698). A table, which supports the work, is mounted near the lower wheel with the blade passing through it. It can be seen that the diameter of the wheels determines the size of work that can be handled, and this dimension is commonly given as the size rating of band saw machines. Sizes from 14 in. to 48 in. are in common use.

The band saw is used primarily with narrow blades, from ¼ in. to ½ in. wide, for sawing irregular or curved work. The work is usually guided by hand, except in circular cutting, and a skilled operator can do very fast and quite accurate work, following an outline drawn from a pattern or template. If the workpieces are thin, a number of them may be fastened together to form a stack several inches thick, which is cut at one time. Only the top piece needs to be marked in this case.

The band saw can be used also for ripping, and for this purpose much wider blades, up to several inches in width, usually are used. The band saw blade is thinner than a circular saw of comparable capacity, so there is less waste of material in the saw cut. This is of particular advantage in the "resawing" of thick planks into several thinner boards. Special types of band saw machines are made for this purpose.

Shaping Operations. In the shaper, a vertical spindle, driven at high speed, projects through a table and carries, on its upper end, a cutter with knives of the proper shape for the cut to be made. It is used to form molding, to shape the edges of table tops and the like, and to cut grooves for "tongue and groove" joints. A wide variety of standard cutters is available. Usually the work is fed manually against these knives, although power feed is sometimes used for production operations. A fence is used as a guide for shaping straight edges, but for curved work a collar of the proper diameter may be used on the spindle which bears against the edge of the work and regulates the depth of cut. The shaper is one of the most dangerous of woodworking machines and on some operations is difficult to guard properly. It should be operated only by experienced personnel and guards should be used to the greatest possible extent.

Double-spindle shapers are sometimes used with the two cutters of the same shape, but running in opposite directions. The operator shifts from one spindle to the other as the grain in the workpiece changes so that he is always working "with the grain" for a smooth cut. Most of the modern shapers use a single spindle operated at much higher speed than the older types and using a small diameter cutter having three or more knives. These cut smoothly either with or against the grain and for most work only a single spindle is needed.

Automatic shapers are also made which are suitable for high-production work. In these machines, the work is clamped to a rotating table and the spindle is guided in the desired path by means of a roller which follows a pattern of wood or metal. Large savings in labor are made by these machines where the production is large enough to justify their cost.

A variation of the shaper is the molding machine, or "sticker," for forming long lengths of molding of various shapes and sizes. These take strips of wood and use from one to four shaper cutters operating against the various edges of the strip to form it into simple or complex molding shapes. Since these machines are designed only for straight work, the cutters can be well guarded and the work can be fed at a predetermined rate against the cutters by means of power-driven rollers. It requires considerable time to set up the molding machine for a given shape of molding and it is not practical to do this unless a substantial quantity is required.

Another variation of the shaper is the tenoner, which is made in either single-end or double-end types. Tenoners are used widely in production furniture and cabinet making to form the tongue or tenon on one or both ends of rails or panels. The cutter spindles are vertical, and, when two of them are used, the spacing between them is adjustable. A power feed carries the workpiece between them and forms a tenon on both ends, at the same time trimming it to the proper dimension. These are also production tools that require quantity runs to show a saving over the simpler, hand-operated machines.

Routing. The router uses a small cutter, usually from ⅛ in. to ¾ in. in diameter, driven at very high speeds of from 10,000 rpm to 40,000 rpm. The cutter is above the work, and the table, carrying the work, may be raised or the cutter lowered to bring the two together. A pin, the size of the cutter and located directly below it in the table, is often used to guide the work by means of a pattern or template. The work is clamped to the top of the pattern, the cutter and the work are brought together, and the work is moved around manually with the pattern in contact with the guide pin. Thus the cutter forms the same shape as the pattern in the workpiece. Originally, the router was used for light cutting of narrow grooves to form shallow flat carvings for ornamental purposes. Routers are now made in a much heavier form and are driven by larger motors which make them very useful for cutting irregular openings of all kinds, even in ¾-in. panels. Because of the high cutter speed, the cut is quite smooth and can be made almost as fast as the work and the pattern can be moved around the guide pin. Routers are widely used in radio cabinet work for speaker grilles, for record changer panels and the like, and in furniture making. Carbide cutters are often used in cutting plywood and composition hardboards where the material is quite abrasive.

Drilling or Boring and Mortising. These are important processes in woodworking just as in the machining of metal. The same types of drill presses can be used, but those made especially for woodworking generally are of lighter construction and have greater clearance between the drill spindle to take larger size work. The spindles also run at the higher speeds which are adapted to use in wood. The drills themselves, usually referred to as "bits," are of different design for faster cutting in this softer material.

In addition to standard vertical drill presses, vertical and horizontal "boring machines" are made which are especially adapted to making holes for use with wooden dowels to form a common type of joint in furniture work. These are really specialized forms of drill presses with work-holding fixtures that do this one job very efficiently.

Drill presses and specialized adaptations of them are used also for cutting square holes for mortising. A conventional bit drills a round hole and a square chisel is forced into the wood behind its cutting edge, forming the square hole. By making several of these square holes side by side, a rectangular mortise is formed. Chain-type mortisers, which form a rectangular mortise, either completely through the work or with a rounded bottom, are faster for production work.

Sanding. While the sanding of wood with coated abrasives is usually thought of as a finishing process, it is often economcial for removing a considerable amount of stock. The abrasive material may be a flint sand, crushed garnet, or aluminum oxide. The latter two, while they are more expensive, stand up much better and are preferred for production work. They are coated on various grades of paper and cloth according to the application. The coarseness of the grit is rated by the scales as follows:

TABLE 6. OLD AND NEW
DESIGNATIONS OF COATED
ABRASIVES

Old	New
3½	20
3	24
2½	30
2	36
1½	40
1	50
½	60
0	80
2/0	100
3/0	120
4/0	150
5/0	180
6/0	220
7/0	240
8/0	280
9/0	320

Finer grits up to 600 are
designated only by number.

The grains of abrasive as they are applied to the backing material may be spaced closely for smooth finishing or spaced widely for rapid cutting, removing paint or varnish, or on glued work where the closely spaced grains would tend to clog up.

For most production work, coated abrasives are used in the form of belts, disks, or drums. Sheets are used for hand sanding or for hand sanding machines.

The overhead belt sander shown in Fig. 708 is in very general use. The abrasive belt travels above the work which rests on a rolling table moving at right angles to the belt travel. The belt is brought into contact with the work by means of a block pressed against the smooth back surface. The block is manipulated either by hand or mechanically to provide an even and uniform cutting or smoothing action over the surface of the work. In some machines, the table may be lowered so that complete cabinets may be sanded after assembly. The overhead belt sander is used primarily for smoothing cabinet work prior to the finishing operations.

The vertical belt sander is quite versatile, especially on small work. A flat metal plate, built into the machine, supports the belt in back of the working point and the work is pressed against the belt. A table that can be adjusted to various angles usually supports the work, which is held manually. In addition to smoothing small pieces, this type of sander is often used for removing a considerable amount of wood in rounding corners, beveling, and truing up roughly sawed edges. With special belts coated with aluminum oxide, the belt sander is often used for metal work also (see Fig. 297, Chap. 5).

The disk sander is a very simple machine. Since it leaves a circular pattern of sanding marks, it is not suitable for finishing work. In small sizes, it can perform some of the wood- or metal-grinding operations of the vertical belt sander; in large sizes, it is often used for cleaning up the backs of cabinets after assembly or for cleaning up and rounding the corners of lock-corner boxes that are to be covered with leatherette for luggage.

The drum sander is used for production sanding of flat lumber or plywood. The work is fed mechanically under the drum which smoothes and reduces the work to uniform thickness. Several drums are often used successively in the same machine with the grit of abrasive becoming finer as the work progresses. Large machines of the multiple-drum type are used in the manufacture of plywood for the final finishing operations on plywood sheets.

Vertical spindle sanders (see Fig. 709), fitted with abrasive sleeves, are used for finishing the edges of curved or irregular work. The spindle often oscillates up and down as it rotates to permit the use of longer sleeves and to prevent the rapid clogging of the abrasive surface. Shaped spindles or drums can be used for sanding molding.

Hand sanders with air or electrically operated vibrating pads are very useful on many of the final sanding and rubbing operations that otherwise would be done by hand.

ASSEMBLY METHODS

Most of the assembly of wood products is done by means of glue joints (see Chap. 15). Usually clamps are required to hold the work while the glue is hardening, although sometimes wood screws or nails are used instead, where their appearance is not objectionable. Wood is not so uniform a material as metal, and there is still a considerable amount of craftsmanship involved in its assembly and finishing. In most small- and moderate-size production work, the glue is still applied by hand, parts are assembled manually (often with some individual fitting), and the clamping is done with a large number of standard clamps of various types.

With larger production, special fixtures replace the clamps, and these are often operated by means of air or hydraulic cylinders. The glue may be applied to flat surfaces by rollers, or, in grooves or narrow spaces, by air-fed guns or spreaders. The newer synthetic resin glues reduce the time the work must be left in the clamps from hours to minutes (15 to 30 min is common). This can be reduced still further by dielectric heating (see Chap. 17), sometimes to a matter of seconds. This reduced clamping time makes it practical to use more elaborate clamping fixtures, with resulting improvement in production, reduction in space requirements, and greater accuracy of the finished work.

Wood screws and special fasteners, without glue, are used chiefly where it is necessary to dismantle the product for shipment or for access to equipment mounted inside a wood cabinet. Wood screws may be driven manually by electric- or air-operated screwdrivers or by automatic feed machines where the work is small enough to be handled easily. Some of the newer recessed-head screws are often preferred to the standard slotted type because of easier use with the power drivers and reduced danger of damage to the work caused by the driver slipping (see Chap. 12).

Nails are used to hold cleats, backs, and bottoms in place while glue is drying and also without glue in packing cases and the like. In addition to hand-driven nails and brads, power-driven staples are used very commonly for attaching upholstery, radio grille cloth, and work of this type. Machines are also available which form nails out of wire and drive them at one operation. These greatly increase production if much nailing work is to be done.

WOOD FINISHING

Wood products may be finished with paint, enamel, varnish, stain, or lacquer, or by combinations of these materials. The use of paint or enamel for preservation or ornament is so well known as to require no comment. These materials can be applied by brushing, dipping, or spraying. The two latter methods are usual in production. Drying can be done at room temperature, but the process is often accelerated by the use of heat in the form of ovens or infra-red lamps.

It is in the finishing of furniture and cabinets that wood finishing becomes most important and often accounts for the major part of the production cost. Most production furniture finishing is now done with lacquer, although some of the synthetic varnishes are sometimes used. These synthetics usually require heat for rapid curing, but they can be formulated for many special characteristics, such as toughness, mar resistance, and resistance to alcohol and other chemicals. The old varnish finishes that required days of drying time in dust-free rooms do not fit into modern production schedules. Lacquers are almost always applied by spraying, with conveyors often used to carry the work to and from the spray booths.

Even at best, a good finish requires many coats and a considerable amount of hand work. Drying of lacquer is usually at room temperature, but it may be accelerated by a moderate amount of heat. A typical schedule for finishing mahogany in good radio cabinets or furniture would be as follows, after careful hand sanding of the finished piece:

1. Stain with non-grain-raising stain, sprayed on. Dry about 1 hr at room temperature.

2. Wash coat, of very thin lacquer, with a little color added. Dry ½ hr and hand sand lightly with 7/0 paper. This wash coat keeps the filler from soaking in too much and causing a "muddy" finish.

3. Fill the grain with a filler and stain combined. This is applied by brush or spray and thoroughly rubbed in by hand, working across the grain with burlap or other coarse material. This fills the pores in the wood and adds most of the necessary color. It is a very important step in obtaining a good finish. The filler should dry at least 4 hrs unless artificial heat is used.

4. Seal with lacquer sealer sprayed on. Dry 1 hr and sand thoroughly by hand or with a vibrating type of hand sander, using 5/0 paper. The sealer is made to sand easily and to provide a good base for the lacquer.

5. Touch up edges and light spots with lacquer shading stain, using a very small spray gun. At this point, also, any small pits or defects in the wood can be "burned in," using colored shellac sticks and a heated knife. This is a hand operation requiring considerable skill.

6. First coat of lacquer sprayed on and dried for 1 hr.

7. Second coat of lacquer, dried over night. Sand by hand or hand machine using #360 paper and rubbing oil until surface is

smooth and level. Then rub by hand with 4/0 steel wool and rubbing wax if a dull finish is desired or with felt and a rubbing compound for a high gloss finish.

Many variations of this schedule are possible, but it gives an idea of why good wood finishes are, by nature, expensive.

The use of special spray equipment, designed to heat the lacquer as it is being sprayed, allows the use of lacquer containing more solids and less solvent. The result is a heavier coating of finish at one application. Two coats of hot lacquer approximate the result of three regular coats and give a very fine finish. If the finish is not too critical, one coat of hot lacquer over the sealer may suffice.

To avoid expensive hand-rubbing operations, a dull or "flat" lacquer is sometimes used as a final coat without rubbing. This is suitable only for low-cost furniture or cabinets, since the effect is not nearly so good as the rubbed finish. In some intermediate applications, the top of a cabinet may be rubbed, and the sides, which are not so conspicuous, may be finished with flat lacquer. This is often done on radio and television cabinets, where cost is very important.

Bleaches are often used to obtain the modern light finishes on darker woods like mahogany or walnut. The bleaching is done on the raw wood before any other finishes are applied and the work must be thoroughly dried before proceeding with the rest of the finishing operation. Bleaching may be done with either a one-solution or a two-solution process, the latter generally being preferred. The basis for most bleaching solutions is either oxalic acid or hydrogen peroxide. Bleaching adds considerably to the cost of the finish and also leads to certain troubles, such as a darkening of the wood upon aging and a deterioration of the finishing coats if the bleach is not properly neutralized and dried. For this reason, naturally light colored woods—such as primavera, avodire, birch, maple, and white gum—are often preferred for light finishes, even in cases where the wood itself may be more expensive.

Simulated bleached finishes can be made by means of toners, which are a thin solution of light pigments in lacquer. If these are applied carefully, before the wood is filled, a result quite similar to bleaching is obtained, especially on open-grained woods such as mahogany and oak. The cost is much less than that of a bleached finish, but the result is not quite so good since there is a tendency for the toner to cover some of the grain, leading to a "muddy" or "painted"-looking finish.

Many of the radio and television cabinets and lower-priced furniture pieces, with surfaces apparently made of beautifully figured veneer or inlaid designs, are actually finished by means of a printed film or decalcomania which is bonded to the surface of low-priced wood or composition hardboard. Lacquer is applied over this and the final appearance is hard to tell from the actual veneer. Of course, any scratch exposes the material underneath and any attempt to remove the finish for refinishing would also remove the film. The film itself is not cheap, but costs much less than highly figured veneers. It has the advantage, from a production if not an artistic viewpoint, of being uniform, so that all pieces are exactly alike. These films are also available in simulated marble, fabric, leather, and, in fact, any surface that can be reproduced photographically.

WOOD COMPOSITION BOARDS

The manufacture of panels made of wood chips or fibers, bonded with plastic adhesives, is rapidly becoming a very important industry, intermediate between the woodworking and the plastic fields. The idea itself is not new since panels made of wood fibers, similar to cardboard, or of loosely bonded fibers of sugar cane or corn by-products, have been made for many years. These have been used mostly in the building industry for wallboard and sheathing. Hardboards of wood fiber, mostly in thicknesses of ⅛ in. to ¼ in., have found many uses in the manufacturing industries as well as building.

However, the new chip-boards greatly extend the field for these "manufactured lumber" products. The wood chips which form the basis for these materials can be made of scrap lumber, of the slabs cut from the outside of logs, or of logs and branches that are too small for lumber use. They make possible the utilization of a much higher percentage of the forest products, and so, greatly extend our potential supply of this raw material. The bonding resins are usually of the phenolic or urea types and the panels may be formed by pressing, rolling, or extruding. They are usually made in thicknesses from ½ in. to 2 in. and, in the thicker extruded types, may be formed with tubular openings which serve to reduce the weight.

The surfaces are hard and quite smooth with the variegated pattern of the chips showing. While this is suitable for certain purposes with only clear lacquer, it can also be painted or enameled.

The panels are also being used as a core for veneering and show greater dimensional stability and less tendency to warp than veneer or lumber cores. The cost is comparable with that of the lowest-priced veneer cores and is much less than for lumber core stock. There is also a good possibility that this cost may be reduced further as production increases. For use as tops and doors, where the edges are exposed, it is usually necessary to veneer or band the edges with solid wood to conceal the rather coarse interior structure of the chip-board.

The material can be worked by standard woodworking techniques, although the use of carbide-tipped cutters is highly desirable because of the abrasive action of the bonding resins on conventional cutting tools.

METHODS OF MANUFACTURE

Rotary Cutting

Log mounted centrally on lathe and revolved against knife

Flat Slicing

Log halved, clamped onto guide plate and sliced parallel to axis of tree

Quarter Slicing

Log quartered, clamped onto guide plate and sliced radially to growth rings

Half-round Slicing

Log halved, mounted off center in lathe and cut slightly across growth rings

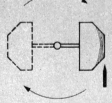

Back Cutting

Log halved and mounted in lathe, with cutting side reversed from half-round slicing

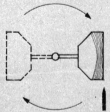

Rift Cutting

Log (oak) quartered, mounted in lathe and cut perpendicular to medullary rays

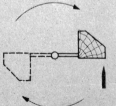

Fig. 685. Methods of cutting veneers and type of grain figure produced. (Courtesy, Fine Hardwoods Association.)

Fig. 686. Rotary-cut veneer as it comes from the lathe. (Courtesy, Fine Hardwoods Association.)

Fig. 687. Typical veneer figures and the parts of the tree where they are found. (Courtesy, Fine Hardwoods Association.)

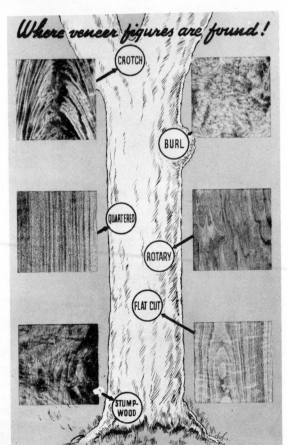

Where veneer figures are found!

CROTCH

BURL

QUARTERED

ROTARY

FLAT CUT

STUMP-WOOD

Fig. 688. A large band saw cuts the waste from a log preparatory to steaming and slicing into veneer. (Courtesy, Fine Hardwoods Association.)

Fig. 689. Slicing veneer with a large 17-ft slicer. (Courtesy, Fine Hardwoods Association.)

Fig. 690. Splicing the edges of veneer sheets with a machine that glues them and applies tape to reinforce the joint until it is used. (Courtesy, Fine Hardwoods Association.)

Fig. 691. A power-driven plywood laminating press with a large 600-gal cold glue mixer and a glue spreader in the background. (Courtesy, The Black Brothers Company, Inc.)

Fig. 692. Small portable sawmills such as this account for a large part of the production of lumber. (Courtesy, Fine Hardwoods Association.)

Fig. 693. A sawmill using a large band saw. (Courtesy, Henry Disston Division, H. K. Porter Company, Inc.)

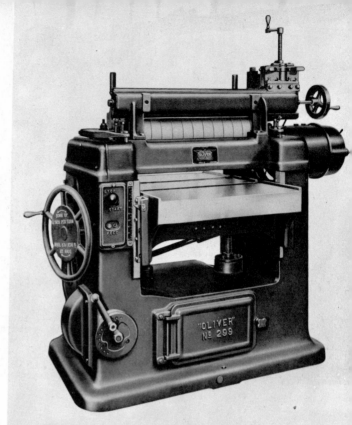

Fig. 694. A medium-size single-surface planer. This one takes work up to 24 in. wide and 8 in. thick with a feed of 18 fpm to 40 fpm. (Courtesy, Oliver Machinery Co.)

Fig. 695. A jointer or hand planer with 8-in. cutting width. (Courtesy, Oliver Machinery Co.)

Fig. 696. A 10-in. tilting arbor saw cutting a compound miter.

Fig. 697. The radial saw used for cutting stock to length. Angular adjustments in all directions make these machines very versatile and capable of a wide variety of work. (Courtesy, DeWalt, Inc.)

Fig. 698. A modern 36-in. wood-cutting band saw with welded steel frame. (Courtesy, The Tannewitz Works.)

Fig. 699. A small high-speed shaper is a versatile machine in both large and small shops.

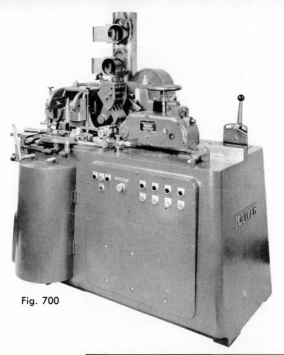

Fig. 700

Figs. 700–701. A modern high-speed molder with double chain feed and cutter speeds of 7200, 5400, and 3600 rpm. Fig. 701 shows cross-sectional views of typical moldings produced on such a machine. (Courtesy, Oliver Machinery Co.)

Fig. 701

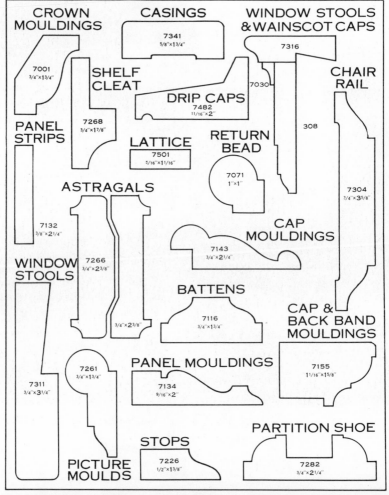

CROWN MOULDINGS

CASINGS

7341
5/8"x1 3/4"

WINDOW STOOLS & WAINSCOT CAPS

7316

7001
3/4"x1 3/4"

SHELF CLEAT

DRIP CAPS
7482
11/16"x2"

7030

CHAIR RAIL

308

PANEL STRIPS

7268
3/4"x1 7/8"

LATTICE
7501
5/16"x1 1/16"

RETURN BEAD

7071
1"x1"

7304
3/4"x3 5/8"

ASTRAGALS

7132
3/8"x2 1/4"

7266
3/4"x2 3/8"

CAP MOULDINGS

7143
3/4"x2 1/4"

WINDOW STOOLS

3/4"x2 3/8"

BATTENS

7116
3/4"x1 3/4"

CAP & BACK BAND MOULDINGS

7155
11/16"x1 5/8"

7261
3/4"x1 3/4"

PANEL MOULDINGS

7134
9/16"x2"

7311
3/4"x3 1/4"

PICTURE MOULDS

STOPS
7226
1/2"x1 3/8"

PARTITION SHOE

7282
3/4"x2 1/4"

Fig. 702. A double-end tenoner with power feed that is adjustable for a wide range of work. These are production machines that turn out a large volume of accurate work. (Courtesy, C. K. L. Machinery Company.)

Fig. 703. A high-speed router making an inside cut on a large panel. (Courtesy, Ekstrom, Carlson & Co.)

Fig. 704. These pieces are typical of the large variety of work done on the router. (Courtesy, Ekstrom, Carlson & Co.)

Fig. 705. A 17-in. drill press is one of the most versatile machines in the woodworking shop. Not only drilling but mortising, routing, sanding, and shaping also can be handled—especially on the lighter jobs that do not justify special machines. (Courtesy, Rockwell Manufacturing Company, Delta Power Tool Div.)

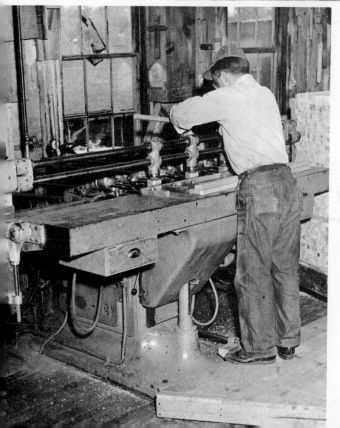

Fig. 706. A multiple spindle borer with hydraulic table feed, widely used in production woodworking. The spindles can be adjusted to any position within the boring area of the machine. (Courtesy, B. M. Root Company.)

Fig. 707. A horizontal multiple spindle boring machine with individually motorized spindles and hydraulic feed. These are used primarily for screw and dowel holes in the edge, or end of stock, but can also be used for certain face boring operations. (Courtesy, B. M. Root Company.)

Fig. 708. The overhead belt sander finishing completed phonograph cases prior to spraying with a two-tone plastic coating.

Fig. 709. An oscillating spindle sander. The spindle can be tilted at any angle up to 45 deg. It rotates at 1800 rpm and oscillates 1⅛ in. with 56 strokes per min. Various types and sizes of drums can be used for both wood and metal. (Courtesy, Oliver Machinery Co.)

Fig. 710. A resilient roll glue spreader for applying adhesives to flat work, here used for laminating plastic sheets to plywood cores for dinette tops. (Courtesy, The Black Brothers Company, Inc.)

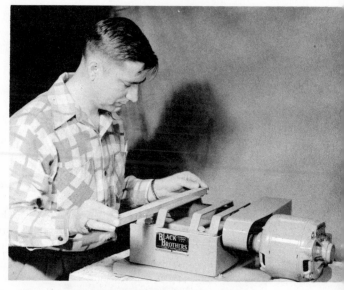

Fig. 711. A small glue spreader with an 8-in. roll applying glue to cleats. (Courtesy, The Black Brothers Company, Inc.)

Fig. 712. The type of sash and frame clamp in general use for assembling and gluing window frames, sash, screen doors, and similar work. (Courtesy, The Black Brothers Company, Inc.)

Fig. 713. A revolving case clamp for the assembly of television cabinets and the like. (Courtesy, The Black Brothers Company, Inc.)

Fig. 714

Figs. 714–715. The old (Fig. 714) and the new (Fig. 715) method of gluing laminated table tops. The old way required slow hand clamping and a three-hour drying cycle. In the new method, using a 20-kw "Thermatron" high-frequency generator, the adhesive coated stock is laid on the infeed table. It is fed by power into the machine which clamps and cures the panels in a three-minute cycle. (Courtesy, Radio Receptor Company, Inc.)

Fig. 715

Fig. 716

Figs. 716–717. The forming of curved veneer panels is efficiently handled in this 225-ton hydraulic press with a 15-kw "Thermatron" high-frequency generator. Simple hardwood forms faced with metal are used (Fig. 717) and the adhesive coated veneer sheets assembled between them. Two and three quarter minutes in the press cures the panels. The old method in a cold press required two and two third hours. (Courtesy, Radio Receptor Company, Inc.)

Fig. 717

Fig. 718. A rotary laminating press for making paper core doors and panels with quick-setting resin adhesives. (Courtesy, The Black Brothers Company, Inc.)

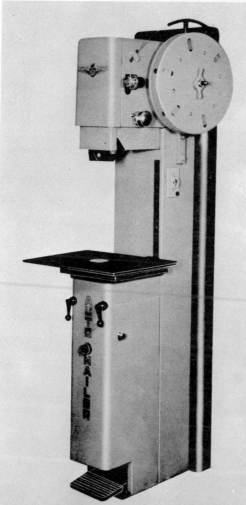

Fig. 719. An automatic nailing machine that cuts its own nails from a coil of knurled wire. Up to 3 nails per second can be driven in a choice of types and sizes. (Courtesy, The Auto-Nailer Company.)

Fig. 720

Figs 720–721. A plastic bonded wood chipboard and (Fig. 721) the same material with veneer facing. (Courtesy, United States Plywood Corporation.)

Fig. 721

Fig. 722. A plastic bonded wood chipboard made by an extrusion process with the chips oriented for maximum strength. This is made either solid or with tubular holes as shown. (Courtesy, The Dean Company.)

20

Ceramics

The production of ceramic articles is probably the oldest of all manufacturing processes, going back, as it does, to the time of prehistoric man. The use of ceramics for tableware, pottery, bathroom fixtures, tile, and brick is so well known as to require no comment. In the field of modern production, ceramics and the related "ceramets" are acquiring increasing importance because of their high temperature resistance and their excellent, and in some cases unique, electrical properties. It is these applications that will be considered here.

CERAMIC MATERIALS

The principal raw materials for ceramics are various natural clays and silicates of aluminum and magnesium. For some of the cruder forms of ceramics, such as brick, tile, and stoneware, the clay may be used in its natural form and shaped by extrusion, with a wire cut-off mechanism, or by molding. The clays often contain various oxides which give the characteristic color to brick and similar products. Some of the clays, notably one known as kaolin, are white in color and retain this after firing. These all-clay ceramics, while suitable for certain purposes, have many limitations, such as lack of uniformity, porousness, low strength, and wide dimensional variations.

A great improvement can be made by blending the clay with natural silicates, such as flint and feldspar, which fuse during the firing into a glass-like form which bonds the clay together. Ceramics containing more than 50 percent of clay, blended with these silicates, are known as "high-clay" compositions, and are used widely for electrical and mechanical purposes and for refractory materials. The standard "electrical porcelain" used for insulators and lighting fixtures is of this type. It is low in cost but does not meet all the requirements of a modern insulating material. One of the serious limitations of the high-clay ceramics is the very high shrinkage (about 25 percent) during drying and firing, which makes it impractical to hold close dimensional tolerances. Moreover, its strength and its electrical characteristics at high radio frequencies are not all that could be desired.

For these reasons, much work has been done and is still being done on the development of specialized ceramics with less clay and more of the silicates and oxides and even with no clay at all. Outstanding physical and electrical characteristics have been obtained in some of these materials, such as the steatites for high-frequency insulation and the ceramets which share some of the desirable characteristics of both metals and ceramics. These materials are formed with much less water content than the high-clay ceramics and can be extruded or molded to much closer tolerances. Dimensions, compared with those of machining standards, still require too much tolerance (of the order of 1 percent or 2 percent) for some purposes. In these cases, machining can be done easily after the material has dried but before firing. After firing, grinding is the only practical machining process.

METHODS OF FORMING

The high-clay ceramics are formed by a wet process which requires enough water to give a rather soft, plastic consistency. In this form, the material can be extruded in much the same way as metals or plastics to form parts of uniform cross section. It can be formed also into round parts by "throwing," "plunging," or "jiggering," which are all only slightly mechanized versions of the old potter's wheel. Parts up to approximately 24 in. in either length or diameter are made by these methods with low tool cost but quite high labor cost.

Larger and more complex parts may be cast in plaster-of-Paris molds, much as metal is cast in sand molds. The plaster absorbs much of the water in the casting material, which must be left in the mold for a considerable time to harden sufficiently to handle it for firing. Large parts up to 6 ft or 7 ft in height and 3 ft or 4 ft in diameter and weighing up to 1400 lb or so can be formed in this way. The parts are expensive, however, because of the slow production rate.

For larger production of parts up to 14 in. or so in maximum dimension, pressing in plaster-of-Paris molds or in steel dies is used. For the steel-die pressing, part of the water is removed from the material by vacuum processing before pressing. This method gives the highest production rates and is economical for large quantities of fairly simple shapes that can be formed without complex coring or undercuts.

For forming the low-clay or clay-free ceramics, the "dry process" is used, wherein the material contains very little water. This can be used with high-clay materials but results in very porous pieces. With the low-clay ceramics, however, excellent characteristics are obtained with close dimensional tolerances. Most of the parts made by this process are relatively small, usually only a few inches in each dimension, although pieces up to 14 in. long have been made. The process is quite similar to powder metallurgy (see Chap. 4) and the parts are subject to about the same shape limitations. The pressures used are less, being a few tons per square inch or less.

All ceramic parts must be dried before they are fired, and this can be done at room temperature although usually it is accelerated by the use of a drying kiln with controlled heat and air circulation. A glaze can be applied either before or after firing by dipping, spraying, or brushing. This fuses to the surface upon firing and forms a smooth, shiny finish that is easy to clean and resists the accumulation of dirt deposits that could cause electrical breakdown. Other than this, the glaze has little except an ornamental function. One surface should be left unglazed to permit support of the piece in the firing kiln.

The firing is quite a critical process, with a low heat applied at first to drive out the small remaining moisture and then gradually increased until the firing temperature of 2000 F or more is reached. This is continued until shrinkage ceases, and then it is reduced gradually to permit slow cooling of the pieces without cracks or strains. In large production plants, the firing may be done by passing the parts, on cars or a conveyor, slowly through a long kiln having various heat zones. In other plants, batch kilns are used which are loaded with work and then carried through the firing cycle.

USES OF CERAMICS

In the field of electrical insulation, ceramics are preferred for many applications to plastics. For high-temperature insulations they are much superior to other materials and are used almost universally in heating elements and in plugs and sockets that must stand heat above 300 F or 400 F. For outdoor insulators, especially on high-voltage lines, their hard, glazed surface which sheds water and dirt and their excellent arc resistance make them the preferred material.

As insulation in household light sockets and plugs, both plastics and ceramics are used, with the ceramics preferred where high temperatures are likely to be encountered. Plastics can be molded to closer dimensional tolerances and are less likely to chip and break.

While ceramics may be losing ground in some fields to the newer plastics, they are finding tremendous new fields in electronic applications, where new developments in ceramics place them in a class by themselves. In coil forms and tube sockets for the high radio frequencies, steatite is preferred to all other materials because of its low losses and moisture absorption and excellent mechanical stability. The only plastics that approach ceramics for this purpose —Teflon, for example—are much more expensive.

As a dielectric for the small capacitors used in tremendous quantities in radio and television sets, ceramics have found another important place for themselves. Special ceramics are formulated which have a very high dielectric constant: 7500 as against 3 to 6 for paper and mica. A small wafer of this material coated with silver on both sides forms a capacitor (condenser) that is much smaller and lighter than other types. It is also competitive in cost, has better characteristics at high frequencies and greater stability under temperature changes. The principal disadvantage of these ceramic capacitors, compared with the paper and mica types used previously, is the difficulty of holding close electrical tolerances on the higher capacity values using the very high dielectric ceramic material.

The lower capacity ceramic condensers can be furnished in close tolerances and have the unique advantage of being able to control the temperature coefficient (change of capacitance with temperature), so that they can be made with zero or with specified positive or negative values of this characteristic.

Ceramic wafers are used also as the base for printed circuits (see Chap. 21) where resistors and capacitors and the connections between them are formed in metallic inks and fused to the ceramic.

Certain specialized ceramic materials can be made so dense that they are comparable with glass in their ability to hold a high vacuum. Since they can operate at much higher temperatures than glass, they are being used in new, extremely small, high-performance vacuum tubes for electronic applications.

Another property of certain ceramics, especially barium titanate, known as piezo-electricity, has opened up other fields to ceramics. Piezo-electricity is the property in a material of generating an electric voltage when subjected to mechanical stress. The process is reversible and the material changes, either in shape or dimension, when voltage is applied. This property is utilized in the ceramic phonograph pick-ups where the slight movement of the needle on the record applies a twisting or bending strain to a small wafer of ceramic and thereby generates a minute voltage that is proportional to the sound waves recorded on the disk. These ceramic pick-ups are not affected by temperature and humidity as were the Rochelle salt crystals formerly used for this purpose.

The same property is used in the transducers that change high-frequency alternating currents into ultrasonic mechanical vibrations. These can be used for various industrial and military applications, such as underwater signaling and depth finding, agitating cleaning baths for small parts (Chap. 16), and emulsifying and mixing various chemicals. The same piezo-electric property of certain metals, notably nickel, is used for ultrasonic machining (Chap. 8) and soldering (Chap. 11).

Another interesting property of certain ceramics that may eventually have commercial applications is the ability of the dielectric constant to change with the voltage applied. Under proper conditions, a small voltage applied to a capacitor formed of certain ceramics may control a larger value of voltage from another source. This operates much as a magnetic amplifier does, and for some purposes may replace a vacuum tube or transistor. These dielectric amplifiers have been used only experimentally up to the present time.

The cermets, mentioned earlier in this chapter, exhibit some of the properties of both metals and ceramics, and their possibilities are just starting to be realized. In one form, known as ferrites, they are being widely used as a core for radio loop antennas. A coil of wire wound over a small rod of the ferrite has a much higher "Q" or factor of merit, and picks up stations better than the older type of flat loop antenna. In addition to taking much less space, it can be mounted closer to the other components and has a great deal to do with the excellent performance of modern compact midget radios.

Other ceramet materials have been developed that can be made into permanent magnets with characteristics that equal, and in some cases excel, those of the best metal alloys. Since they replace alloys containing large percentages of nickel and chromium, which are both critical materials, they may be of great value in any future emergency. It is quite possible that they will also offer substantial cost savings as they come into more general use.

Other ceramets are being made experimentally which combine the heat conduction of metal with the heat resistance of a ceramic. These materials show great promise for turbine blades and other parts of jet engines and gas turbines. Still to be overcome is the characteristic brittleness that is typical of all the ceramic materials, and that limits their usefulness in mechanical applications. New techniques of infiltrating a porous ceramic with metals of high strength and temperature resistance show considerable promise in this direction. These ceramets are formed by methods similar to those used in powder metallurgy, which permit close tolerances and a high degree of uniformity.

Another approach to the problem of high temperature and the abrasive action of hot gases in turbines is the use of ceramic coating on metals. Progress is being made along this line, although the process is still largely in the laboratory. One serious difficulty is the difference in expansion between the metal base material and the ceramic coating, which causes cracks under severe temperature conditions. Progress is being made in developing materials to overcome this problem.

Ceramics are also finding use as material for inspection gages where their extreme hardness gives much longer life than steel and at a cost considerably less than carbides. For measuring other ceramic parts, they have a special advantage, since the abrasive nature of the ceramic material causes rapid wear on steel gages. Ceramics have even been used for surface plates where their long wear and dimensional stability are superior to the cast iron or granite usually used for this purpose.

The resistance of ceramics to most acids and chemicals is excellent, and many mechanical parts which must operate in contact with these materials are made of ceramics. Among these are pump and valve parts and bearings.

A new use of ceramics for the tips of metal cutting tools shows great promise. When these tips are mounted properly and backed up in steel shanks, the extreme wear and heat resistance give phenomenal life and smooth cutting qualities, at high cutting speeds (see Chap. 5).

Fig. 723. Cars of ceramic parts ready for loading in the kiln for firing. (Courtesy, Frenchtown Porcelain Company.)

Fig. 724. Spray glazing in a machine such as this is an important step in making spark plug insulators. (Courtesy, Frenchtown Porcelain Company.)

Fig. 725. Porcelain spark plug insulators have been standard for many years. Here these insulators are given a dielectric test with 30,000 v at 1.5 megacycles plus a careful surface inspection. (Courtesy, Frenchtown Porcelain Company.)

Fig. 726. A precision ceramic part being ground to size, after firing, with a diamond wheel. (Courtesy, Frenchtown Porcelain Company.)

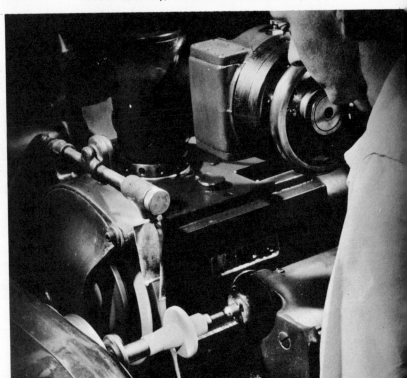

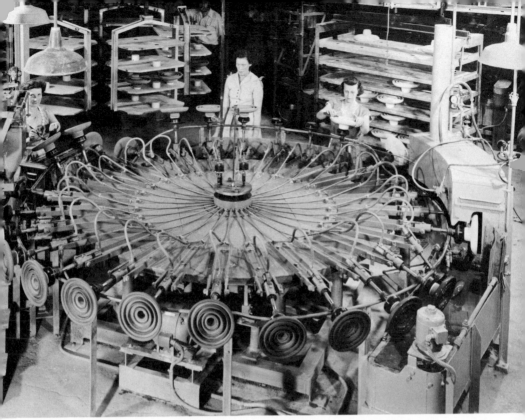

Fig. 727. This automatic glazing machine for high-voltage electric line insulators uses close controls to assure uniformity of glaze coverage and thickness and give high impact resistance. Sand bands for the later application of hardware are applied automatically. (Courtesy, Locke Department, General Electric Company.)

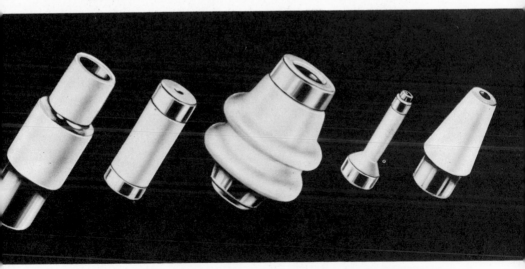

Fig. 728. A group of ceramic parts with "Nicote" metallized bands which may be hard or soft soldered to metal parts. (Courtesy, Frenchtown Porcelain Company.)

Fig. 729. A stack of six switch and bus bar insulators for use in power stations. Power switches or other electrical equipment for operation at 230,000 v may be attached to this. (Courtesy, Locke Department, General Electric Company.)

Fig. 730. A three-ton antenna lead-in bushing, 26 ft high, indicates the size possibilities of ceramic parts. (Courtesy, Locke Department, General Electric Company.)

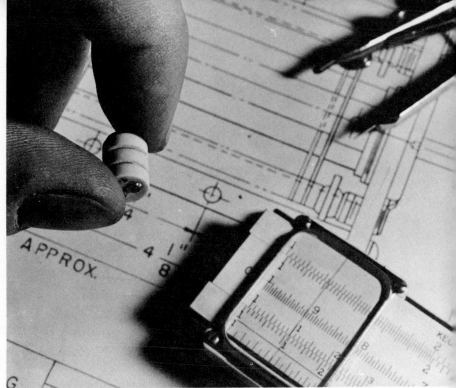

Fig. 731

Figs. 731–732. The high heat resistance of ceramics makes possible this new micro-miniature receiving tube designed to give low noise performance at ultra-high radio frequencies. Fig. 732 shows the parts that make up this tiny tube. (Courtesy, General Electric Company, Electronics Div.)

Fig. 732

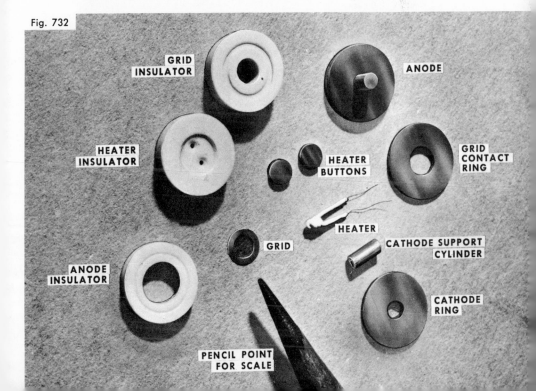

21

Electronic Printed Circuits

It is something of an anachronism that the radio, television, and electronics industry, which has been the most progressive of all industries from a design point of view, has been the slowest in modernizing its own production processes. Factories that are turning out the control instruments that make automation possible in other plants are still mass producing television sets by the same methods used by the first "hams" on their "wireless" sets. They are still riveting tube sockets and other parts onto metal "chassis bases" and attaching wires, resistors, and condensers to them by hand with pliers and soldering irons.

This situation is rapidly being changed by the various forms of printed circuits that have only begun to come into general use since 1953. The development of these printed circuits has followed several lines.

ETCHED WIRING BOARDS

The one that is leading in popularity at the present time is, strictly speaking, not a printed circuit but a printed wiring board which serves to connect together more or less standard components. These boards are produced from sheets of laminated plastic material such as the phenolics, the epoxies, the melamines, or the silicones, to which copper foil has been bonded on one or both sides. The desired wiring pattern is printed by one of several methods on the surface of the copper in an acid-resisting material and the unwanted portion is etched away by an acid bath. The resist material is then washed off, leaving the desired circuit in copper foil on a plastic base. Holes are punched or drilled through the circuit board, and components are inserted in the proper places. Small holes are provided for the wire leads of standard resistors and condensers which project through the copper foil. Larger components, such as tube sockets, electrolytic condensers, and coils, are made with special terminal lugs for use with the printed wiring. When the components are all in place, a dip soldering operation completes all of the electrical connections at once. It is obvious that a considerable saving in labor can be made by this method, although hand work is still required to assemble the components on the board.

The most commonly used base material for printed wiring boards is a good grade of paper-base phenolic known as XXXP. It has good mechanical and electrical properties, punches easily when heated, has fairly low moisture absorption, and is the least expensive of the satisfactory materials. Its disadvantages are a tendency to warp, especially when the copper foil is applied to one side only, low arc resistance, and rather high electrical losses at high radio frequencies. It is made in thicknesses from 0.005 in. to $\frac{1}{2}$ in. or more, but thicknesses of $\frac{1}{16}$ in., $\frac{3}{32}$ in., and $\frac{1}{8}$ in. are the most popular.

Laminates of fiber glass with binders of epoxy, melamine, or silicone resins have better high-frequency characteristics and much better arc resistance, and are more stable mechanically. The silicones especially, while they are quite expensive, have excellent electrical and mechanical properties, very low moisture absorption, and withstand high temperatures. All of these fiber glass laminates are hard to machine, and the life of punches and cutting tools is relatively short.

The foil used for coating these laminates has almost always been electrolytic copper, which is available in wide sheets, has excellent conductivity, and is easy to solder. Recently, rolled copper foil has become available in wide sheets and is taking over some of this market. The copper is usually furnished in "1 oz," which is 0.00135 in. thick, or "2 oz," which is 0.0027 in. thick. Heavier foils are also available. Foil may be applied to one or both sides of the plastic according to the circuit requirements. Various adhesives are used to bond the foil to the plastic base, with epoxy and phenolic resin types apparently the most satisfactory. These adhesives must not only provide a strong bond but also stand the heat of the dip soldering without losing their strength. This was one of the weak points in the early printed wiring boards, but is now quite satisfactory. The current-carrying capacity of the foil conductors is surprisingly large because of their large surface area, which provides good heat dissipation. A line $\frac{1}{16}$ in. wide of the 0.00135-in. foil will carry up to 5 amp with free air circulation.

The pattern of acid-resist material is applied in any of several ways. The photographic and the silk-screen methods are the most commonly used. In the photographic method, a "photo-resist" material is used like that used in photoengraving. The foil surface is completely covered with this material, and, when it is dry, a negative of the circuit pattern is placed on top of it. This is then exposed to a strong light, the negative is removed, and the board is developed in certain chemicals which have the property of removing the unexposed resist material but leaving the exposed parts intact.

In the silk-screen process, the resist material is applied only to the required pattern through a photographically prepared screen (see Chap. 22) of silk, rayon, or fine wire mesh. Both methods are entirely satisfactory for the usual printed wiring work, and the screen process is somewhat less expensive. The photographic process gives smoother edges to the lines and is preferred where very close spacing (less than 0.030 in.) is required between the lines, as is sometimes the case between switch contacts and in other special applications.

A photo-offset printing process has also been used for applying the resist material and is probably the most economical method of all for large-quantity production. Special techniques must be used to obtain a sufficiently heavy coat of the resist.

A new process for applying resist material is especially adapted to the making of short-run or sample wiring boards, since it requires no screen or negative. The copper foil is coated with a material which has the property of holding a strong electrostatic charge. This charge is applied in a darkroom by a high-voltage electrostatic field and the coated board is then exposed, by photographic techniques, either by contact printing or projection to a positive image of the desired pattern. Where the light strikes, the electrostatic charge is removed, leaving the charge only on the pattern. A special powder having an opposite charge is dusted over this surface and adheres only to the pattern. This powder is then fused by heat to form the resist material, the coating on the rest of the sheet is washed off in a selective solvent that does not attack the desired pattern, and the board is ready for etching. Progress is being made toward mechanizing this process for use in automatic, large-scale production also.

The etching away of the unwanted foil is done by any one of several chemicals, ferric chloride being used most commonly. The board may be dipped in the etchant, but a preferred method is to suspend the board in a horizontal position over the surface of the acid and subject it to an acid spray, by pressure, splashing, or air agitation. This gives cleaner lines and less undercutting than the immersion process, and is much faster. The etchant is usually heated to further speed up the process. After etching, the boards are washed clean and sometimes rinsed in a mild alkali to neutralize any remaining acid. The resist material is then removed by a solvent.

Either before or after etching, the copper surface may be plated with silver, tin-lead solder, or other metal to prevent oxidation, to increase the ease of soldering or to improve the wearing properties of the surface if it is to be used for switch contacts. For the latter purpose, a nickel plating with a thin overplating of rhodium is excellent. In most cases, electroplating is done before etching since electrical continuity of the surface is required. Some platings resist the etching acid, and in this case the wiring pattern may be printed in reverse in a plating "stop-off" material. The plating then adheres only to the desired wiring pattern. After plating, the "stop-off" is removed and the unwanted foil is etched away, with the plating itself acting as a resist material to protect the circuit pattern.

Small inductances (coils) and capacitors (condensers) may be formed by the etching process. The inductances are simply spiral lines of foil in either a round or a rectangular shape. Inductance values up to about 5 microhenrys can be obtained before the size becomes cumbersome. Capacitors are formed between areas of foil on opposite sides of a sheet. These are most practical if very thin base material, 0.005 in. to 0.010 in. is used. The capacitance value will depend on the area of foil, and the thickness and the dielectric constant of the insulation. Small capacitance values, up to 5 or 10 micromicrofarads ($\mu\mu f$), can be formed on one side of a sheet by means of closely spaced lines in the form of interlocking combs. The capacitance is formed between the edges of the foil, and the dielectric is partly air and partly the insulating base material. Resistors can be printed by the silk-screen process on the insulating base material in semiconducting inks. They usually are made to bridge across between parts of the copper foil wiring. The resistance is varied by changing the composition of the ink and the length and the width of the resistance path. It is difficult at the present time to hold close enough tolerances on the resistance value, and very difficult to make repairs in the field. For these and other reasons, standard resistors, soldered in place, have proved more satisfactory and are preferred.

Switch contacts and commutators are often formed by the etching process and these can be in very complex forms that would be extremely difficult to make by any other process. For operation at speeds over about 500 rpm it is necessary to have the surface of the foil flush with that of the insulation. This may be done by etching the desired pattern on a semicured base material which is somewhat soft, and then placing the piece between two flat plates and curing it under heat and pressure. Usually switch contacts are plated to reduce contact resistance and improve wear. Silver plating is often used for contacts that are not subject to much wear. For switches and commutators that turn rapidly, nickel plating with a very thin overplating of rhodium is preferred. The life of switches made in this way, used with brushes of the proper design and tension, is often 50 million cycles or more.

Wherever possible, the circuit pattern is kept on one side of the board. This simplifies the etching, the assembly of the components, and the dip soldering. If it is necessary to have an insulated crossover between the conductors, it is made by means of a U-shaped piece of wire, inserted from the back and soldered in place along with the other components in the dip-soldering operation.

If it is necessary to form the circuit on both sides of the board, crossovers are usually required at numerous points in the circuit. These may be formed by eyelets inserted through holes and crimped over to make contact on both sides of the sheet. They are then dip-soldered to make a good connection. They also furnish a strong mechanical bond for components and wires. Another method of making crossovers is by means of plating through the holes. This is done by first coating the holes with a conductive material and then electroplating over this. The plating makes contact with the foil on the two sides of the sheet, and, when the sheet is dip-soldered, the solder follows through the holes and completes the job. If component leads are inserted through the plated holes, the solder flows in around them and greatly improves the strength of the joint. Opinions differ as to the relative merits of the eyelets and plated crossovers, but both are being used successfully in production.

OTHER WIRING BOARDS

Other methods of forming the wiring pattern on the plastic laminates do not involve etching, and these are preferred by some manufacturers. One of these forms the pattern by electroplating after the desired pattern has been made conductive by chemical reduction or by coating with a conductive paint or ink. Early attempts to use this method were not too successful because of difficulty in getting good adhesion of the plating to the plastic. New techniques have at least partially overcome this difficulty. It has the advantage of using copper more efficiently since copper is deposited only where needed. In the etching process it is seldom economical to recover the copper that is dissolved in the etchant. The principal advantage of the plated circuits is that the holes for mounting the components can be punched or drilled before plating and the plating can extend through them to form a better joint in the dip soldering. If a double side circuit is needed, the crossovers can also be a part of the plating, either through holes or around the edges of the board. The surface of the plated copper is rougher than the foil, which is good for dip soldering but not so good for use as switch contacts.

Another method of applying the conductive pattern is by a hot stamping process. A die is made, usually by photo-etching, and this die is used with a combination of heat and pressure to partially imbed the desired pattern of metal in the plastic surface. In some cases, adhesive coated foil is used and the die is made with sharp edges that cut through the foil, and a flat inner section that bonds the pattern to the plastic by heat and pressure. The unwanted foil is peeled off by hand. In another variation of the stamping or embossing process, a liquid suspension of metal powder, usually silver, is sprayed over the entire surface of the board. The hot die is then pressed on the surface, fusing the wiring pattern to the backing. The coating on the rest of the surface is then washed off.

In still another variation of the stamping or embossing process, the pattern is pressed below the surface of the sheet of plastic at the time it is being cured and laminated. The unwanted portion, which is raised above the wiring pattern, is removed mechanically by a sanding operation. No adhesive is used, the combination of heat and pressure forming a secure bond. The silver is a better conductor than copper and solders more easily, although it is, of course, more expensive. Its special advantage is in the forming of switch and commutator contacts where the silver requires no plating and gives low contact resistance and long life.

One difficulty that has been experienced with silver printed circuits under conditions of high humidity is the condition known as "silver migration." When a voltage exists between nearby conductors in the presence of moisture, minute filaments of silver tend to "grow" across the surface and cause leakage or short circuits. Techniques have been developed to minimize this effect, but it is still not very well understood and is a problem under humid conditions.

Many special components are being made for use with printed wiring boards. Tube sockets snap into holes in the boards and make contact with the foil connections, ready for dip soldering. Resistor and condenser leads may be formed by hand or in simple, foot-operated machines, to slip through small holes punched in the boards and hold themselves in place until soldered. Variable resistors, such as volume and tone controls, are made with special terminals to mount either vertically or horizontally on the boards. Plug-in connectors are available which make contact with printed leads which are brought out to one edge of the board and properly spaced to match the plug contacts.

After the components are mounted in place, the soldering to the printed conductors can be done by hand with a soldering iron, or by dip soldering. The latter method is used almost universally because of the saving in labor and the danger of applying too much heat with the hand iron. Dip soldering is done in thermostatically controlled pots made especially for this purpose. The solder used should have the lowest melting point, which is known as the "eutectic alloy," 63 percent tin, 37 percent lead. (A close approximation is the standard 60/40 solder, which is quite satisfactory.) The solder is maintained at a temperature of from 410 F to 490 F, the usual temperature being around 450 F. The assembled board is dipped in a flux (special fluxes are available for this purpose) and then into the solder, where it is held for about 5 to 10 sec. It is then withdrawn, the surplus flux is rinsed off, if desired, and the assembly is ready for use. This method can be used for either single- or double-sided wiring boards, provided that the components are all on one side. If components must be mounted on both sides of the board, the side having the most parts is assembled first and dip-soldered. The components on the second side are then assembled and soldered by hand. This, of course, adds considerably to the cost and should be avoided, if possible.

The greatest saving in labor cost between printed wiring and hand wiring is on jobs where substantial quantities are involved. However, there are many cases where it may be economical to use printed wiring even in lots of 50 or 100 pieces. By the electrostatic printing method, even lots of 5 or 10 pieces may be made economically. Printed wiring is more uniform, involves less chance of error and also makes it possible to reduce the size of many types of electronic equipment.

FABRICATION AND ASSEMBLY OF WIRING BOARDS

The manufacture of printed circuits by any of these methods involves the punching or drilling of a large number of small holes for component leads. In most cases, the size of these holes is standardized at around 0.052 in. A number of methods have been worked out for reducing the cost of this perforating process. In small quantities, the holes may be drilled or punched individually, using center marks, formed as part of the wiring pattern, as a guide. Where larger quantities are involved, a drill jig may be used which gives greater accuracy but not much reduction in labor.

Where the quantity required of a single wiring board is large enough, a multiple perforating die can be made which will punch not only the small component holes but also larger openings for sockets and other larger parts all at one operation. This method is very fast, but the cost of the die makes it impractical unless quantities of at least a few thousand pieces are involved.

Several machines have been developed to do this perforating operation rapidly and without the expense of a multiple die. One of these, shown in Fig. 740, uses a single punch operating at high speed with the wiring board moved around underneath it automatically to the positions where holes are required. The holes must all be of the same size (0.052 in.) and must be located at the intersection of lines running vertically and horizontally at 0.1-in. spacing. The movement of the board under the punch and the consequent location of the holes is controlled by a perforated tape which is inserted in the control unit. The preparation of the master tape requires about 4 hr, and, when this is once on file, all that is necessary to change from one board to another is to interchange these tapes, which can be done in about 6 min. Boards up to 6 in. x 17.6 in. in size can be handled and the time required to punch any pattern of holes in such a board is about 45 sec. Any larger holes needed have to be punched in a separate operation.

The use of a 0.1-in. grid for hole spacing shows promise of being adopted as a standard. This would simplify the design of machines for automatically forming and inserting components, such as resistors and condensers. It would also simplify the use of larger components such as controls and electrolytic condensers with straight terminals made especially for use in printed circuits since these could be designed to fit the standard hole spacing.

Another machine, shown in Fig. 741, for rapidly perforating printed wiring boards, is an adaptation of the turret punch press used in the sheet metal industry (see Chap. 2 and Figs. 94–96). This machine carries 12 different sizes and shapes of dies up to $1\frac{1}{2}$ in. in diameter, and any one of them can be brought into position by means of a foot pedal in about $1\frac{1}{2}$ sec. Holes are punched at a rate of 80 to 120 per minute. The board to be perforated is clamped in a carriage, the movement of which, in both directions, is controlled by the operator. Boards up to 14 in. x 14 in. can be handled. The location of the holes is determined by a template, in front of the operator, having a $\frac{1}{16}$-in. or a $\frac{1}{8}$-in. hole at each point to be perforated. A sample of the wiring board itself, properly drilled, usually is used for this template. The operator moves a plunger, attached to the work-holding carriage, into position and allows it to drop through each of the holes in the template. The plunger makes an electrical contact, which triggers the operation of the press. Since most printed-circuit laminates must be punched hot, the table on which the work rests is heated electrically to the proper temperature. The low-cost templates and the quick setup make this machine practical for runs as low as 10 pieces, and it is also economical for quantities of several thousand pieces.

In another perforating machine (see Fig. 743), the same method of locating the holes, by means of a template and a manually operated carriage, is used, but a high-speed drill head is used instead of a punch. The boards do not have to be heated for drilling and the hole size can be changed within reasonable limits by changing drills. Large holes must be punched in a separate operation.

The production of etched wiring boards and the dip-soldering process lend themselves readily to automatic production. A further step in this direction is found in several machines now coming into use, which automatically cut and form the component leads and assemble the parts on the board, ready for dip soldering.

A major problem in the design of these machines is the necessity of keeping them flexible enough so that model changes, which are frequent in the fast-moving electronics industry, are not too difficult to make. This means that they must be, basically, a series of assembly heads or stations, each of which can be adjusted to handle components of various sizes and to form the leads in various manners. These stations are then positioned adjustably along a conveyor, so that each can insert its particular component in the proper place on the wiring board as it is carried from station to station. When one considers the large number of components in even a subassembly of a modern television set, it is easy to see why these machines are necessarily complex and expensive and practical only on units produced in large quantities. However, it is certain that many, if not most, of the radio and television sets produced in the next few years will be made automatically, and will use printed circuits in one form or another. Component manufacturers are contributing to the trend toward automation by designing parts especially adapted to printed-circuit wiring and by packaging them in a manner that will permit easy handling by the automatic assembly machines.

CERAMIC PLATE PRINTED CIRCUITS

Another approach to printed circuits and the automatic production of electronic equipment is found in the small ceramic wafers on which are printed not only the wiring but also the resistors and the capacitors. Small units of this kind, combining a few resistors and capacitors, for specific applications in standard radio and television circuits, have been in use for quite a few years. They are made by a silk-screen process with silver and carbon inks which are fused to the ceramic base by a firing operation. Capacitors up to 0.01 microfarad (μf) are formed by areas of silver on opposite sides of the thin ceramic plates which vary in size from $\frac{9}{16}$ in. x $1\frac{3}{16}$ in. to $1\frac{1}{4}$ in. x $1\frac{1}{8}$ in.

Resistors with values up to several megohms are also formed on these plates and are usually held to a tolerance of ± 20 percent, which is close enough for many applications. After firing, the circuit plate is given a plastic coating for insulation and mechanical protection. The leads brought out from these printed circuits can be either wires for connection to standard wired circuits or straight metal tabs for mounting and dip soldering on the etched wiring boards described before. The cost of these units is about the same as that of the several components they replace, plus a small allowance for the labor of assembly. The saving of space and of labor often makes them economical.

A further extension of this principle into much more complex circuit assemblies is the so-called "Project Tinkertoy" or MDE (Modular Design of Electronics) developed by the National Bureau of Standards in co-operation with private industry. The ceramic wafers which form the basis of this system are of standard size and shape, approximately $\frac{7}{8}$ in. square and $\frac{1}{16}$ in. thick. Three notches are provided in each side. On these wafers are printed various combinations of wiring, resistance, and capacitance. Points requiring interconnection are brought out to one of the 12 notches in the edge. Wafers are also made in the form of tube sockets. All of the circuits associated with a tube are assembled in a stack of wafers mounted below the tube socket and connected together mechanically and electrically by means of wires running vertically through the notches in the edges of the wafers and soldered to the printed leads. These wires may be extended either above or below the stack to make connection with an etched wiring board for connections between tubes.

Elaborate machines, controlled by punched cards and tapes, have been developed and a pilot plant set up to form, assemble, and test these units on a completely automatic basis. The system has great flexibility. Resistors can be of several types, with varying degrees of precision. They are carbon composition, applied either directly or in the form of strips of flexible adhesive tape, evaporated metal precision resistors, or wire-wound resistors formed around an entire wafer. Resistance values from a fraction of an ohm to 10 megohms are practical. Capacitors may consist of conducting areas on opposite sides of a thin ceramic wafer or they may be built up of layers of foil and plastic film with values up to 0.01 μf. Small inductances may be formed on one or several of the wafers, but larger inductances are mounted separately.

Each stack of wafers (usually four to six), with its associated tube socket, is called a module. A group of six modules mounted on an etched wiring board can form a six-tube radio. If repairs are necessary in the field, usually an entire module would be replaced. The first applications of the "Tinkertoy" modules have been on military equipment, but large-scale production facilities have been set up and it is anticipated that the cost will be competitive with other production methods for use in radio and television sets. Experimental radio and television sets have been made with satisfactory results. Of course a major redesign of equipment would be required to adapt it to this construction, but it seems probable that both ceramic wafer circuits and printed wiring boards and combinations of the two will be used in electronic equipment in the near future.

Other modular systems, such as the one shown in Figs. 758 and 759, represent different approaches to the same problem.

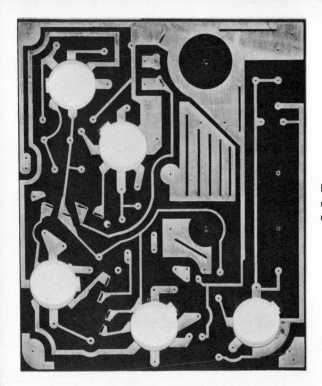

Fig. 733. A printed wiring board for a five-tube home radio receiver. (Courtesy, Photocircuits Corporation.)

Fig. 734. A group of typical printed circuits made by the etching process. The two in the center are switch circuits; the one at the lower right has inductances and capacitors as part of the circuit. (Courtesy, Photocircuits Corporation.)

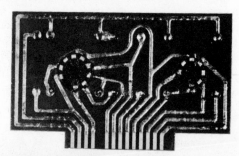

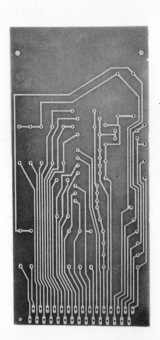

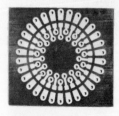

Fig. 735. Assembling the components on a printed circuit amplifier prior to dip soldering. (Courtesy, Arthur Ansley Mfg. Co.)

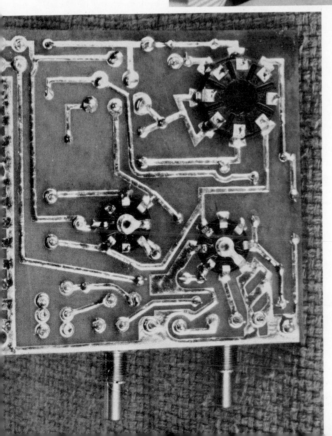

Fig. 736. Bottom view of the amplifier shown in Fig. 735 after dip soldering. (Courtesy, Arthur Ansley Mfg. Co.)

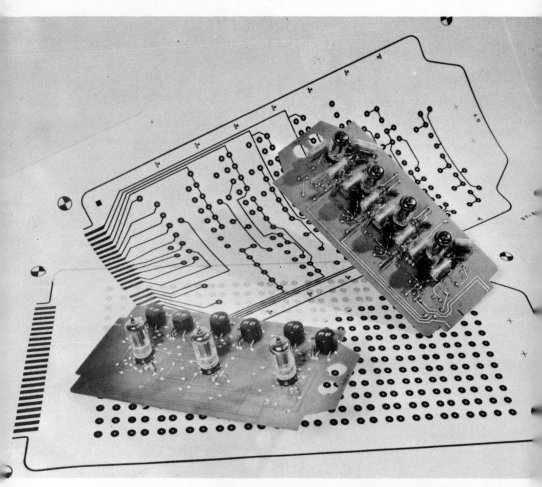

Fig. 737. Printed circuits are widely used in the computer field. These units are from Burroughs desk size digital computer. In the background are two master drawings from which such circuits are made. (Courtesy, Burroughs Corporation.)

Figs. 738–739. A printed circuit board made by the plating method with the plating extending through the holes. The wiring can be on one or both sides of the board. These boards are produced in large quantities in a highly mechanized production setup which includes the 75-ft long automatic plating tank shown in Fig. 739, with the completed boards about to be unloaded. (Courtesy, General Electric Company, Electronics Div.)

Fig. 738

Fig. 739

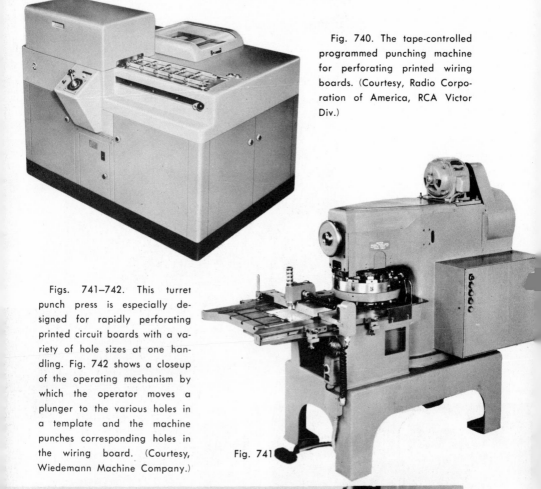

Fig. 740. The tape-controlled programmed punching machine for perforating printed wiring boards. (Courtesy, Radio Corporation of America, RCA Victor Div.)

Figs. 741–742. This turret punch press is especially designed for rapidly perforating printed circuit boards with a variety of hole sizes at one handling. Fig. 742 shows a closeup of the operating mechanism by which the operator moves a plunger to the various holes in a template and the machine punches corresponding holes in the wiring board. (Courtesy, Wiedemann Machine Company.)

Fig. 741

Fig. 742

Fig. 743. A semi-automatic drill press for rapidly perforating printed wiring boards in small or medium lots. The drill is guided by a template which can be a manually drilled board of the type to be made. Boards up to ⅜ in. thick can be drilled, or two thinner boards at one time. No heating of the board is required, as is necessary for punching most plastics used for printed circuits. (Courtesy, Allen B. DuMont Laboratories, Inc.)

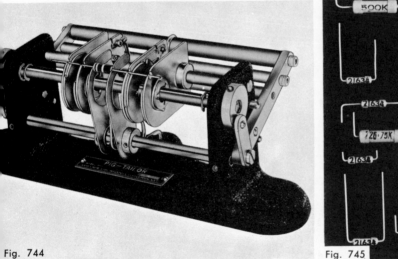

Fig. 744

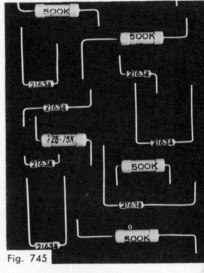

Fig. 745

Figs. 744–745. The "Pig-Tailor" is a simple, foot-operated machine for cutting and forming leads on components for insertion in printed wiring boards. It is easily adjusted to form a wide variety of shapes, as shown in Fig. 745. (Courtesy, Bruno-New York Industries Corporation.)

Fig. 746. A forty-station machine for assembling components on printed wiring boards. Each station inserts one component as the boards pass through the line. (Courtesy, United Shoe Machinery Corp.)

Fig. 747. Axial lead components, like resistors and condensers, are held in belts by means of tape and fed to the inserting unit, which cuts the leads, forms them, and inserts them through the board. (Courtesy, United Shoe Machinery Corp.)

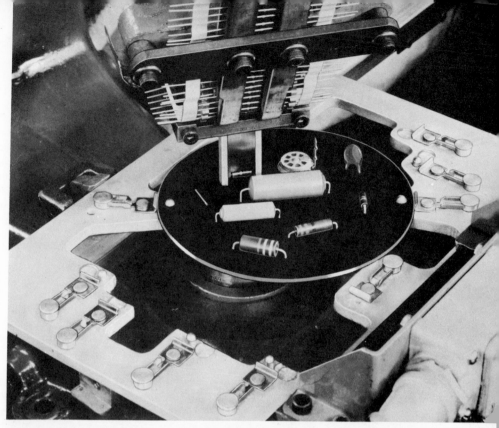

Fig. 748. The pallets which carry the printed wiring boards through the equipment can be designed to handle various shaped boards and components can be inserted at any angle. (Courtesy, United Shoe Machinery Corp.)

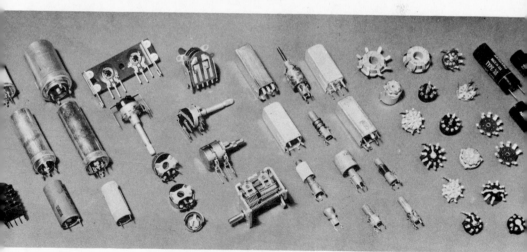

Fig. 749. A few of the many electronic components designed with short, straight terminals especially for use with printed wiring boards. (Courtesy, *Electronics.*)

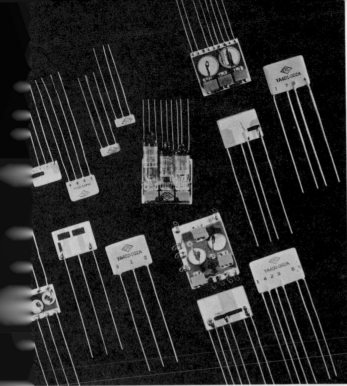

Fig. 750. A group of printed or packaged electronic circuits which contain resistors and capacitors as well as the wiring, fired on ceramic plates. Units of this type have been in successful use for many years. (Courtesy, Centralab, Div. of Globe Union, Inc.)

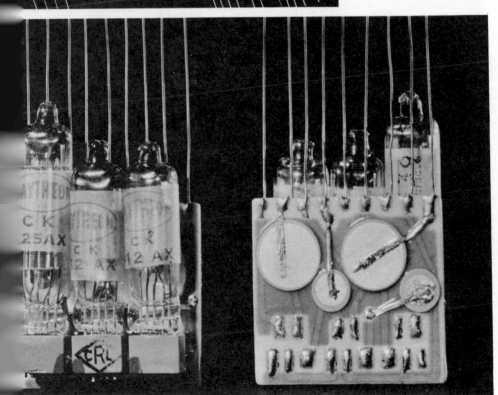

Fig. 751. A three-tube amplifier using subminiature tubes and a packaged electronic circuit. (Courtesy, Centralab, Div. of Globe Union, Inc.)

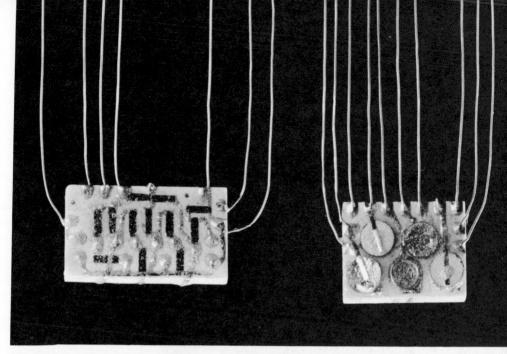

Fig. 752. Two- and three-stage transistor amplifiers made as packaged circuits.
(Courtesy, Centralab, Div. of Globe Union, Inc.)

Fig. 753. A module of the MDE or "Project Tinkertoy" type, with the tube socket on the upper wafer. A standard miniature tube is shown beside it for a size comparison. Each module is designed for the particular circuit in which it is to be used. (Courtesy, ACF Electronics, Div. of ACF Industries, Inc.)

Fig. 754. Two of these modules shown on a circuit diagram with the group of condensers and resistors one module would replace. (Courtesy, ACF Electronics, Div. of ACF Industries, Inc.)

Fig. 755. A three-tube video amplifier using these modules on a printed circuit board 2½ in. x 5¼ in. (Courtesy, ACF Electronics, Div. of ACF Industries, Inc.)

Fig. 756

Figs. 756–757. Top and bottom views of a television receiver using ACF modules. Of the 195 components in the set, 153 are replaced by 17 modules, making an outstandingly clean chassis well adapted to automatic assembly. (Courtesy, ACF Electronics, Div. of ACF Industries, Inc.)

Fig. 757

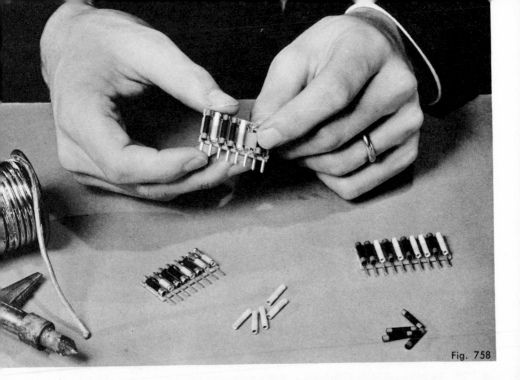

Fig. 758

Figs. 758–759. A new approach to electronic circuit modules is this "packaged assembly circuit" based on uniform component elements ⅛ in. diameter and ⅝ in. long. These are mounted with standard spacing on plastic boards (Fig. 758) with embossed copper wiring between components. The strips, carrying any number of components up to 92, are dip soldered and coated with a protective plastic. These modules are designed for mounting on printed wiring boards which make the connections between them, as shown in Fig. 758. (Courtesy, Erie Resistor Corporation.)

Fig. 759

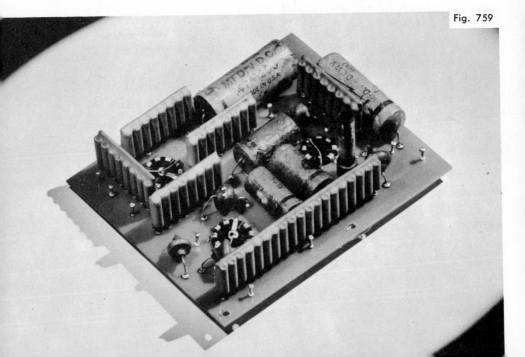

22

Marking Processes

Most products require markings of various kinds for identification of the part itself or of the manufacturer, or for information to the user of one kind or another. Sometimes this marking may be purely utilitarian, but often it forms an integral part of the design or the appearance of the product. Sometimes these markings may be molded into the piece, as part of the forming operation. This is often done in castings or plastic moldings and sometimes in metal stampings. In many cases, however, the markings are applied as a separate operation after forming or assembly. This may be done by any of the methods described in this chapter.

HOT AND COLD STAMPING

The hot-stamping method is often used to apply a permanent marking to the softer materials, such as plastics, wood, leather, and coated fabrics. A heated die is used, carrying the marking in raised letters. A plastic film carrying the desired color on one side is placed between the die and the workpiece and the die is brought against the work with considerable pressure. The heat and the pressure transfer the color to the work, leaving the marking in slightly depressed characters of the desired color. Gold and silver, either in actual metal leaf or in simulated pigments, are applied very commonly by this method to pencils, book covers, leather products, or plastics. A wide variety of colors is also available.

The process may be done in simple hand presses for small quantities or in power-driven, automatically fed machines for large production. The roll of film carrying the color is usually advanced automatically after each stroke just enough to bring a fresh section under the die for the next operation.

The dies are usually made of brass, either by engraving or by an etching process, and are not expensive. Interchangeable type can be used for short runs or for individually personalized items carrying a name or initials. Standard linotype slugs are often used for this purpose.

On harder materials, principally metals, steel dies are often used to mark letters, numbers, etc., on a surface. They may be in the form of individual characters used by hand with a hammer or movable type set in a holder and used manually or in a press; or a special die may be used for production marking. This method is often used for filling in blanks on metal name plates with model or serial numbers or other data. It is also used to mark identification or other information on any fairly smooth metal surface. Dies made in the form of rollers are often rotated against a curved surface under pressure to imprint names, part numbers, or other markings. Small, hand-operated machines, carrying a complete set of letters and numbers on a wheel which can be rotated quickly to bring any one of them into position, are used for filling in name plates and similar work.

DECALCOMANIAS OR TRANSFERS

These are used very widely for applying trade marks, names, or instructions to articles of almost any material. They are attractive in appearance, being made in any pattern and in one or more of a wide variety of colors. They can be made economically in fairly small quantities by the silk-screen process, described later in this chapter, or in larger quantities by lithographic methods.

Several types of "decals," as they usually are called, are made according to the requirements of a particular job. The commonest type carries the letters on a thin, transparent film, temporarily supported by a paper backing. To use, the decal is dipped in water for a few seconds to soften the adhesive; the film, carrying the markings, is slid from the supporting paper to the work and rolled or pressed onto the surface by hand. These are easy to apply and on most surfaces give good permanent adhesion.

In some cases, the transparent film which remains on the work is considered undesirable. Another type of decal is made to eliminate this objection. The pattern is applied in reverse form to a backing of thin, translucent paper and is then coated with a solvent-activated adhesive. To apply this type, the design side of the decal, or the work, is moistened with a solvent and the decal is applied, paper side up, to the work. The paper is then moistened and peeled off, leaving only the desired pattern on the work. This type is a little more difficult to apply than the first one described, but better adhesion can be obtained. After application, decals are often sprayed over with a coat of clear lacquer or varnish to increase their durability.

ADHESIVE LABELS

The development of improved adhesives has made it practical to use permanent paper or metal foil labels in place of the heavier metal name plates that usually are attached by means of screws, nails, or drive pins. These labels can be made with pressure-sensitive adhesives and the adhesive formulation can be varied from the type that is used for temporary marking on inspection labels, stock identification, etc., to a type that gives reliable permanent adhesion. Other types of adhesives, applied by means of solvents or by heat and pressure, give even stronger bonds. None of these bonds properly to very rough or porous surfaces.

SILK SCREENING

This is a printing process using a stencil made of very fine fabric or wire mesh. The portion of the screen corresponding to the pattern is left open and the rest of the screen is covered with an impervious film which closes the pores. The screen is stretched tightly over a frame which serves to support it and to retain the special ink or enamel that is used with it. In use, the screen is pressed tightly against the surface to be marked and the ink is squeezed through the open portions of it onto the surface of the work with a flat rubber blade called a "squeegee." If two or more colors are desired, a screen is made for each and they are used successively, allowing one color to dry thoroughly before the next is applied.

Silk-screen printing is used for advertising displays where the quantities are not large enough for other printing processes. It is also excellent for applying markings to the panels and the chassis bases of electronic equipment and similar articles. In this case, permanent markings are made by the use of baking enamels. Silk screening is also one of the commonest methods of applying an acid-resisting material to copper foil-coated plastic sheets in the manufacture of electronic printed circuits (see Chap. 21).

The screens are made by photographic methods and are quite inexpensive. The process, therefore, is well adapted to short runs, using hand-application methods. For larger quantities, fairly simple machines are used for applying the ink.

MASKED SPRAYING

A somewhat similar process involves the spraying of the colors through masking stencils onto the work. The stencils must be shaped to fit tightly against the surface of the work and they must be washed and dried after each few pieces to prevent smearing of the work. The process has been mechanized, however, with a number of masks or stencils in use at one time. These are carried by automatic conveyors through a solvent and dried before coming back into the work position.

Very beautiful name plates, having a three-dimensional effect, are made by molding the required shape in clear plastic and spraying the back with colors which follow the molded pattern. These are widely used on automobiles, refrigerators, and other products where the name plate forms an important part of the product design. They are practical only where large quantities are required because of the high mold and mask costs.

EMBOSSING

In embossing, the desired pattern is formed in thin metal or other material, usually by means of matched dies which raise the lettering or other markings above the surface. The reverse side shows a corresponding depression. The embossing dies often form part of a forming die, so that the piece is shaped and embossed at one operation. In this way it is economical, the only additional cost being in the die. The embossed pattern may also serve the additional function, if it is properly designed, of stiffening the entire piece. This is especially useful on large unsupported areas of thin metal or plastic. Some expense can be saved by using a rubber pad of the proper hardness for one half of the die, although the impression will not be as sharp as it could be if made in matched metal dies. An embossed effect can be obtained in thin thermoplastic sheet material by the vacuum-forming process (see Chap. 14). In this case, the embossing is usually only part of the forming process and does not add anything to the cost of the piece.

ETCHING ✓

Etching is used very extensively for marking and decorating the surface of metal products and also for forming metal name plates and panels. The raised portion of the pattern is protected by an acid-resisting coating and the rest of the surface is etched away to whatever depth is required by means of suitable chemicals.

Often the etching is very slight, as when the name or the trade mark is applied to the polished steel surface of a saw blade or other tool. In other cases, the lettering may be protected and the background area etched away, often to a considerable depth, as in the case of reverse-etched name plates of brass, aluminum, or other metals which are widely used on machinery, instruments and many other products.

The acid-resisting material, which protects the raised portions during the etching, may be applied by any of several methods, such as silk-screen printing, offset printing, or a photographic process. The best method will depend on the size and the complexity of the piece and the quantity involved. After etching, the resist is washed off with a solvent, leaving the original surface of the metal on the raised portions.

Color is often applied to the etched portions by spraying the entire surface before the resist is removed with a type of lacquer or enamel that will not be affected by the solvent used to remove the resist. Then when the resist is washed off, the raised portions show the original metal surface while the etched areas retain the color.

For a lightly etched marking on a smooth or polished metal surface, an electrolytic etching process can be used. A pad saturated with an electrolyte is covered with a thin stencil of rubber or plastic or of material similar to a silk screen. This is pressed against the work and a low-voltage direct current is passed between the electrolyte pad and the work, causing an etching effect wherever contact is made. The process can be done on a production basis or small hand stamps are made for toolroom use or small quantity marking.

ENGRAVING

This is a machining process wherein a small cutter, revolving at high speed, is moved across the surface of the work, forming the required pattern or lettering in a narrow groove of controlled depth. The cutter is guided by means of a pantograph mechanism, under the control of the operator, who moves a guide point or a stylus around grooves in a master pattern. For letters or numerals, these patterns usually are made up as standard alphabets of individual letters which are assembled as required. Various sizes of symbols can be made from the same master by changing the ratio of the pantograph arms in the machine.

Engraving is used primarily for small quantities, or on work, such as certain dial calibrations and measuring scales, where extreme accuracy is required. The engraved characters are often filled with a colored enamel to increase contrast and legibility. A special plastic material called "Lamicoid" is made with a center layer that contrasts in color with the surface. The engraving tool cuts through the surface layer so that the marking shows up clearly. This material is excellent for name plates and markers on single units or small quantities of equipment. Lettering engraved in methyl-methacrylate (Lucite or Plexiglas) sheets stands out clearly when the sheet is edge lighted, and is often used for signs and displays.

Sometimes effects similar to etching or engraving are obtained by abrasive-blast methods (see Chaps. 10 and 16). Usually this is done on glass or plastic surfaces, but it can be done also on wood or metals. A mask or stencil, usually made of rubber having openings in the shape of the marking required, is applied tightly to the work surface and the piece is then subjected to the blast of abrasive, which may be either wet or dry. The particles may be thrown either by air pressure or by centrifugal force. In glass, particularly, which would be hard to work by other methods, very striking and beautiful effects can be obtained in this manner.

Fig. 760. The marking on tools must be permanent and attractive. This one is applied by steel stamping to the polished surface of the saw. (Courtesy, Henry Disston Division, H. K. Porter Company, Inc.)

Fig. 761. Silk-screen printing by hand with a circular work table. (Courtesy, Frank A. Clarici & Sons.)

Fig. 762. A group of silk-screen printed articles, signs, displays, decalcomanias, luggage, etc. These are printed on plastics, paper, fabrics, metals, felt, and leatherette. (Courtesy, Frank A. Clarici & Sons.)

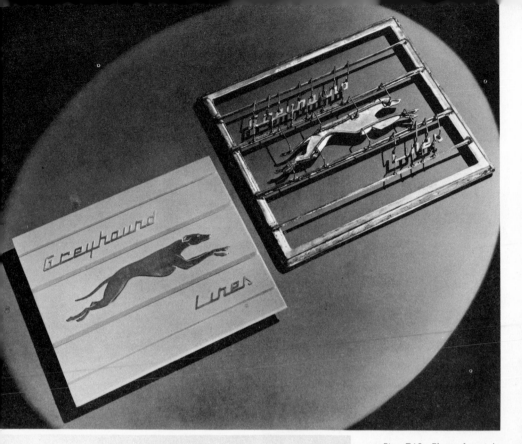

Fig. 763. Electroformed spray masks (see Chap. 6) are widely used for selective coloring of markings on a production basis. This photograph shows an attractive emblem and the mask used in spray painting it. (Courtesy, Conforming Matrix Corp.)

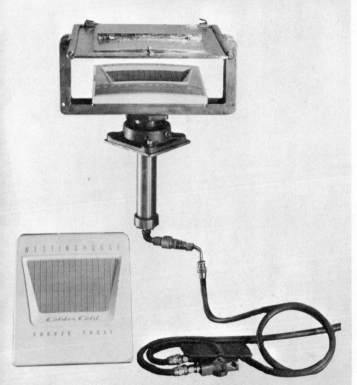

Fig. 764. An air-operated fixture for mask spraying of the refrigerator inner door shown below. (Courtesy, Conforming Matrix Corp.)

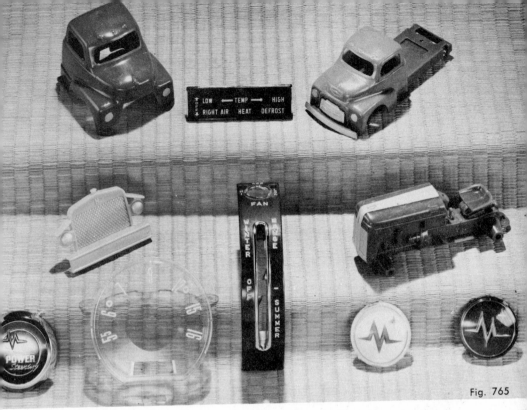

Fig. 765

Figs. 765–766. Two groups of parts marked or decorated by means of selective spraying with electroformed spray masks. (Courtesy, Conforming Matrix Corp.)

Fig. 766

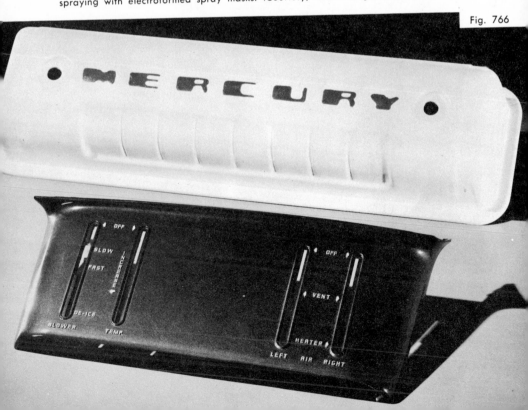

Fig. 767. A hand-operated press for stamping data on name plates, identification tags, etc. The plate is automatically advanced one space after each impression. (Courtesy, The Clearview Co.)

Fig. 768. An inexpensive, manually operated engraving machine, working on the pantograph principle for engraving name plates, dials, etc., from changeable type masters. A rotating cutter is used, or on very hard materials, a fixed diamond cutter. (Courtesy, New Hermes Engraving Machine Corp.)

Fig. 769. An engraving machine with an electric arc etching unit for clear marking on tools and other hard metal surfaces. (Courtesy, New Hermes Engraving Machine Corp.)

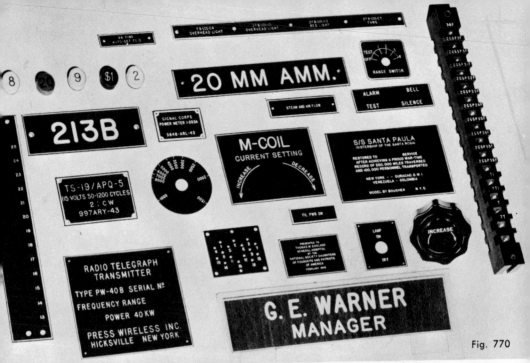

Fig. 770

Figs. 770–771. A group of plastic and metal plates with engraved markings and (Fig. 771) a group of tools engraved with the electric arc unit. (Courtesy, New Hermes Engraving Machine Corp.)

Fig. 771

23

Automation

Automation has become a magic word in modern industry and a fruitful subject for arguments, pro and con. These tend to obscure the fact that automation is not new, either in concept or in practice, although the development of electronics has greatly extended its application. The steam-engine governor of James Watt was definitely automation, since the flyballs of the governor acted to sense a change of speed in the engine and to control a valve which regulated that speed. As early as 1830, a completely automatic flour mill was made using highly ingenious mechanical controls over the entire process from the time the wheat was dumped from the wagons into a storage bin until the flour came out in barrels at the other end.

To the layman, automation means the "push-button factory," with a few highly skilled technicians controlling a vast plant from a little room lined with dials and knobs. In a very few cases, such as oil refineries and highly specialized chemical plants, this is not far from the truth. In most manufacturing operations, however, automation comes gradually, being adapted to certain machines and processes and not to others. In many cases, it is difficult to determine where mechanization ends and automation begins. The dividing line is sometimes drawn when the handling of the work between machines or operations becomes automatic rather than manual. In other cases, the distinction may be made when the control of the machines is taken over by electronic or highly developed mechanical devices rather than by human operators. Basically, automation is an outgrowth of the concept known as "feedback," which means that information about the result of a process is used to control the process itself. This is not a new idea, although the concept and its applications have been exploited much more fully in recent years than ever before.

An example of the feedback principle that is so common it is often overlooked is the modern home heating system. Here, the room thermostat is the sensing element. When the room temperature drops below a predetermined point, the thermostat conveys this information to the burner, and, through suitable relays, causes it to generate more heat. When the room temperature rises to the upper limit, the thermostat operates to turn the burner off. These automatic heating systems have been developed over a considerable period of time to the point where they often operate for years with no human attention whatsoever.

It is easy to see how the same principle can be applied to the control of dimensions in a machining operation. An automatic gaging device can measure the critical dimensions on the pieces that have been machined or are being machined, and when these start to run too large or too small, the information can be relayed to an automatic device that adjusts the cutting tools to correct the condition. This is commonly done on the automatic machines that produce large quantities of complex parts like automobile cylinder blocks with no human control other than maintenance.

In a similar manner, a sensing device might determine when the cutting tool was becoming worn, by measuring either the cutting force required or the surface finish on the completed work. When these indicated the need for a new tool, they could operate an alarm so that the change could be made manually, or, if the additional complication were justified, additional tools could be mounted in such a way that they could be brought into use automatically when they were needed. It is even conceivable that the tools might be sharpened automatically and put back into use without any human intervention at all.

These elaborate controls are made possible by electronics, since a very small force, such as that provided by a gaging device, can be amplified, transmitted to a remote point, and used to control the largest motors, hydraulic cylinders, or other power sources.

Going beyond a single machine, it is easy to see that the raw material for these automatic machines can be picked up automatically from a storage point and conveyed to the machine as required. Sensing devices can tell the conveyor when more material is needed, and, after inspecting the finished pieces coming out of the machine, can control the mechanism carrying them to the next operation or to a suitable storage point. Here other sensing devices might measure the inventory and tell the machine when to stop production and when more parts are needed.

If we give rein to our imaginations, we can visualize such a completely automated factory whose production is controlled automatically by a computer which could receive information daily from sales offices all over the country. This information could be classified and broken down into the quantity of each item required and the machines could then be instructed by the computer to make this many pieces and no more. If none of the machines ever got out of order (which is quite unlikely), the factory might run indefinitely without human aid.

Unfortunately (or perhaps fortunately), many factors prevent our factories from converting overnight to such automatic operation. From an economic point of view, it is doubtful whether all the workers not needed in the factories could be put to work immediately making and maintaining the machines or selling the vast quantities of products produced by them. A more immediate deterrent to widespread automation is the cost of the machinery and the controls required and the fact that a great many products are not needed in large enough quantities to justify this cost.

The processes best adapted to automation, and where the most progress has been made in this direction, are: (1) continuous processes such as oil refining, and the production of some chemicals, and (2) mass production of repetitive mechanical parts, such as some of those found in the automotive and the household appliance industries. In these fields, automation can justify its high initial cost and can show substantial savings. The quality of the product is often better and more uniform than that produced by human operators.

The more specialized a machine is, and the more standardized its product, the easier it is to equip it with automatic controls and the more likely it is to show cost economies. However, progress is being made in adapting small-quantity production of complex parts to automation.

A good example of this is a new automatic milling machine used for making aircraft parts. All motions of this machine are controlled by an electronic unit, and the information needed to produce a given part is furnished to this control unit in the form of a magnetic tape. Once this is set up, the machine completes the entire sequence of operations needed without manual control of any kind. On work adapted to it, this is often economical even if only one piece is required. To change to another part, it is only necessary to change the tape in the control unit.

A similar principle is used in the machine shown in Chap. 21, Fig. 740, for perforating printed wiring boards for electronics. The operation of this machine is described in that chapter.

From the two examples shown above, it will be seen that certain processes can be automated without sacrificing flexibility and versatility. A machine of this type requires some source of information to control it in the absence of a human operator. This source may be a perforated card or tape or a magnetized tape indicating the sequence of operations to be performed or the dimensions to be followed. The preparation of these masters requires considerable skill and experience in many cases, but the cards or tape can be stored away for future use on reruns of the part for which it was made.

The decision to automate a plant or parts of a plant should be made only after a careful analysis by experienced engineers. The idea of automation is so appealing to management that much money has been spent without sufficient consideration of all the factors involved. Questions such as the following should receive careful scrutiny before a decision is reached:

1. Is the process adapted to automation?
2. Can the cost of the necessary equipment be amortized in a reasonable length of time by the savings in labor?
3. Is the product well enough standardized or the proposed automatic equipment flexible enough so that a change in product design will not make it obsolete before it has paid for itself?
4. Is trained personnel available to set up, operate, and maintain the equipment?
5. Is the rate of production constant enough or high enough to keep the equipment operating on an efficient schedule?
6. Is a drastic change in product design or in consumer demand likely to affect the situation radically?

There are many places in industry where the answers to such questions are favorable and the trend to automation is certain to continue and probably accelerate. However, there are many other places where the factors are not right for automation and where the more conventional methods for improving efficiency and reducing cost are still the most fruitful.

If it seems that automation is likely to be practical, the study of the problem should begin with the product itself. An analysis of the market and of competition should be made to determine whether the design is likely to find a good market for a long enough period so that it can be frozen in its present form. It should then be examined to determine whether the design is well adapted to automatic manufacture in its present form, or, if changes are needed from this angle, whether they will improve or harm the sale of the product. After the design and the production methods are decided on, serious consideration should be given to the degree of automation that will be economical. The highest possible degree of automation is very seldom the ideal one from this angle. The initial cost of the equipment is likely to be prohibitive and too much of a sacrifice in flexibility may have to be made, since the most highly automatic machines are usually the least flexible.

There has been some opposition on the part of labor unions to the introduction of automatic machines and methods, and this is only natural. In most cases, some disruption of established work patterns is involved in any such change. However, the more far-sighted labor leaders see in automation simply an extension of the trend toward the more efficient mass production that has made our modern industrial system possible. If the change in methods is gradual enough, as it seems to be at the present time, there is little doubt that it will help to continue the trend toward increased productivity, lower costs, and a higher standard of living for the entire country. A more probable unfavorable effect of the long-term development of automatic manufacturing may be the freezing out of the smaller producers and the concentration of production in the hands of the larger corporations. Evidences of this effect are already seen in the automobile industry and in the production of television receivers.

Promising fields for automation that are often overlooked are found in packaging, material handling, and office work. Tremendous savings can often be realized in the packing and wrapping of food, drugs, and similar products where the product is well standardized and quantities are large. Conveyors, automatically controlled by the needs of the production machines, are less spectacular than automatic production machines but may show large savings for a moderate investment. The routine mathematics of payroll, production and cost records, inventory control, and sales analysis are ideal applications for the smaller electronic computers that are now coming into use, and it is quite possible that the largest labor savings and most drastic changes in methods during the next few years may be in this field. Here computers not only do the job much faster than human operators but also more accurately. They can often furnish management more complete data on which to base decisions and keep this information more up-to-date.

It is certainly essential for every manufacturing executive to keep informed of current developments in the rapidly growing field of automation. It is bound to result in changes in competitive position of the companies in many industries, and those which are first to realize and take advantage of its possibilities will find themselves in the best position in our rapidly growing economy.

Fig. 772. Petroleum refining is one of the most highly automated of all industries. This cycle timer co-ordinates the opening and closing of electrically operated valves in a catalytic cracking unit at Sun Oil Company's Marcus Hook Refinery. (Courtesy, Sun Oil Company.)

Fig. 773. An automatic line for machining a V-8 engine block. Regarding this, Pontiac Motor says: "We avoid the use of the word 'Automation' when referring to our new automatic handling machinery because we do not feel that it is far enough advanced to be considered automation." Most factories would be happy to reach this stage in the process. (Courtesy, Pontiac Motor Division, General Motors Corporation.)

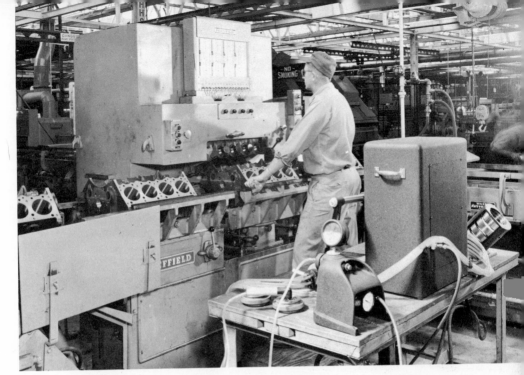

Fig. 774. A gaging station on the engine block line where a Sheffield precision air gage checks the cylinder bore. (Courtesy, Pontiac Motor Division, General Motors Corporation.)

Fig. 775. A series of multiple drill stations along the V-8 engine block line. (Courtesy, Pontiac Motor Division, General Motors Corporation.)

Fig. 776. An automatic line for machining hydraulic valve lifters. (Courtesy, Pontiac Motor Division, General Motors Corporation.)

Fig. 777. Machining crankshafts in an automatic line. (Courtesy, Pontiac Motor Division, General Motors Corporation.)

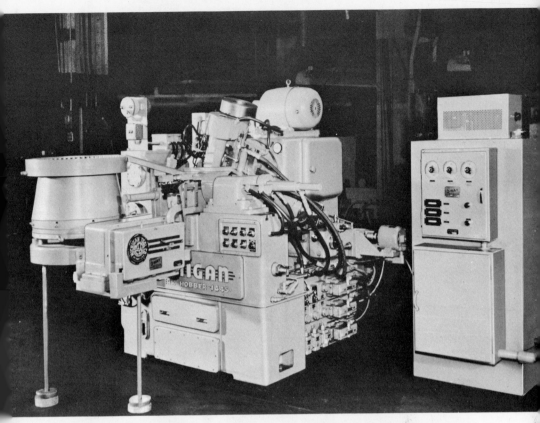

Fig. 778. An automated gear hobbing machine. Blanks are fed from the hopper at the left into the cutting position. After being cut, they are checked for size in an automatic measuring device which sorts them according to pitch diameter into three groups. (Courtesy, Michigan Tool Company.)

Figs. 779–780. This automatic gear classifier checks the production from a gear-cutting machine. Probes at the top and the bottom (Fig. 780) measure the pitch diameter and actuate a mechanism that sorts them into oversize, undersize, or correct size. (Courtesy, Michigan Tool Company.)

Fig. 780

Fig. 781

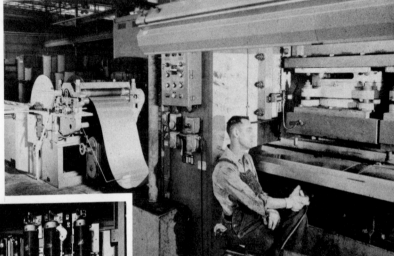

Fig. 782

Fig. 783

Figs. 781–783. A large automatic transfer feed press in operation at Ford Motor Company. Figure 782 shows the input end of this press. Figure 783 shows the complex controls typical of automatic machinery. In this unit, for example, if two blanks stick together, a trap door opens and throws them out, without interrupting the operation of the press. (Courtesy, E. W. Bliss Co.)

Figs. 784–786. Electronic controls of this concrete batching plant provide a selection of some 1500 different formulas and give approximately twice the output of manually operated plants. Figure 785 shows the one-man control board and Fig. 786 the punched card unit that determines the formula for each batch. (Courtesy, Fairbanks, Morse & Co.)

Fig. 785

Fig. 786

Fig. 787. This automatic television assembly line inserts over 70 percent of the 231 electrical components on three printed circuit boards used in the set. The three panels carry 13 tube sockets and nearly four fifths of the circuitry in the chassis. Inserted automatically are condensers, resistors, wire jumpers, and tube sockets. Over 400 hand-soldered connections are eliminated. (Courtesy, Admiral Corporation.)

Fig. 788. Packaging is one of the most fruitful fields for automation. This machine can fill and seal from 25 to 30 2-gal cans of motor oil per minute. (Courtesy, Sun Oil Company.)

Index

Page numbers set in **boldface** refer to illustrations.

MANUFACTURING METHODS AND PROCESSES was set in 11 point Caledonia, leaded 2 points, a face designed by W. A. Dwiggins, a well-known American type designer.

The book was composed, printed by off-set, and bound by Quinn & Boden Company, Inc., Rahway, New Jersey. Typography and binding design are by Leonard W. Blizard and staff of the printer.

Date Due